VITAMINS AND HORMONES

ADVANCES IN RESEARCH AND APPLICATIONS

Edited by

ROBERT S. HARRIS
32 Dwhinda Road
Newton, Massachusetts

EGON DICZFALUSY
Karolinska Sjukhuset
Stockholm, Sweden

PAUL L. MUNSON
University of North Carolina
Chapel Hill, North Carolina

JOHN GLOVER
University of Liverpool
Liverpool, England

Consulting Editors

KENNETH V. THIMANN
University of California, Santa Cruz
Santa Cruz, California

IRA G. WOOL
University of Chicago
Chicago, Illinois

JOHN A. LORAINE
University of Edinburgh
Edinburgh, Scotland

D1496881

Volume 31
1973

ACADEMIC PRESS, New York and London
A Subsidiary of Harcourt Brace Jovanovich, Publishers

ACADEMIC PRESS, INC.
111 Fifth Avenue, New York, New York 10003

United Kingdom Edition published by
ACADEMIC PRESS, INC. (LONDON) LTD.
24/28 Oval Road, London NW1

LIBRARY OF CONGRESS CATALOG CARD NUMBER: 43-10535

PRINTED IN THE UNITED STATES OF AMERICA

Contents

Retinol-Binding Proteins

J. GLOVER

Vitamin D, Calcium, and Protein Synthesis

R. H. WASSERMAN AND R. A. CORRADINO

Erythropoietin

ALBERT S. GORDON

v

Immunology of Gonadal Steroids

Michel Ferin, Sam M. Beiser, and Raymond L. Vande Wiele

Hormonal Control of Ovoimplantation

Alexandre Psychoyos

Hormonal Effects on Human Myometrial Activity

Lars Philip Bengtsson

Contributors to Volume 31

Numbers in parentheses indicate the pages on which the authors' contributions begin.

SAM M. BEISER,* *Departments of Obstetrics and Gynecology, and Microbiology, and the International Institute for the Study of Human Reproduction, Columbia University College of Physicians and Surgeons, New York, New York* (175)

LARS PHILIP BENGTSSON, *Department of Obstetrics and Gynecology, University Hospital, Lund, Sweden* (257)

R. A. CORRADINO, *Department of Physical Biology, New York State Veterinary College, Cornell University, Ithaca, New York* (43)

MICHEL FERIN, *Departments of Obstetrics and Gynecology, and Microbiology, and the International Institute for the Study of Human Reproduction, Columbia University College of Physicians and Surgeons, New York, New York* (175)

J. GLOVER, *Biochemistry Department, University of Liverpool, Liverpool, England* (1)

ALBERT S. GORDON, *Laboratory of Experimental Hematology, Department of Biology, Graduate School of Arts and Science, New York University, New York, New York* (105)

ALEXANDRE PSYCHOYOS, *Centre National de la Recherche Scientifique, Laboratoire de Physiologie de la Reproduction, Hôpital de Bicêtre, Bicêtre, France* (201)

RAYMOND L. VANDE WIELE, *Departments of Obstetrics and Gynecology, and Microbiology, and the International Institute for the Study of Human Reproduction, Columbia University College of Physicians and Surgeons, New York, New York* (175)

R. H. WASSERMAN, *Department of Physical Biology, New York State Veterinary College, Cornell University, Ithaca, New York* (43)

* Deceased September 7, 1972.

Preface

The Editors of *Vitamins and Hormones* are pleased to present this volume, the thirty-first in a series of critical reviews of advances in vitamin and hormone research.

The present volume comprises six chapters: Retinol-Binding Proteins (Glover); Vitamin D and Protein Synthesis (Wasserman and Corradino); Erythropoietin (Gordon); Immunology of Gonadal Steroids (Ferin, Beiser, and Vande Wiele); Hormonal Control of Ovoimplantation (Psychoyos); and Hormonal Effects of Human Myometrial Activity (Bengtsson). We are deeply indebted to these authors for their fine contributions.

The Editors wish to announce that after serving for thirty-two years as an Editor of *Vitamins and Hormones,* Professor Robert S. Harris is becoming Consulting Editor of the same publication and Professor Paul L. Munson will replace him as Senior Editor.

Now is a propitious time for a few comments on the early history of *Vitamins and Hormones.* The *Ergebnisse der Vitamin-und-Hormon Forschung* was first published by Akademische Verlagsgesellschaft in Germany in 1939. Because of World War II, only two volumes of this critical review serial were published. Mr. Walter Johnson and Mr. Kurt Jacoby, who had been associated with the German company, migrated to New York City and established Academic Press, Inc. in 1942. Very soon after their arrival, they traveled to Boston to invite Dr. Robert S. Harris (Massachusetts Institute of Technology) and Dr. Kenneth V. Thimann (Harvard University) to accept editorial responsibility for producing a successor to the *Ergebnisse* which would similarly present critical reviews of the current literature relating to vitamin and hormone research. Dr. Thimann and Dr. Harris accepted this interesting challenge and became the first editors of a new volume of annual reviews which was named *Vitamins and Hormones* and was published by Academic Press, Inc. The first volume was published in March, 1943. The Editors stated the objectives of this book in the Editors' Preface as follows:

> The basic research on vitamins and hormones is conducted by investigators in the fields of organic chemistry, biochemistry, physiology, biophysics and medicine. The results of this research are published in a large number of medical, biological and chemical journals, many of which are not readily available to the scientist or clinician.
>
> To accumulate, correlate and digest the current literature in a field in which research is active and to point out where knowledge is incomplete requires a thorough grasp of the subject. To indicate the directions in which future research would be most fruitful and useful one must have sound imagination. Each chapter

in this volume was written by a well-qualified investigator who endeavored to evaluate the present status of his special subject and to indicate what knowledge is lacking.

This volume contains a very complete subject and author index because it is intended primarily as a reference book. With each succeeding volume, "Vitamins and Hormones" will rapidly become a complete reference on all active research in the vitamin and hormone field.

During the past 31 years, the following several devoted scientists have served as Editors or Consulting Editors:

Name and academic location	Volumes published while serving	
	As Editor	As Consulting Editor
Robert S. Harris, Massachusetts Institute of Technology	1–31	[a]
Kenneth V. Thimann, Harvard University	1–17	18–31[a]
G. F. Marrian, University of Edinburgh	10–17	18–25
Dwight J. Ingle, University of Chicago	18–19	—
Ira G. Wool, University of Chicago	18–27	28–31[a]
John A. Loraine, University of Edinburgh	21–27	28–31[a]
Paul L. Munson, University of North Carolina	27–31[a]	
Egon Diczfalusy, Karolinska Institutet	28–31[a]	
John Glover, University of Liverpool	29–31[a]	

[a] Continuing as Editor.

ROBERT S. HARRIS
PAUL L. MUNSON
EGON DICZFALUSY
JOHN GLOVER

Retinol-Binding Proteins

J. GLOVER

Biochemistry Department, University of Liverpool, Liverpool, England

I. Introduction

Following the discovery of the importance of vitamin A (retinol) to the animal in preventing night blindness and maintaining normal growth of the animal body, in replacement of epithelial tissues and in reproduction, it was appreciated that knowledge of the level of the vitamin circulating in the bloodstream would assist in determining the nutritional status of the subject with respect to this essential nutrient. In examining blood, the vitamin was found to be associated with the plasma fraction and it was necessary to denature the proteins with ethanol before it could be extracted into light petroleum (Kimble, 1939), and from fractional precipitation studies it appeared to be associated with serum globulins (Pett and LePage, 1940).

From the early work on the isolation of the vitamin in pure form it

1

was known that the stores of the vitamin found in liver oils were mainly in the esterified form, consequently the observation of Clausen *et al.* (1942) that almost all of the vitamin obtained from extracts of denatured serum was present as the free alcohol was unusually interesting. This was later confirmed by Hoch and Hoch (1946) in human, and Glover *et al.* (1947) in rat serum. The normal fasting level of the vitamin in humans seemed to be controlled in the region of 100–150 IU/100 ml (35–50 μg/100 ml) (Leitner *et al.*, 1952) irrespective of the amounts of the reserves in liver. The fact that the fat-soluble vitamin normally did not exceed the above level and was uniformly dispersed in aqueous medium and completely in the alcohol form in the fasting animal, implied that a protein carrier was involved. In one of the early attempts to determine its nature, the plasma proteins were resolved by fractional precipitation with ammonium sulfate. Chicken, ox, and pig plasma were examined in this way by Ganguly *et al.* (1952), and in each case retinol was found to be associated with the globulins precipitated after the 25% fraction containing mainly the γ-components. Some albumin is also brought down in that fraction, but this was eliminated as the carrier after its precipitation with specific antiserum (Krinsky *et al.*, 1958), the complex being devoid of retinol.

Using density gradient ultracentrifugation, Hack (1956) and Krinsky *et al.* (1958) observed that the vitamin was associated with a protein in the fraction having a density greater than 1.21. Thus the carrier protein behaved more like a high density α-globulin than a β-type globulin. Similarly, resolution of the proteins of rat serum by preparative zone electrophoresis also revealed that the vitamin was associated with α-globulins, and particularly α_1-lipoproteins rather than α_1-glycoprotein (Garbers *et al.*, 1958, 1960). The degree of resolution of each of the above procedures, however, was adequate to establish that the carrier protein was an α-globulin, but the concentration in plasma being so low, it was necessary to purify and characterize the protein further by using additional procedures such as chromatography and gel filtration.

Using anion exchange cellulose along with paper electrophoresis, Glover and Walker (1964) observed that the retinol carrier protein behaved more like an α_2-globulin since its electrophoretic mobility on paper was slightly less than that of ceruloplasmin used as a marker. Furthermore, on diethyl aminoethyl cellulose (DEAE-32) it was among the last proteins to be eluted off the column using combined gradients of increasing salt and H^+ ion concentrations.

Alvsaker *et al.* (1967) later chromatographed serum successively on Sephadex-gel and DEAE-Sephadex. The retinol-containing protein fraction was then further subjected to paper electrophoresis. On the basis of fluorescence and immunological reactivity tests on their purified material, they concluded that retinol was transported on tryptophan-rich pre-albumin (PA).

At the same time, however, Kanai et al. (1968) purified human serum labeled with ^{14}C-retinol by Cohn fractionation, chromatography on Sephadex and DEAE-Sephadex to yield a 650-fold purified preparation D. The latter was resolved further by electrophoresis on preparative polyacrylamide gel and shown to contain PA in addition to the retinol-binding protein (RBP), which had a much lower electrophoretic mobility. Final traces of PA were removed from the RBP by chromatography on Sephadex gel (G-100). This purified sample of RBP was found on examination by disc-gel electrophoresis to contain apo- as well as holo-protein, the former having a slightly greater electrophoretic mobility. In this system RBP was found to have the mobility of α_1-globulin. Its molecular weight as determined by Sephadex gel chromatography, ultra-centrifugation, and amino acid analysis was shown to be approximately 22,000; holo RBP contained 1 mole of retinol, but no other lipids. Like PA, the retinol-binding protein was found to contain a relatively high concentration of aromatic amino acids. Furthermore RBP as isolated readily associated with PA to form a 1:1 complex.

This indirect connection between retinol and PA explained in part the previous observation of Alvsaker et al. (1967) that retinol was bound directly to PA. The latter group after further analysis of their purified preparation by disc electrophoresis and ultracentrifugation, however, revised their earlier work and agreed that retinol was bound to a low-molecular weight protein having α_1-mobility (Johannesson et al., 1969). They, however, reported a sedimentation constant $s_{20,w}$ of 1.85 S compared with 2.26 S as reported by Kanai et al. (1968).

While it is abundantly clear that retinol is attached to a specific carrier protein of the α-globulin type there have been some inconsistencies between the various reports in detail with regard to its true electrophoretic mobility and sedimentation constant and to the nature of its association with thyroxine-binding prealbumin. The aim, therefore, of the present article is to review the recent work on the chemistry and biochemistry of human RBP which leads to a better understanding of retinol metabolism. At the same time, an attempt will be made to resolve some of the discrepant observations so that a greater consensus on the properties of this carrier protein may be reached. Available information on the comparable carrier proteins isolated from other animal species will also be discussed.

II. METHODS OF ISOLATION

The various groups of workers have used some or all of the four basic protein fractionation procedures: fractional precipitation, ion-exchange chromatography, molecular sieving on Sephadex gels, and preparative-scale electrophoresis in different combinations. Fractional precipitation was used in the early work as an initial stage to reduce quickly the absolute amount of protein to be handled. Retinol binding protein is precipitated by ethanol mainly (75–80%) in Cohn fractions I and III (Kanai et al., 1968) and in 22.5–37.5% $(NH_4)_2SO_4$ (Kirby et al., 1971), but the degree of purification achieved by either of these steps was generally less than 5-fold and not so efficient as the ion-exchange procedure, and they were usually omitted in later work since they also tend to cause extensive denaturation of the proteins.

A. ISOLATION OF RBP–PA COMPLEX

In later work with human RBP, serum or plasma, suitably equilibrated with buffer, was applied to an ion-exchange column such as DEAE–Sephadex-A.50 (Raz and Goodman, 1969; Peterson, 1971a) or DE 32 cellulose (Haupt and Heide, 1972), or the bifunctional (anionic and cationic) exchanger arginine–Sepharose 6B (Kirby et al., 1971). In the former systems, RBP is bound with a few other proteins having low isoelectric points and tends to be among the last group of proteins to be eluted. In the arginine–Sepharose system first used by Porath and Fornstedt (1970) for the isolation of ceruloplasmin, the plasma or serum must be dialyzed against running distilled water for at least 24 hours to reduce its ionic strength before application to the column. During the dialysis a considerable portion of the fibrinogen, lipoproteins, β- and γ-globulin fractions are precipitated and can readily be separated off in the centrifuge. The supernatant is then applied directly to the arginine–Sepharose column equilibrated against 0.01 M Tris buffer pH 7.5. RBP is bound with a few other low isoelectric point proteins, whereas the bulk of the remaining proteins pass through the column. Stepwise elution with 0.01 M up to 0.15 M Tris buffer, pH 7.5, enables RBP to be collected in a final fraction containing thyroxine-binding prealbumin, ceruloplasmin, and some albumin, as main contaminants (see Fig. 1). The purification achieved by any of the above procedures is of the order of several hundredfold.

The next step to be applied was generally chromatography on Sephadex gel G-200 (Raz and Goodman, 1969) or G-100 (Peterson, 1971a; Kirby et al., 1971). This enables the higher molecular weight proteins such as ceruloplasmin to be removed from RBP which is mainly complexed with thyroxine-binding prealbumin at this stage. However, a small amount of unbound RBP may also be found in the final fraction to be eluted from G-100 system.

More recently a procedure involving affinity chromatography has been used by Vahlquist *et al.* (1971). Prealbumin coupled to Sepharose 6B is the specific binding agent for RBP, which can be separated quickly from other serum proteins.

B. SEPARATION OF RBP FROM PREALBUMIN

The further separation of RBP from minor contaminants and PA was accomplished in different ways by the various groups. Raz *et al.* (1970) and Peterson (1971a) passed their preparations through DEAE–Sephadex for the second time. This removed the minor contaminants but left RBP still complexed with PA. The complex was largely dissociated by subjecting it to electrophoresis in a preparative column of polyacrylamide gel (Kanai *et al.*, 1968) and the free RBP was finally purified on Sephadex G-100 (Raz and Goodman, 1969) or by passing the complex through Sephadex gel G-200 and G-100 in succession (Peterson, 1971a). It was claimed by Peterson (1971a) that the reduction of the concentration of the pH 8.0 buffer medium down to 2 mM enables the separation of the two components to occur. This procedure, however, was quite different from that of Raz *et al.* (1970), who found 6 M urea to be the effective agent when the complex was chromatographed on G-100 equilibrated with a much higher strength buffer of 50 mM.

With a view to exploring whether the complex between RBP and PA could be resolved satisfactorily by the gel-permeation procedure rather than by preparative electrophoresis, the dissociation of the complex was also examined in our laboratory using Sephadex gels G-50 and G-100. It was confirmed that better separations of the two components were achieved using low ionic strength buffer but that optimal resolution was obtained only in the presence of at least 2 M urea, which does not appear to have any serious deleterious effect on the holo RBP component. Chromatography of complex in such a medium on G-50 gel, as opposed to G-100, did not yield any separation of the two proteins. This was unexpected since the respective molecular weights of RBP (22,000) and PA (53,000) should be within the capacity of the G-50 gel to resolve as indeed it does a mixture of RBP and albumin. Separation on a column of G-100 gel, on the other hand, does take place, but again the passage of the mixture through it must be at a relatively slow rate ($<$10 ml/ hour) for it to be effective. It was felt, therefore, that the resolution of the two components depended to some extent on a specific property of the G-100 gel. The yield of RBP at this stage was generally in the region of 30% of the starting material.

Separation of RBP and PA by the gel permeation procedure was never as satisfactory as the electrophoretic separation, which was more reproducible and invariably led to a purer final product. Indeed, it is possible to resolve much of the higher-mobility "apo" material from the holo RBP by preparative electrophoresis.

Following the resolution of RBP and PA by electrophoresis, it is necessary to pass the holo RBP preparation through a column of G-50 or G-100 gel in order to change the separation buffer solution to one more appropriate for other biochemical work and at the same time to eliminate any residual traces of albumin, which occasionally persist up to this stage.

The state of purification of the RBP as prepared by the various procedures is readily monitored by disc-gel electrophoresis on polyacrylamide (Fig. 1a). It is usual to find that RBP preparations homogeneous as far as molecular weight is concerned show three closely spaced bands on disc-gel electrophoresis. A nonfluorescent component corresponding to apo RBP and two fluorescent bands corresponding to holo RBP_f and holo RBP_s (f = fast and s = slow) in decreasing order of electrophoretic mobility, which extend from the α_1- to α_2-globulin region relative to albu-

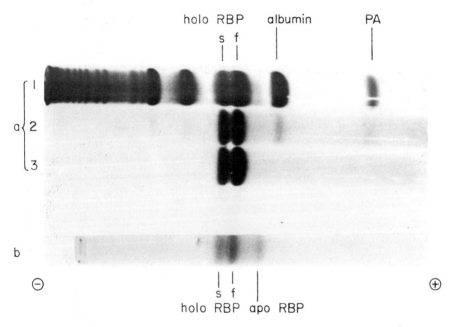

FIG. 1. Disc-gel pherograms of RBP fractions of human serum at various stages of purification. (a,i) After chromatography of serum on arginine–Sepharose 6B. (ii) After preparative electrophoresis of (i) on polyacrylamide. (iii) After final chromatography on Sephadex G-100 to remove traces of albumin. (b) A preparation of RBP showing presence of apoprotein in addition to the two holo components, RBP_{fast} and RBP_{slow}.

min (see Fig. 1b). Holo RBP$_f$, however, appears to be found in appreciable quantity only when the isolation is protracted. It appears to arise artifactually from the slower native component (Raz et al., 1970). RBP has been isolated in pure form and crystallized out as long needles, so it should soon be possible for the structure to be determined by X-ray analysis (Haupt and Heide, 1972).

III. Chemical Nature

A. Heterogeneity of the Preparation

The differences in electrophoretic mobility of the fast, slow, and apo-components arise from differences in the net charge per unit density through the loss, perhaps, of either amide groups (Raz et al., 1970) or a terminal amino acid (Peterson, 1971a) or possibly a peptide during isolation. At the same time some conformational changes probably occur, because not all the apo fraction as isolated seems to have the capacity to take up added retinol (Kirby et al., 1971; Peterson, 1971c) and differences in the fluorescence spectra have been noted between fast and slow components; holo RBP$_s$ shows stronger fluorescence emission at 340 nm than holo RBP$_f$ when irradiated at 278 nm (Kirby et al., 1971) as indicated below in Fig. 6 (Section IV, B, 2).

It has been established that serum several weeks old yields a higher proportion of the faster moving components than does fresh serum (Raz et al., 1970), suggesting that a hydrolytic or proteolytic process is occurring with some denaturation of the protein. Furthermore when RBP is subjected to isotachophoresis on acrylamide gels containing ampholines, at least three faster moving retinol-binding proteins are resolved from the main RBP zone, implying that several amide groups may be lost in turn (Kirby, 1971), as indicated in Fig. 2. Serum contains the proteolytic enzyme plasmin, and perhaps traces contaminating RBP concentrates in the earlier stages could cause some loss of the holoprotein. However, when precautions were taken by adding ϵ-amino hexanoic acid as an inhibitor of proteolytic digestion and by adding some free retinol at various stages of the isolation with a view to keeping RBP loaded with the vitamin, appreciable amounts of apo RBP and RBP$_f$ were generally found in the final purified preparations of RBP. Although some of this heterogeneity appears to have arisen largely during isolation, the existence of some RBP$_f$ or apo RBP in the fresh serum should not be ruled out. They might also be formed as part of normal metabolic processes. The range of conditions of pH used throughout the isolation, 5.5 to 9.5, are not sufficiently strong to break down a peptide bond, but some of the relatively unstable amide groups might be lost. It has been noted that

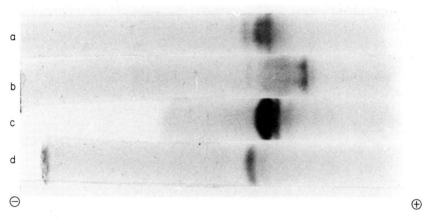

FIG. 2. Isotachophoresis of RBP fractions on acrylamide gel containing ampholines shows microheterogeneity of RBP preparations. (a) $RBP_{fast_{1-3}}$. (b) apo RBP with small amounts of holo RBP_f. (c) holo RBP_{f_1} with a little holo RBP_{f_2}. (d) holo RBP_s and a trace of holo RBP_{f_1}.

amide groups can be removed from asparagine in peptides and proteins even under conditions commonly used in protein isolation procedures (Flatmark, 1966). The deamidation reaction occurs readily even at pH 7 in phosphate buffer, ionic strength 0.15 at room temperature (McKerrow and Robinson, 1971).

1. *Formation of RBP Congeners in Vitro*

It would appear that Visking dialysis tubing is not completely inert with respect to proteins even though it has been carefully treated and washed with chelating agents before use. The loss of peptides from enzymes during purification by prolonged dialysis in Visking membrane has been reported previously (Di Prisco and Strecker, 1970) but not yet fully explained. It is clear that it is advisable to allow proteins to remain in contact with Visking for only the minimal possible time. In our isolation procedure, therefore, we avoided the use of Visking after the initial dialysis to remove fibrinogen and concentrated protein solutions in ultrafiltration cells. The artificial membranes used in the latter cells, however, have also a disadvantage in that some retinol is lost from the protein when concentrates of RBP are passed through them, for example, in concentrating chromatographic and preparative electrophoresis fractions at various stages of the purification process. Some apoprotein is presumably also produced after loss of retinol by oxidative processes. Further changes, however, apparently take place in the apoprotein, since a high proportion of the isolated material is found to be denatured and incapable of binding retinol again. This is illustrated in Fig. 3, which

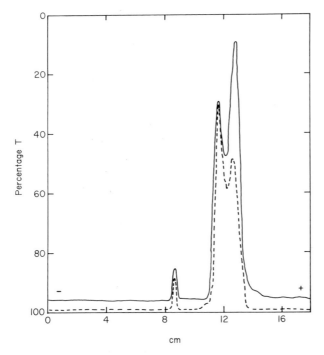

FIG. 3. Scans of protein-stained cellulose–acetate pherograms of an RBP preparation before (—) and after (- - - -) incubation with free retinol. The ratio of the higher mobility apo RBP/holo RBP has changed from being >1 to <1 following the uptake of retinol by apo RBP.

shows scans of protein-stained pherograms of a purified RBP preparation on cellulose acetate before and after incubation with a small amount of free retinol. The treated portion of the preparation can be seen to contain a smaller proportion of the faster moving apoprotein relative to the holo-component, but there still remains a large amount of protein incapable of taking up retinol. Thus the native apoprotein would appear to denature readily so that the high-mobility fraction should perhaps be referred to as "apo"-protein. Apo RBP has been prepared *in vitro* in several ways. Direct extraction of the holoprotein by vigorous shaking with heptane yields apo material (Goodman and Raz, 1972; Peterson and Berggard, 1971). In our experience, however, this occurs only with extreme difficulty and is usually accompanied by considerable denaturation of the RBP. In several trials where purified holo RBP was shaken with heptane under N_2 for 4–5 hours, only a few percent of retinol was extracted and the amount appeared to be closely related to the quantity of the carrier protein which was denatured and unable to take up retinol again. On the other hand, when whole serum is extracted in this way under N_2, the retinol was completely removed, leaving the apoprotein capable of taking the vitamin up again to about 90% of the original level. The other serum proteins must have afforded some protection to the RBP in this case.

Futterman and Heller (1972) have prepared apo RBP in good yield by extracting the lyophilized holo RBP with ethanol in the cold. When this material was redissolved in aqueous solution and freshly prepared retinol added, a rapid reconstitution of the holoprotein took place in 15–20 seconds to a level about 90% of the unextracted control. Again, if holo RBP is dissolved in 6 M guanidine hydrochloride, the retinol is easily extracted by shaking the solution with heptane (Rask et al., 1971), and a good yield of apoprotein is obtained after removal of the guanidine hydrochloride (White, 1973).

Evidence has also been obtained that RBP_f can be produced arti- factually during the isolation and purification of RBP_s. Raz et al. (1970) first noted that preparations of RBP from fresh serum contained smaller amounts of the faster moving holo RBP than those from older batches of serum. Again, after careful stepwise elution of RBP preparations on arginine–Sepharose-6B, Kirby (1971) obtained fairly pure holo RBP_s containing only a few percent of RBP_f. When this material was recon- centrated and passed through the ion exchange column a second time, an increased amount of RBP_f appeared in the eluate. This could only have arisen as an artifact of the procedure. Thus both RBP_f and the "apo" component found in preparations isolated from serum could arise en- tirely artifactually.

2. Possible Formation of Some RBP Congeners in Vivo

It is important to know, however, whether perhaps some apo material is normally present in serum in vivo. This could, perhaps, be encountered after the carrier protein from the liver has given up its retinol to the target tissue cells and then is possibly returning to the liver or the in- testine for recharging with a further load. Smith et al. (1970) carried out radioimmunoassay of RBP in human serum using specific antibody raised in rabbit serum and compared the values obtained with those for free retinol present. On the basis that there is 1 mole of retinol per mole of protein, they found that the two sets of values were in close agreement within experimental errors, implying that there could at best be only a very small amount of apo RBP in normal serum. In a similar exercise the retinol attached to RBP in several samples of fresh normal human serum has been estimated by fluorescence and the protein by immunoassay using rabbit antiserum to RBP, and again good agreement between the values for RBP content was obtained confirming that the amount of apo component which is usually present in normal subjects must be small (Glover *et al.*, 1973).

Recently, Rask *et al.* (1971) isolated from urinary RBP obtained from proteinuric patients a protein with mobility corresponding to an apo-component unable to bind retinol. This, on detailed amino acid analysis, was found to have lost a carboxy-terminal arginine residue compared with a fraction capable of taking up the vitamin. Some of this "apo" material may, therefore, be present in the serum of these patients, or even in normal patients. Furthermore, Smith and Goodman (1971) had clear evidence that the ratio of RBP:retinol was markedly raised above the normal value in patients with chronic renal disease, demonstrating that apo RBP must be present in the sera of these subjects (see Section V, C, 1, *c*). Apo RBP is also present in vitamin A-deficient subjects. The presence, therefore, of apo RBP in pathological serum would suggest that probably traces at least are present in normal serum, but further work still needs to be done to settle this point satisfactorily.

The detection of minor amounts of RBP_f in concentrates of RBP_s is possible by electrophoresis and fluorescence analysis, but it is more difficult to detect traces of RBP_f if present in serum in this way because of the limitation of the sensitivity of the method and the poorer resolution of the two components in the presence of the large excess of serum proteins. Certainly visual examination of the pherogram under UV-radiation indicates that only one symmetrical zone of RBP fluorescence is present and this is shown by the scans in Fig. 4. Thus the main form

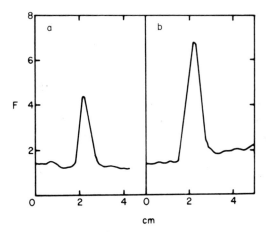

Fig. 4. Fluorescence scan of RBP zone in disc-gel pherograms of (a) normal human serum and (b) pathological serum with an elevated level of RBP. The symmetry of the fluorescence implies the presence of only one holo RBP component.

of holo RBP in normal human serum would appear to be the component with lowest electrophoretic mobility.

B. ELECTROPHORETIC MOBILITY

As mentioned in Section I, RBP was found to have an electrophoretic mobility similar to that of α_1- or α_2-globulin. However, several different procedures were used and some of these introduce, by virtue of the small pore size of the support system, molecular sieving factors which can markedly affect the true electrophoretic mobility of RBP relative to albumin. The problem has been reexamined in our laboratory with a view to determining the influence of these factors so that the various findings may be rationalized and agreement reached concerning the relative mobility of RBP to albumin.

Pure RBP was, therefore, subjected to electrophoresis on (a) cellulose acetate support which has a relatively large pore diameter of 0.4 μm (Chin, 1970) and free from appreciable molecular sieving and adsorption effects and on (b) a 5–15% range of polyacrylamide gels which have increasing molecular sieving effects as the degree of polymerization is raised. Comparable runs were also carried out with human serum under the same conditions. Commercial ceruloplasmin was also used as an additional reference protein on the cellulose acetate system. The results obtained showed clearly that the mobilities of RBP$_s$ and ceruloplasmin relative to albumin were 0.56 and 0.74, respectively. This confirms the previous observations of Glover and Walker (1964) using paper support that RBP has a lower mobility than ceruloplasmin and can be regarded as an α_2-globulin or possibly a fast β-globulin.

With the various strengths of polyacrylamide gels, the following mobilities for RBP (alone) relative to albumin in serum were recorded: 0.70 (5%), 0.75 (7.5%), 0.90 (10%), 1.03 (15%). It is clear that in the highly cross-linked 15% gel, albumin has been retarded relative to RBP so much that it travels behind the latter, so making RBP appear to be a protein with mobility comparable to a prealbumin, and this molecular sieving effect is present to some extent even in 5% gel. Furthermore, the relative mobility of RBP in the presence of other serum proteins as determined from the fluorescence zone in the electrophoretogram on 5% polyacrylamide has been found to be slightly less at 0.65 than when examined alone. Thus when molecular sieving factors are removed the electrophoretic mobility of RBP is that of an α_2-globulin rather than α_1. More recently, Cejka and Poulik (1971) isolated a low molecular weight α_2-globulin from the urine of patients suffering from tubular proteinuria. This has since been identified with urinary RBP as isolated by Peterson and Berggard (1971). Thus, the higher mobility (α_1) reported by Kanai

TABLE I

MOLECULAR WEIGHT (MW) OF HUMAN RETINOL-BINDING PROTEIN

Reference	Ultracentrifugation		Gel filtration (MW)	Amino acid analysis (MW)	Other procedures (MW)
	MW	$s_{20,w}$ (S)			
Kanai et al. (1968)	20,800 ± 200	2.26	20,400	21,600–22,600	—
Raz et al. (1970)	21,300	2.13	—	—	—
eterson (1971a)	21,000	2.3	—	20,600	—
Peterson (1971b)	20,300	—	20,500	—	—
Peterson and Berggard (1971)	21,400	2.3	—	20,500	—
Kirby et al. (1971)	21,940 ± 800	2.05, low concn. 2.03, high concn.	22,400	22,000–22,700	—
White et al. (1972)				22,100	22,130 (osmometry) 21,500 SDS-(electrophoresis)

et al. (1968) and by Peterson (1971a) would appear to arise from the molecular sieving effects of the 7% polyacrylamide system used. Again, the preparative-scale separation on cellulose powder reported by Garbers *et al.* (1960) and on Pevikon C-870 block by Peterson and Berggard (1971) would not really provide sufficiently good resolution to differentiate easily between α_1 and α_2 values.

C. MOLECULAR WEIGHT

The molecular weight of RBP has been determined directly and indirectly by a variety of standard procedures such as (a) ultracentrifugation by sedimentation equilibrium method as described by Edelstein and Schachman (1967), (b) amino acid analysis (Spackman *et al.*, 1958), (c) gel filtration (Andrews, 1965), (d) electronic membrane osmometry (Knauer instrument), and (e) by comparison of the electrophoretic mobility of the complex with sodium dodecyl sulfate (Weber and Osborn, 1969) with values for known standards. Very good agreement has been obtained between the values found by the various research groups using the different techniques. The values set out in Table I show that the molecular weight of human RBP (HRBP) is in the region of 21,000–22,000.

The protein sediments as a single homogeneous component in the ultracentrifuge with sedimentation constants obtained by the various groups as given in Table I. The fact that the value for the constant does not vary with a 5-fold change in concentration indicates that there is no concentration-dependent dimerization of the molecule. Furthermore, when the protein is treated with mercaptoethanol and incubated with sodium dodecyl sulfate to form the SDS complex, and the latter is subjected to electrophoresis on polyacrylamide gel, only one protein zone is present; this indicates that RBP is a single protein and not composed of smaller subunits.

D. AMINO ACID COMPOSITION

The amino acid analysis of pure RBP as prepared by the different groups is given in Table II, which shows that there is reasonably good agreement between the various groups as to the contents of a large number of the amino acids in the protein. The Scandinavian group, however, consistently tend to have a slightly lower total number (179–183) of acids than the others (about 194). RBP contains a high proportion of dicarboxylic acid residues, a proportion of which would be in the amide form in the original protein. It also contains a relatively high concentration of aromatic amino acids, just as does thyroxine-binding prealbumin (PA) (Schultze *et al.*, 1962), with which it readily associates during the isolation procedure (see Section V, B). The few minor differ-

TABLE II
AMINO ACID COMPOSITION OF RETINOL-BINDING PROTEIN

Amino acid	Kanai et al. (1968)	Peterson (1971a)	Vahlquist et al. (1971)	Rask et al. (1971)	Kirby et al. (1971) a	b
Lysine	10–11	10	10	10	11–12	10
Histidine	2	2	2	2	3	2
Arginine	14–15	14	13	14	13–14	13
Aspartic	29	26	26	26	27	29
Threonine	9–10	9	9	9	11	9
Serine	11	11	11	11	12	11
Glutamic	21	18	18	18	20	20
Proline	5–6	6	7	7	6	6
Glycine	12	11	11	11	13	12
Alanine	14–15	13	14	14	15	14
Half-cystine	5–6	5	3	5	6	6
Valine	14	12	12	12	13	11
Methionine	3–4	4	4	4	4	4
Isoleucine	4	4	3	4	4	3
Leucine	14	12	13	13	13–14	13
Tyrosine	8	8	8	8	8	9
Phenylalanine	10–11	10	10	10	10–11	11
Tryptophan	4	6	5	5	4	4
Total residues	189–197	181	179	183	192–196	185

[a] Hydrolysis with 6 N hydrochloric acid.
[b] Hydrolysis with toluenesulfonic acid.

ences in the number of residues found by the different groups for particular amino acids will be resolved once the full sequence has been determined. As mentioned previously (Section III, A), it has been possible to separate the different components in RBP preparations by chromatography on arginine–Sepharose (Kirby, 1971). Some of the faster moving holoprotein RBP_f was isolated in this way from RBP_s and examined for amino acid composition (Kirby et al., 1971). The two were identical within experimental error in respect to the total number of amino acid residues.

E. N-TERMINAL AND C-TERMINAL RESIDUES

Peterson and Berggard (1971) observed that there was one less arginine residue in their higher mobility component (A_1) obtained from urine, which does not bind retinol, compared with the slower moving component which does (B_1). This was confirmed in a more detailed study (Rask et al., 1971) involving (a) the determination of the carboxy- or C-terminal amino acids of the two preparations isolated by affinity chromatography on a prealbumin–Sepharose 6B support and (b) of the "peptide maps" obtained from the tryptic digests of the two preparations. The preparation A_1 was again found to correspond to B_1 with the C-terminal arginine residue removed. This material has an electrophoretic mobility corresponding to that of genuine apoprotein. If it were present to a slight extent in normal serum preparations, it might possibly account for the previous finding that not all the fast-moving apofraction can take up retinol.

A start has been made on the determination of the amino acid sequence of the protein. The N-terminal amino acid has been shown to be glutamic acid by Morgan et al. (1971) and confirmed by others (Rask et al., 1971; White et al., 1972). Morgan and colleagues furthermore determinated the partial sequence of amino acids from the N-terminal end by degrading the reduced and carboxymethylated derivative of RBP using the Edman (1950) procedure as outlined by Blombäck et al. (1966), in a Beckman protein/peptide sequencer. The sequence obtained was as follows:

NH₂-Glu-Arg-Asp-Cys-Arg-Val-Ser-Ser-Phe-Arg-Val-Lys-Glu-Asn-Phe-
　　1　 2　 3　 4　 5　 6　 7　 8　 9　 10　11　12　13　14　15

Rask et al. (1971) have also determined the carboxy-terminal amino acids of their A_1 and B_1 protein preparations of RBP isolated from human urine. They subjected the reduced and alkylated proteins to carboxypeptidases A and B separately and together. The former enzyme alone did not digest the peptide but carboxypeptidase B and the mixture of the two readily degraded both proteins. Arginine was liberated from the C-terminal end of the B_1 protein, with lysine appearing as the penultimate acid, whereas lysine was the terminal residue in protein A_1. Glutamic acid and serine were the next internal residues to lysine in both proteins. A similar study was carried out on holo RBP preparations from human serum by White et al. (1972). They were unfortunately unable to confirm the above findings. Both carboxypeptidases acted on the RBP and from short term as well as longer term digests, the carboxy-terminal sequence was found to be as follows:

NH₂-Glu- - - - - - - - - - - - -Lys-Arg-Tyr-Ala-Gly-Ser-Leu-COOH

This was repeated several times on different preparations. The marked difference between these two sets of results is difficult to understand unless the urinary protein may have lost a small peptide portion in passing through the kidney. Yet the amino acid composition of the RBP obtained by Peterson (1971a) from plasma appears to be similar to that for the RBP from urine. Again, Vahlquist and Peterson (1972) have confirmed the previous finding that arginine is the C-terminal residue in RBP preparations from both human and cynomolgus monkey plasma. Thus a different explanation seems more likely. Since the total number of residues in the RBP isolated by the Scandinavian group tends to be lower than that found in Goodman's laboratory and ours, it may be that their preparation lost a small peptide artifactually during the isolation procedure, which involved ultrafiltration through Visking dialysis tubing: The latter process has been found by Di Prisco and Strecker (1970) to cause a loss of terminal peptides of certain enzymes concentrated by it, but the manner by which this is done has not yet been explained. Perhaps something similar may have happened in this case. Further work is needed to clarify this point.

RBP has been examined for components other than the polypeptide. Hydrolyzates have been examined for sugar residues, but none have been found (Peterson, 1971a; Kirby, 1971). Again, all groups who have isolated RBP in a pure state have reported the absence of phospholipids from the molecule so the attachment of retinol must be direct to the protein in a specific hydrophobic pocket rather than by admixture with other lipids in micellar form as with the larger lipoproteins.

IV. Physical Properties

A. Isoelectric Point

Purified RBP isolated from the urine of subjects suffering from proteinuria was examined by the isoelectric focusing technique on a gradient of pH 3 to 6 stabilized by a sucrose gradient from 0 to 50%. Four protein peaks were recorded in the pH range from 4.4 to 4.8 (Peterson and Berggard, 1971) and from the intensity of UV absorption at 330 nm, the major holoprotein component was focused at the upper end of the pH range. The other components with lower isoelectric points will correspond to the higher mobility RBP components which result from minor modifications of the slower moving holo RBP by the loss of amide groups. This is the expected region for the isoelectric point from the evidence of its behavior on columns of the anion exchanger DEAE-cellulose where it is eluted close to ceruloplasmin and after albumin (Glover and Walker, 1964).

B. Spectrophotometric Studies

1. UV Absorption

The absorption spectrum of RBP$_s$ shows two absorption bands with λ_{max} at 278 nm and 329 nm with a shoulder at 283 nm and λ_{min} at 246 nm

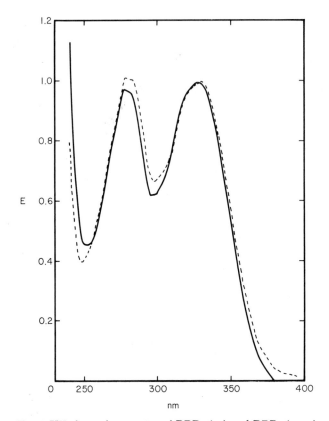

Fɪɢ. 5. UV-absorption spectra of RBP$_s$ (—) and RBP$_f$ (- - - -).

and 298 nm (Fig. 5). These bands correspond to the specific absorption
of the aromatic amino acids and retinol, respectively. The spectrum of
RBP$_f$ is almost identical with that of RBP$_s$ except for some loss in persistence of the protein band in RBP$_f$ as reflected in the bathochromic
shift of λ_{min} from 248 to 252 nm. There is also some loss of absorption at
290 nm relative to the retinol component. The $E_{1cm}^{1\%}$ value at 278 nm as
determined by the various research groups is given in Table III.

The optimal ratio of maximal absorption of retinol component to that
of protein E_{329}:E_{280} obtained in our laboratory for pure RBP$_s$ was 0.97
and for pure RBP$_f$ 1.05. Kanai *et al.* (1968) have also obtained preparations of RBP where the retinol absorption exceeds slightly that of the
protein band. When such preparations are extracted with organic solvent
approximately 0.95 mole of retinol is recovered per mole of protein indicating that the latter has only one specific acceptor site for the vitamin.

TABLE III

THE UV-EXTINCTION COEFFICIENT OF RETINOL-BINDING PROTEIN

$E_{1\,cm}^{1\%}$, 278 nm	Reference	Remarks
16.5 (corr. to 19.4)	Kanai et al. (1968)	Protein determined by Lowry procedure
18.7	Peterson and Berggard (1971)	Assayed on preparation depleted of retinol
17.5	Kirby et al. (1971)	Protein assayed by number of interference fringes in synthetic boundary formed in ultracentrifuge
18.6	Peterson (1971a)	Calculated from ϵ 39,100 and MW 21,000
17.5	Rask et al. (1972)	Value stated, but Peterson (1971a) reference given

2. Fluorescence

Retinol-binding protein has a characteristic green fluorescence very similar to that of free retinol in hydrocarbon solvent but considerably stronger in intensity. The fluorescence yield of retinol in human RBP is of an order of magnitude greater than that for the free vitamin dissolved in light petroleum, which is superior to some more polar solvents for inducing fluorescence (Peterson and Rask, 1971; Goodman and Leslie, 1972).

The emission spectra of aqueous solutions of both RBP_s and RBP_f when irradiated with UV at 278 nm are given in Fig. 6. The main fluorescence λ_{max} at 456 nm is the same for both proteins, but the subsidiary λ_{max} at 340 nm representative of tryptophan has about 50% lower intensity relative to that of retinol in the case of RBP_f indicating a marked change in conformation of the protein from the native state. This is consistent with the lowered UV absorption in the 290 nm region for RBP_f compared with RBP_s. The fluorescence spectra determined on a Hitachi-Perkin Elmer MPF 2A instrument are corrected for variations in the energy source. The excitation spectra for these two proteins with emission measured at 456 nm are also the same (Fig. 7).

The effects of increasing concentrations of urea up to $9\,M$ on the intensity of fluorescence of solutions of holo RBP_s and holo RBP_f have been examined (Kirby, 1971; White, 1973). The optical densities of the RBP solutions were kept low at 0.08 to minimize any self-absorption effects. Exposure of RBP_s to urea solutions of up to $6\,M$ concentration causes the fluorescence intensity of retinol as irradiated by UV at 332 nm to increase gradually above normal for about 2 hours; after this time the intensity slowly declines. At higher concentrations of urea, i.e., from

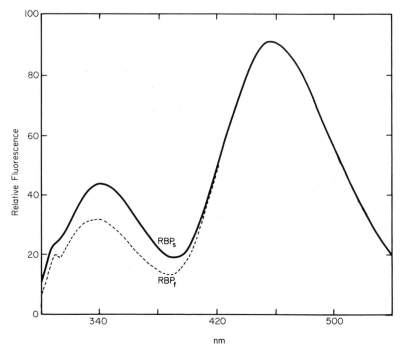

Fig. 6. Fluorescence spectra of RBP$_s$ (—) and RBP$_f$ (- - - -) excited at 278 nm.

8–9 M, the fluorescence declines slowly from the outset and more rapidly after about 2 hours. The tryptophan fluorescence of RBP$_s$ is also increased by 2–6 M urea to a level about 35% above the normal value, when the molecule is irradiated at 270 nm or 292 nm. A quick rise occurs in the first hour, and a more gradual one subsequently. At higher concentrations of urea the tryptophan fluorescence rises much more rapidly with time.

RBP$_{f_1}$ is less stable than RBP$_s$ to urea concentrations above 6 M as evidenced by a more rapid decline in retinol fluorescence with time particularly when irradiated with UV at 292 nm or below. However, both forms of RBP are fairly stable to urea even up to 6 M since little or no loss of retinol fluorescence occurs until after about 4 hours. The urea may be dialyzed away and the holoproteins appear to return to their original state.

RBP$_{f_2}$ is much less stable than the other forms; its retinol fluorescence falls quickly on exposure to UV in the presence of increasing concentrations of urea. Thus the binding region around the retinol molecule becomes relatively polar more quickly than in the case of the other

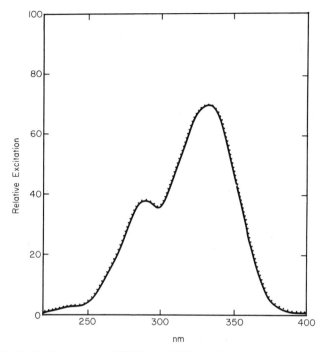

FIG. 7. Excitation spectra of RBP$_s$ and RBP$_f$ with emission measured at 456 nm.

proteins. It seems likely that the molecules with greater mobility, and therefore increased number of negatively charged groups (through loss of amide groups), have a more open structure as a result perhaps of the increased mutual repulsion of these similarly charged carboxyl groups.

C. CIRCULAR DICHROISM AND OPTICAL ROTATORY DISPERSION

Circular dichroic spectra were determined on solutions of human RBP and PA individually and together as complex and also on apo RBP by Gotto et al. (1972). Their findings were subjected to computer analysis, and it was concluded that RBP contained a high proportion (80%) of disordered structure with no α-helical and only 20% β-type structure. The spectra of RBP and PA in approximately equimolar mixture as in complex were additive, indicating that no change in secondary structure of RBP took place on binding to PA. The differences in the CD spectra of holo and apo RBP did not give any indication of a significant change in conformation of the protein arising from the binding of retinol.

The optical rotatory dispersion spectrum of holo RBP was also reported by Rask et al. (1972) and Kirby et al. (1971), and the observed Cotton effects were also regarded as indicating that the molecule contained little α-helical or β-pleated sheet type of structures. Thus the protein is coiled in a highly organized and specific manner with three –S–S– bridges but containing only very little repetitive type structure.

V. Biochemistry

A. Apo Retinol-Binding Protein and Specificity of Binding Site

As mentioned in Section III, A, there is often some apo RBP formed during the isolation of the holoprotein. This apo material can be resolved electrophoretically from the holo compound, but it is not suitable for use in studies on the binding site, because of further deterioration which has taken place in the protein rendering a substantial portion of it incapable of taking up retinol again. It is, therefore, necessary to prepare fresh apoprotein for binding studies.

Goodman and Raz (1972) prepared apoprotein by extracting RBP in 0.02 M phosphate buffer at pH 7.4 with heptane by shaking it at 100 strokes per minute for 6 hours in an N_2 atmosphere. The holoprotein was extracted to the extent of approximately 80%. This material was capable of taking up retinol dispersed on Celite and shaken with it. By this procedure retinoic acid was found to combine with apo RBP to the extent of 75% of that of all-*trans*-retinol and the isomers, 13-*cis*- and 11′,13′-di-*cis*-retinol were taken up to 50% and 80%, respectively, of all-*trans* material. The capacity of the apoprotein to bind other terpenoid alcohols, such as phytol and cholesterol, however, was small, and it was negligible in the cases of retinyl esters and β-carotene. The fact that some retinoic acid and *cis* isomers of retinol can be bound to the protein, all of which have the β-ionone ring, polyene side chain, and a polar end group, whereas other cyclic and straight-chain terpenoid alcohols cannot, indicates that the hydrophobic pocket in the molecule is highly specific. Greater specificity, however, may well be expressed by the protein *in vivo* in a competitive situation where the all-*trans*-retinol could be taken up preferentially to, say, neo-vitamin A (13′ isomer) or the specific 11′-*cis* isomer found in the retina. Although retinoic acid from the above type of experiment seems to be capable of entering the RBP-binding site *in vitro*, there is recent evidence indicating that it is really transported by serum albumin in vitamin A-deficient animals maintained on retinoic acid (Smith *et al.*, 1973). Such animals have only a comparable amount of apo RBP circulating in their bloodstream as that encountered in retinol-deficient animals (Muto *et al.*, 1972), and the release of more protein from the liver is not triggered by the administration of retinoic acid, as it is with retinol dosing (see Section V, C, 2, *e*). The behavior therefore of retinoic acid toward apo RBP *in vivo* is substantially different from the *in vitro* situation, further highlighting the specificity of the protein.

B. INTERACTION OF RETINOL-BINDING PROTEIN WITH PREALBUMIN

During the isolation of RBP it is invariably found to be associated with thyroxine-binding prealbumin (Alvsaker *et al.*, 1967; Kanai *et al.*, 1968; Raz *et al.*, 1970; Vahlquist *et al.*, 1971; Kirby *et al.*, 1971). There has not, however, been complete agreement about the properties of the complex and indeed as to its size in the earlier work. It has been suggested (Kanai *et al.*, 1968) that complex formation between the two proteins is of considerable physiological importance in preventing the loss of RBP from the plasma by glomerular filtration of the relatively small protein molecule which has a molecular weight of 22,000 daltons compared with 70,000 or 85,000, respectively [as reported by Raz *et al.* (1970) and Peterson (1971b)] for a 1:1 complex with prealbumin which has a molecular weight of 56,000 daltons approximately (Gonzalez and Offord, 1971). Equally well the possibility should perhaps be considered, however, that such a complex might inhibit the passage of retinol into target tissues and be therefore disadvantageous to the organism. Retinol has to be transferred to epithelial tissues and consequently must penetrate some distance from blood vessels, and the lower the molecular weight of the transport protein, the easier becomes the passage through the tissues. Furthermore, from the facts that retinol is more difficult to extract from the complex than from RBP and more stable toward oxidation in the former, it has been suggested that complex formation is also important for protecting the labile conjugated unsaturated molecule during its transport to the target tissues. This carries the implication, however, that the transfer of the retinol from RBP to its acceptor in the target cell is possibly made more difficult unless a mechanism is invoked which can readily dissociate the retinol from the complex when required.

It is generally accepted by all groups that RBP, as isolated from plasma by ion-exchange chromatography, reacts readily with prealbumin in this purified form, but in the isolation process a considerable portion of RBP has undergone change in that some amide groups are lost which may influence its affinity for prealbumin. Again interaction of the two native proteins may be influenced *in vivo* by the presence of the other proteins in large excess in serum. These observations together with the difficulty in obtaining an agreed molecular weight for the complex prompted a more detailed examination of the interaction between these two proteins and in particular tests on serum using the mildest possible physicochemical procedures to determine the degree of affinity of RBP for PA under conditions obtaining in serum (White *et al.*, 1971).

1. *Examination of RBP-PA Complex Prepared from Pure Components*

Raz *et al.* (1970) examined the chemical and physical properties of the two individual proteins and factors affecting their interaction in solution such as pH, temperature, and urea concentration. From sedimentation velocity tests in the ultracentrifuge using mixtures of the two components they observed that a 1:1 complex was formed with Svedberg sedimentation constant 4.57–4.7. Again, chromatography of mixtures of RBP and PA on Sephadex G-100 columns equilibrated with a range of buffers indicated that most of the RBP was eluted in the form of complex at pH 5, but at pH 8.6–10.3 appreciable dissociation occurred. At physiological pH 7.4, however, only 5% of the RBP was in the free form. The addition of $6\,M$ urea completely disrupted the complex and also reduced the affinity of PA for thyroxine but did not affect the binding of retinol to RBP.

The observations on the behavior of RBP and PA mixtures in the ultracentrifuge have been confirmed by Kirby (1971), who obtained similar values of 4.80 and 4.78 for the Svedberg coefficients of synthetic 1:1 molar mixtures of the two proteins by successive scans at 330 nm and 280 nm, respectively. Confirmation that RBP and PA interact to form a complex in physiological saline containing phosphate buffer, pH 8.0, has been obtained by White (1973) through measurements of the osmotic pressures of the pure components and of various mixtures of the two using a Knauer electronic membrane osmometer. When PA was in excess, the osmotic pressures exerted indicated that the RBP was largely bound as approximately 1:1 complex, but when RBP was in excess more than 1 mole of RBP appeared to become associated with 1 mole of PA, but not in reproducible proportions. The affinity constant for the first site was calculated to be of the order of 10^6 mol/liter as opposed to an earlier value of 10^8 suggested by Raz *et al.* (1970). The binding between the two could possibly involve more than one site. This would not be surprising since PA is assembled from 4 identical subunits (Gonzalez and Offord, 1971). The affinity of PA for the additional molecules of RBP, however, could be influenced allosterically by the first one to become bound.

The fluorescence of retinol does not appear to be appreciably different when bound in the complex compared with that in free form (Goodman and Leslie, 1972; Peterson and Rask, 1971), but studies on fluorescence polarization (Goodman *et al.*, personal communication) clearly indicate that there are 4 binding sites on prealbumin for retinol-binding proteins.

2. Examination of Plasma for RBP–PA Complex

First, human plasma diluted slightly with acid citrate dextrose anti-coagulant during collection was subjected to ultrafiltration directly through the wide-diameter UM 20, PM 30, and XM 50 Amicon membranes in the 2-liter vessel. The membranes permit proteins with molecular weights less than approximately 20,000, 30,000, and 50,000, respectively, to pass but retain those of higher molecular weight. The ultrafiltrates were examined for the presence of RBP and PA, respectively, by allowing portions to react with the appropriate specific rabbit anti-RBP sera on agar plates by the radial diffusion procedure (Mancini et al., 1965). A positive reaction for RBP was observed in all ultrafiltrates, and the concentrations of RBP in the first runnings through the membranes were approximately 25% of the value for the original whole plasma in the case of the XM 50 membrane, falling down to 5–10% level for the UM 20. No prealbumin was detected in any ultrafiltrate even that from the XM 50 experiment, after concentrating it 10-fold. The fact that ultrafiltration can separate the two proteins would suggest that a significant proportion of RBP must be in the free state in serum despite the presence of a 2–3-molar excess of prealbumin. Smith and Goodman (personal communication), however, using fresh serum and smaller diameter membranes have repeated the ultrafiltration on fresh serum but not been able to detect RBP in the ultrafiltrate in significant amounts. It is appreciated, however, that the immunological method of assay includes apo- as well as holoprotein so that some of the material passing through the membrane in the former experiment may have been in the apo form, and this is known not to combine with PA as readily as the holoprotein.

Second, serum (6.5 ml) was chromatographed directly on Sephadex gel G-50 and G-100 columns to determine whether it is possible to resolve by molecular sieving the smaller RBP molecule away from prealbumin or the complex. Successive fractions eluted from the column were examined by double diffusion against the specific antisera to RBP and PA on Ouchterlony (1962) plates. Qualitatively it was established that some RBP tended to be retained longer on the columns than PA. From estimates of the level of precipitation formed by immunodiffusion with the same aliquots for each fraction, the peak concentration of RBP occurred later than that for PA, implying again that some RBP was present in the free form. In studying the turnover of RBP and PA, respectively, in the monkey, Vahlquist (1972) added ^{125}I-labeled PA and ^{3}H-retinol-labeled RBP to serum and chromatographed the mixture on Sephadex gel G-100. From measurements of the elution pattern of both RBP and PA using the respective antisera and of the radioactivity, he found that most of the RBP appeared to be bound to PA in the serum, but a significant fraction (10%) was free; of this, 25% was holoprotein. It would seem from the above experiments, therefore, that a significant amount of RBP must be in the free form *in vivo*, and presumably this could normally pass through the glomerulus.

Third, human serum was examined for complex directly, using specific rabbit antisera to RBP and PA on Ouchterlony plates (White *et al.*, 1971). Peterson (1971c) observed that when RBP-PA complex is treated with anti-RBP, it dissociates and only RBP is precipitated, whereas when anti-PA reacts with the larger PA component of the complex, the RBP is precipitated with it. The first observation, but not the latter, has been confirmed in our laboratory. Rabbit anti-PA was added directly to serum in sufficient excess to precipitate completely all PA, and the mixture was allowed to diffuse against the specific antiserum to RBP. The RBP remained unaffected and diffused out to form precipitin to the same extent as the controls, an observation clearly indicating that the RBP was free. Similar experiments with purified RBP:PA (1:1) complex yielded the same result. Thus the complex is very readily dissociated by either type of antibody, so the association between the two proteins is relatively much weaker than that for their respective antibodies. Further confirmation that the affinity constant of the complex is not so high as 10^8 mol/liter (Raz *et al.*, 1970) but nearer 10^6 mol/liter was obtained from the findings of Smith and Goodman (1971) that, in chronic renal disease, RBP accumulates in serum to a level in excess of that of PA on a molar basis whereas the concentration of PA remains unchanged. From estimates of the amount of free RBP resolved from complex by chromatography of the plasma on Sephadex G-100, and from the different effects the kidney exercises on the two proteins, it was calculated that a considerable portion of the holo RBP must be free to account for the findings. These can best be explained on the basis that some RBP normally undergoes glomerular filtration and reabsorption, as has been shown for other low molecular weight proteins, such as insulin (Chamberlain and Stimmler, 1967), and L chains or Bence-Jones protein (Mogielnicki *et al.*, 1971). It is considered that in kidney disease filtration is impaired. Similar observations have been made by Peterson (1971c). Using fluorescent labeled antibodies, the distribution of RBP and PA has been studied by White (1973) in histological sections of normal human kidney obtained postmortem. PA was confined entirely to the blood capillary network within the glomerulus whereas RBP was observed in approximately equal concentration in the tissue surrounding Bowman's capsule and cells lining the convoluted tubules, as in the blood capillaries. It is clear, therefore, that an appreciable amount of RBP is normally filtered through the glomerulus and is reabsorbed in the tubules. It was suggested by Peterson (1971c) that each holo RBP molecule is used once, and that when the retinol is removed from it, the carboxy-terminal amino acid arginine is also removed, so making the protein incapable of reaction with PA again. This free apo RBP is then thought to be filtered through the glomerulus. This concept would not be in accord with the known high concentration of retinol which occurs mostly in the free alcohol form and is probably bound to RBP in normal kidney. Again, from the well-known high level of autofluorescence observed in kidney sections in renal tubules, it would seem much more likely that a significant amount of the RBP passing through the glomerulus is probably in the holo form. Furthermore, in cases of infection of the kidney where reabsorption is impaired, holo RBP is often found in the urine, which has been used as a source for its isolation (Peterson, 1971a).

C. Factors Affecting Retinol-Binding Protein Level in Plasma

Direct analysis of a number of samples of normal plasma from groups of men and women by Kimble (1939) and of some subjects dosed with retinol (Week and Sevigne, 1950) has clearly shown that the level of retinol in plasma tends to be higher in the male than the female. This has also been confirmed in experimental rats (Moore et al., 1951). That this previously observed difference is merely a reflection of the changes in level of the specific carrier proteins has been borne out by the recent work of Smith et al. (1970). The mean values for adult males and females were found to be 47 μg/ml and 42 μg/ml, respectively. Similarly, the prealbumin levels of males (263 $\pm$ 7 μg/ml) was significantly higher than the level for females (238 $\pm$ 6 μg/ml).

In addition to the above sex difference, the plasma level of RBP increases with age, the correlation being closer in male than in female subjects (Smith et al., 1972). The level rises from 1.5 mg/100 ml, approximately, in children (3–4 years old) to nearly three times this amount in the adult. Hormonal activity will probably also affect the RBP level, particularly in the female since changes in retinol concentration have previously been noted to occur over the menstrual cycle (Laurence and Sobel, 1953). Direct measurements of RBP have not yet been done, however, to check whether the latter observed changes also arise through alterations in the concentration of the carrier protein in plasma.

Superimposed on the fluctuations caused by normal physiological responses are the effects arising from infection and disease. Any disorder of metabolism which causes an alteration in either the supply of retinol or the biosynthesis of its carrier protein or the rate of catabolism and excretion of the holoprotein and its components will affect the equilibrium level in plasma. Thus nutritional disorders arising from a deficiency of either retinol or of first-class protein would markedly lower the vitamin A status of the individual, as has been found in cases of kwashiorkor. Similarly, diseases like tropical sprue and jaundice affecting the absorption of the vitamin from the intestine could also bring about a lowering of RBP levels. Again, any disorders affecting (i) the liver, where retinol is stored and RBP is synthesized, and (ii) the kidney, controlling its retention in the body, should also have an important influence on the "normal steady state" level of RBP. Some of these effects are discussed in the following section.

1. *Plasma RBP Levels in Disease*

The retinol levels in plasma of subjects suffering from various diseases have been observed previously to change significantly from normal, and the findings of many workers have been reviewed and discussed fully by Moore (1957). It is interesting now to find, largely through the work of Goodman and colleagues, that many of these earlier observations can be explained as arising principally from alterations in the metabolism of the carrier protein rather than of retinol per se. At present, most studies have involved diseases affecting the liver and kidney, but some work has also been done on disorders affecting the retina.

a. Liver. Previous studies on retinol metabolism have shown that the retinol level in plasma changed in patients with disorders affecting the liver. Abnormal dark adaptation, one of the earliest signs of vitamin A deficiency, was encountered in patients with cirrhosis of the liver (Patek and Haig, 1939), and administration of vitamin A relieved the dark adaptation. Furthermore examination of patients with other liver disease, such as chronic hepatitis (Popper *et al.*, 1943) and infective hepatitis (Harris and Moore, 1947), also revealed depressed levels of retinol in plasma. Smith and Goodman (1971) have investigated the effect of liver disease on RBP levels in plasma. In patients suffering from such liver disorders the plasma levels of retinol, RBP, and PA were all found to be lower than normal. Despite the reduction in plasma levels, the molar ratios of the three components remained within the normal range, indicating that the effect of the disease in reducing the rates of synthesis and release of RBP from liver was comparable to that on PA. Examination of serial samples from 19 cases with acute hepatitis showed that the plasma concentrations of all three substances returned to normal with gradual improvement in the condition of the patients. Negative correlations between RBP concentration and the levels of bilirubin, glutamate–oxaloacetate transaminase and alkaline phosphatase were also found in patients with acute hepatitis. It was also noted that in patients with cystic fibrosis, plasma retinol, RBP, and PA levels were significantly lower than in normal controls (Smith *et al.*, 1972). The correlation was mainly with patients showing hepatic involvement rather than with those where gastrointestinal and pulmonary tissue was involved. This diminished capacity of the liver to synthesis these proteins in the diseased state has also been confirmed by Kindler (1972), who comments on the possible diagnostic value of estimating RBP levels in the serum of patients with liver disease. Knowledge of the RBP level can be useful in assessing the course of acute infective hepatitis and to a limited extent in the differentiation of various forms of jaundice.

b. Thyroid. Administration of thyroxine induces vitamin A deficiency and the onset of xerophthalmia (Sure and Buchanan, 1937) whereas dosing A-deficient animals with thyroid inhibitor prolonged their lives (Wiese *et al.*, 1948) implying an inverse relationship between the two. In 14 hyperthyroid cases examined by Smith and Goodman (1971), PA and RBP levels in serum were significantly lower than normal although the molar ratios of retinol:RBP and RBP:PA remained unaffected. In 7 hyperthyroid cases, however, the absolute levels of the above components as well as their molar ratios remained within the respective normal ranges.

c. Kidney. The elevation of retinol in plasma of patients suffering renal disorders had been noted in earlier clinical studies (Popper *et al.*, 1948), but unexplained, and the presence of retinol in the urine of patients suffering from nephrosis had also been reported (Boller and Brunner, 1936; Catel, 1937). From the fact that retinol is fat soluble, its excretion in the aqueous medium in the presence of protein was taken to mean that it was probably secreted as a lipoprotein complex across the damaged glomerular membrane. This excretion of the vitamin, together with the elevated level in plasma of nephritic cases, although not fully understood, indicated that the kidney played some role in vitamin A metabolism. Again, it had also been shown that male experimental rats made deficient in the vitamin and then given small doses of retinol, stored more of the free alcohol form in the kidney than in the liver (Moore and Sharman, 1950). This confirmed that the kidney was involved with some aspect of retinol metabolism. It was of some interest, then, when Peterson and Berggard (1971) isolated a form of RBP from the urine of proteinuric patients. This protein was similar to that previously isolated from blood plasma by Kanai *et al.* (1968), and it became clear that the presence of retinol in the urine was due to the leakage of this specific retinol-binding protein across the damaged glomeruli or to failure of reabsorption of normally excreted materials.

The ability of RBP to form a complex with PA (MW 56,000) under physiological conditions, led Kanai et al. (1968) to suggest that this interaction was a necessary mechanism of physiological importance for preventing the loss of the vitamin and its carrier protein RBP (MW 22,000) across the glomeruli. Although this provides a most satisfactory explanation for the interaction of these two proteins, it is also possible that reabsorption of the secreted protein would equally well prevent the loss of the vitamin from animal body. Later experimental work showed that both these processes were involved in preventing the loss of the vitamin. Smith and Goodman (1971) examined the changes in retinol, RBP, and PA levels in 26 patients with chronic renal disease and made several significant observations. First, retinol levels were elevated but the PA levels were normal. Second, the molar ratios of RBP:PA and RBP:retinol were markedly raised above the normal range. In many cases the level of RBP was in molar excess over PA instead of being approximately one-third of the latter. The addition of more PA to serum from such patients caused some of the free RBP to become bound. It was established, therefore, that RBP was present in serum in three forms, holo RBP complexed with PA, free holo RBP, and some apo RBP. This observation has also been made independently by Peterson (1971c), who has at the same time shown that the free apo RBP does not bind to PA as well as the normal native holo RBP. Amino acid analysis of the purified free fraction indicated that it differed from the native protein in that it had lost a C-terminal arginine residue. Peterson suggested that the unbound RBP in the serum of these patients with renal failure represented material which had lost its retinol in carrying out its function and would have been metabolized by the kidney under normal conditions. The high levels of RBP in cases of nephritis has also been confirmed in our laboratory, but in the fluorescence assay used for the holoprotein only one fluorescent band with the same electrophoretic mobility as normal RBP was observed (see Fig. 4b). Thus, if there were two forms of holo RBP present, they must either have had the same mobility or not been sufficiently well resolved.

d. *Retinal Disorders.* The plasma level of RBP has been investigated in 51 male and female patients suffering from retinitis pigmentosa and from 8 carriers of the disease (Rahi, 1971). The etiology of this disease, which is characterized by progressive degeneration of the neuroepithelium, is not known (Duke-Elder and Dobree, 1967), but there is some evidence that cases appear to be associated with vitamin A deficiency (Campbell et al., 1964). Although it is known that the retinol level is not always low in subjects suffering from retinitis pigmentosa (Krachmer et al., 1966), the form in serum has not been examined in detail and possibly a partial deficiency of RBP could be a contributory factor to this disorder.

Rahi (1971) estimated the RBP levels in the above cases (28 males and 23 females) by radial immunodiffusion of the serum samples against rabbit antiserum to human RBP and compared the results against the mean value obtained for healthy adult males (10) and females (10). He found that 82% of the patients had a mean value of 76% of that for the normal adult value, indicating that the RBP level tended to be low in these patients, but it is not known whether there is any etiological relationship between the low levels of RBP and the degree of retinal degeneration. The above results should, however, be treated with caution since the immunoassay estimates total RBP (i.e., both apo and holo forms), and no information is available on the proportion of holo RBP present.

e. Protein-Calorie Malnutrition and Retinol Deficiency. Vitamin A deficiency is still prevalent in many countries and is a major cause of preventable blindness among preschool children, particularly in some socially and economically deprived regions of Central and South America, Southeast Asia, and the Middle East (McLaren *et al.*, 1964). It is usually associated with a low level of protein-calorie nutrition caused by the poor diet, which often lacks a good source of retinol or provitamin A. The various degrees of deficiency from night blindness to corneal xerosis and keratomalacia are encountered in many of these young children after weaning. Although their protein-calorie malnutrition can be treated, in a considerable number of cases regrettably the deficiency symptoms in the eye have proceeded beyond the less severe reversible stages, so that permanent blindness results. The various public health authorities, therefore, have an immediate major problem in attempting to prevent these severe deficiency symptoms developing in young children until longer-term educational and better nutritional programs can be instituted.

Since retinol is transported to the eye and indeed to other target tissues on a specific carrier protein, clearly the retinol deficiency can be caused either through a lack of the vitamin itself or of the various carotenoid provitamins A in the diet or through deficiency of protein in the diet to make the carrier. Again there is the additional problem that, as the organism runs out of available retinol, the intestinal mucosa like other epithelial tissues would be affected. This could lead to a deterioration in absorptive capacity so that even the marginal diets cannot be used optimally. It is therefore useful to know when treating certain deficient children not only the level of holo RBP in the plasma, but also whether protein must also be administered to ensure that there is sufficient carrier in the bloodstream to enable the administered retinol to be effectively utilized. This has now become possible with the development of new sensitive techniques for the assay of RBP in very small quantities of plasma or serum (see Section VI). Since it has been isolated in pure form, its antiserum has been prepared and is now commercially available. This has enabled total RBP to be determined either by the radial immunodiffusion procedure of Mancini *et al.* (1965) or by the radioimmunological assay devised by Smith and Goodman (1971). Holo-RBP can now be measured fluorimetrically on small quantities of serum (20 μl) and independently of any other form of the vitamin present, so it should now be possible to gain a better understanding of the changes which take place in RBP levels as protein and retinol deficiency develop. Protein deficiency presumably has a marked effect on RBP because, from its amino acid composition compared with that of albumin, it has higher contents of the essential amino acids leucine, methionine, tyrosine, and tryptophan, but half that of lysine, which is known to be low in cereal proteins, particularly rice, usually a major dietary component for many groups of people living in tropical and subtropical zones.

Preliminary studies by Goodman and colleagues (personal communication) have confirmed the importance of restoring adequate protein to the diet of certain groups of children suffering from kwashiorkor and retinol deficiency despite the presence of provitamin A in the diet. The restoration of good quality protein to the diet enabled the children to synthesize RBP for the mobilization of latent reserves of the vitamin in the liver. In our own laboratory and in collaboration with Dr. D. Karjadi, Indonesia, some investigations have been carried out on the relative levels of holo and apo RBP to albumin in groups of young children suffering from different degrees of malnutrition and vitamin A deficiency. In cases where the albumin level of the serum had declined from a good normal level of $>4\%$ to about 3.5%, there were still traces of holo RBP present in amounts equivalent to retinol levels of 3–10 μg/100 ml, but the patients showed night blindness. When the albumin content dropped below this level, holo RBP was absent, but there was still an appreciable amount of apo RBP in circulation at a level ($\equiv$20 μg of retinol per 100 ml). In the more severely affected patients with xerophthalmia index down to X_2, the protein level had declined below 3.0%. It seemed, however, that while traces of retinol were present in the serum, the organism was capable of maintaining a modest level of serum albumin, but once the retinol had disappeared from the serum, the organism lost the capacity to regulate or maintain its albumin level, which declined to very low levels indeed in the region of 1.5–2.5% of serum.

It is this group of severely protein-deficient children who clearly needed both retinol and protein to be restored urgently. In fact in view of their weak condition and presumably poor digestion and absorption capacity, it would be better to administer initially protein hydrolyzates along with retinol or preferably retinal, which is absorbed more efficiently (Glover *et al.*, 1948).

Some apo RBP was invariably encountered in these vitamin A-deficient children, but none of it was found to be capable of taking up free retinol *in vitro* from a 10-fold excess adsorbed on Celite and shaken with it, whereas holo RBP in normal serum from which the retinol has been extracted with heptane will readily take up the vitamin under the same conditions (Muhilal and Glover, unpublished work). Similarly sera from retinol-deficient rats containing extremely low levels of holo RBP were found not to take up any additional retinol from a Celite dispersion of the vitamin shaken with them indicating that any apo-RBP present was unable to do so.

2. Regulation of Retinol-Binding Protein Metabolism

When weanling rats are run out of vitamin A, the level of total RBP declined gradually during the onset of deficiency from 50 ± 4 $\mu g/ml$ to 20 ± 2 $\mu g/ml$ after 27 days and then more slowly down to 13 ± 2 $\mu g/ml$ after 75 days. After 3–4 weeks most of the circulating RBP was in the apo form, the retinol level having dropped from the normal 30 $\mu g/100$ ml down to 2 $\mu g/100$ ml. Animals maintained on retinoic acid-supplemented diet continued to grow normally when the retinol disappeared, but they also showed similar levels of RBP in the deficient state.

The level of immunoreactive RBP in the livers of the deficient animals, however, were approximately 4 times higher than the control level. Administration of retinol to similar groups of these rats caused the RBP level in serum to rise rapidly to a concentration well above the normal steady-state value within 5 hours (the first interval sampled). This then declined slowly back to the normal value after approximately 24 hours (Muto *et al.*, 1972). This has been confirmed by Muhilal and Glover (1973), who examined the effect of retinol and protein deficiency on serum RBP levels in the rat. When retinol was restored to their deficient animals orally, the level of RBP in the serum reached its peak value between 1.5 and 2 hours after dosing. It would appear that apo-RBP accumulates in the liver in the absence of retinol and that once retinol is available the holo RBP is formed and released immediately into the bloodstream. Thus the retinol appears to be involved in triggering the release of the holoprotein from the liver. It was interesting to find that the level of retinol bound to RBP reached in the serum of vitamin A-deficient rats on the low protein diet (5% of total calories) did not reach so high a peak value (65 $\mu g/100$ ml) as in the serum from rats on the more normal protein diet (20% of total calories) where 97 µg/100 ml was attained. Not only were the livers of the former group smaller, but the rate of RBP synthesis was presumably lower so that apo RBP would not accumulate in them to the same extent. Smith, Goodman, and colleagues established that the release of RBP occurred just as readily in the presence of inhibitors of protein biosynthesis, indicating clearly that it was the preformed apoprotein which contributed to the rising serum RBP levels. This raises the problem of the origin of the small amount of immunoreactive apo RBP invariably present in the deficient rat or human plasma.

The fact that a small amount of apo material ($\equiv$13 µg/ml) was present even after 75 days on the retinol-deficient diet (Muto et al., 1972) points to the possibility that a small amount of apo RBP or similar immunoreactive metabolic fragments can escape from the liver, when retinol is absent to complete the assembly of the whole carrier protein. This is supported by experimental work on the turnover of RBP.

3. *Turnover of RBP*

From experiments on the administration of radioactivity labeled RBP-^{125}I, Vahlquist (1972) has shown that in male cynomolgus monkeys (*Macaca irus*) the half-life of RBP associated with prealbumin was 6–7 hours, whereas that of uncomplexed RBP was only 2 hours. The more rapid time for the uncomplexed material is believed to arise from the fact that it can be filtered across the glomerular membranes in the kidney and becomes metabolized readily after reabsorption; the complexed material does not escape in this way and must therefore undergo additional metabolic steps in other tissues before being completely broken down. It would seem, however, from the above experimental work that the level of holo RBP in plasma, like that of other proteins, represents the steady-state position between its rate of biosynthesis and release from the liver and its metabolism in the tissues, particularly the kidney, and clearly any disorder affecting these two tissues, as was shown earlier, can markedly affect the serum level.

VI. Methods of Assay

A. Methods Involving Extraction of Retinol

Previous analytical procedures for retinol in serum generally involved denaturation of the proteins with ethanol followed by extraction of the lipid fraction from the aqueous ethanol phase with diethyl ether or mixtures of diethyl ether with light petroleum to inhibit the loss of ether in the aqueous layer or the uptake of water and ethanol by the ether layer. The organic solvent is then evaporated off in a stream of nitrogen leaving the lipid residue, which contains the free retinol originally attached to the specific protein carrier along with the retinol within chylomicra, in transport from the intestine to the liver. The latter retinol is mainly in the esterified form and can be separated from the free alcohol by chromatography. In general the amount of ester in normal plasma constitutes less than 5% of the total vitamin A except perhaps when a food rich in the vitamin is undergoing absorption. Usually samples are collected from subjects in the fasting state so that assays for total vitamin A can be regarded as a reliable estimate of the physiologically active retinol present without having to eliminate esterified retinol from the assay by chromatography.

All these procedures can result, however, in some loss of the vitamin before the final colorimetric or fluorimetric measurement is carried out. Again, the free retinol is labile and the color formed with either antimony trichloride or trifluoroacetate is transient so that assays must be completed quickly and in duplicate for accuracy. The smallest volume of serum required for an acceptable assay for total retinol using a standard 1-cm cuvette in the spectrophotometer is 2–3 ml. With modern microcells and rapid recording spectrophotometers, it is possible to assay the total retinol colorimetrically in about 0.2 ml of serum, and in 0.1 ml by the fluorimetric procedure of Thompson *et al.* (1971). The latter assay, however, is affected by the presence of fluorescence from variable amounts of other lipids in the extracts, such as phytofluene, and from color quenching materials like the carotenes, so that corrections have to be applied.

B. Direct Fluorometric Assay

A new microfluorometric method has now been devised which enables the retinol attached to holo RBP to be determined directly with very little processing of the sample required (Glover *et al.*, 1972, 1973). Advantage is taken of the fact that the fluorescence of retinol attached to its carrier protein is approximately 10-fold more intense than free retinol in hydrocarbon solvent. Furthermore, by leaving the retinol attached to the protein it remains stable throughout the assay. The process involves subjecting a small amount (20 μl) of the sample to electrophoresis in the dark in the standard polyacrylamide disc gels. The electrophoretic mobility of the RBP relative to albumin is 0.6, so that it lies in a zone of the gel free from other chromoproteins* which would

---

* Heavily hemolyzed samples can give trouble due to hemoglobin running close to RBP, and conditions of the electrophoresis have then to be altered slightly to overcome the interference.

quench its fluorescence. Again the larger β-lipoproteins do not penetrate the gel easily so their possible interfering lipids are also well separated from RBP. The gel is transferred into a long quartz cuvette and mounted on a carriage to enable it to be scanned by a narrow beam of UV light in a modified recording Chromoscan (Joyce-Loebl, Mark II), the fluorescence of the RBP produces a peak in the recording and since the intensity of fluorescence is linearly related to concentration of the material, the area of the peak gives a direct quantitative measure of the amount of holo-RBP present in the sample (see Fig. 4). The instrument can be calibrated directly using quinine sulfate as a reference standard for checking its performance, and with a series of blood sera whose holo-RBP has been established by assay of the retinol present in extracts from large quantities. The electrophoresis takes only 2 hours, and the scanning only a few minutes. Many samples (16–24) can be run in parallel. Thus with duplicate assays the reproducibility of the method has been found to be <2–3%, and extremely good between different operators. These new techniques should now permit a much more accurate study of the biochemical changes which occur in RBP than has been possible hitherto and should lead to a better understanding of vitamin A metabolism generally.

C. Immunoassay

The immunoassay procedures using specific antisera for the protein carrier are much more sensitive than the colorimetric methods for retinol. Consequently they are potentially capable of providing a more reliable estimate of the microquantities of retinol bound to the protein in serum and tissues. However, the antiserum can also react with the apoprotein as well as with large metabolic fragments; hence under circumstances where apoprotein is likely to be present, it is necessary to carry out both types of assay to obtain the complete picture.

Smith et al. (1970) devised a radioimmunoassay procedure using the specific rabbit antiserum to RBP and ^{131}I-labeled RBP. It enables the total protein to be assayed (in the 10–100 ng range) with accuracy and a good degree of reproducibility ($\pm 8\%$ SD), and yet requires only 1 μl of plasma per assay tube. This covers more than adequately the very low plasma levels likely to be encountered in retinol and protein-deficient subjects. The procedure does require the extra preparation of the pure labeled RBP and other special reagents which may tend to limit its use for much routine work, which can be done satisfactorily by the slightly less accurate but more widely used radial immunodiffusion procedure of Mancini et al. (1965), which is almost equally sensitive. The latter still requires the preparation of pure RBP as control standard but is simpler and quicker to carry out on a large number of samples. It involves measurement of the diameter of the ring of precipitin formed when the RBP in the test solution diffuses from a small well into the surrounding thin layer of agar gel containing sufficient excess of the specific antiserum dissolved in it. The concentration of RBP is directly related to the area of the circle of precipitin formed within a reasonable concentration range. Standard solutions within the appropriate range are run alongside the unknowns for each thin plate of gel. Duplicate assays by this procedure generally do not differ by more than 10%.

More recently attempts have been made to raise antibodies to vitamin A itself, using it as a hapten linked to albumin (Conrad and Wirtz, 1973). This may prove to be useful in locating the vitamin within target tissues, but further development appears to be necessary before the procedure will be fully effective at the micro level.

Using the radioimmunoassay technique, Goodman and colleagues have studied the degree of homology between the retinol-binding proteins of the different species. As might be expected there is a marked resemblance between the RBP molecules of the different primates and some domesticated animals, but those of the rodents are appreciably different with the guinea pig lying in between.

VII. Species Differences in Retinol-Binding Proteins

A number of the retinol-binding proteins have now been isolated in the pure state from various species, such as the monkey (Vahlquist and Peterson, 1972), ox and pig (Huang *et al.*, 1972; McCullough *et al.*, 1973), and rat (Muto and Goodman, 1972), so that when their sequences of amino acids have been determined it will be possible to check the changes which have taken place in their evolution.

In isolating the above proteins it has been necessary to modify the procedures as used for human-RBP, except in the case of the cynomolgus monkey, which resembles the latter more closely. The first differences encountered are those of affinity for the anion exchangers used in their chromatography. For example, the rat-RBP (RRBP) is eluted from the column of DEAE–Sephadex along with albumin instead of much later as in the case of human RBP (HRBP) (Muto and Goodman, 1972). Again the pig protein (PRBP) does not bind to arginine–Sepharose 6B compared to HRBP but binds to sulfanilic acid–Sepharose 6B (McCullough, 1973). Some of these differences arise partly from variations in the respective prealbumin proteins with which they associate to form complexes as in the case of the human complex, but there are other intrinsic differences reflected in their physical and chemical properties summarized in the Tables IV and V. Although the C-terminal amino acids appear

TABLE IV

Properties of Retinol-Binding Proteins from Different Animal Species

Property	Human[a]	Cynomolgus monkey[b]	Ox[c]	Pig[c]	Rat[d]
Molecular weight					
a. By sedimentation equilibrium	20,000–22,000	20,500	20,000	20,300	20,000
b. By amino acid analysis	20,500–22,700	Similar to human	—	21,000	—
c. By SDS-gel electrophoresis	21,500	—	20,700	20,600	19,600
Isoelectric point	4.4–4.8	4.4–4.8	—	—	—
Mobility relative to albumin	α_1, α_2	α_1	α_2	α_2	β
UV Absorption, λ_{max} (nm)	280, 330	280, 330	279, 329	279, 329	280, 330
$E_{1\,cm}^{1\%}$, 280 nm	17.5	—			19–20
Fluorescence					
excitation λ_{max} (nm)	332		333	333	343, 463 (uncorrected)
emission λ_{max} (nm)	456		457	457	—
NH$_2$-terminal residue	Glutamic acid	Glutamic acid	Glutamic acid	Glutamic acid	—
COOH-terminal residue	Arginine,[e] leucine[f]	Arginine	Leucine	Leucine	—

[a] Kanai et al. (1968), Peterson (1971a), Kirby et al. (1971).
[b] Vahlquist and Peterson (1972).
[c] McCullough et al. (1973).
[d] Muto and Goodman (1972).
[e] Peterson (1971a).
[f] White et al. (1972).

TABLE V

AMINO ACID COMPOSITION OF RETINOL-BINDING PROTEINS
FROM DIFFERENT ANIMAL SPECIES

Amino acid	No. of residues/mole protein		
	Monkey[a]	Pig[b]	Ox[c]
Lysine	10	12	10–11
Histidine	2	4	3–4
Arginine	14	10	10
Aspartic acid	26	25	24
Threonine	9	8	9
Serine	11	12	12
Glutamic acid	19	21	20
Proline	6	6	8
Glycine	11	13	14
Alanine	14	13	15
Half-cystine	5	6	5
Valine	12	11	10
Methionine	3	4	3
Isoleucine	5	5	6
Leucine	13	12	12–13
Tyrosine	8	8	8
Phenylalanine	10	10	11
Tryptophan	5	4	3

[a] Peterson (1971a).
[b] McCullough (1973).
[c] C. Jay, S. M. Weston, and J. Glover (unpublished observations).

to be the same for some of the species examined so far, differences have already been noted in the order of the amino acids internal to leucine (unpublished observations). It is clear from these that the molecular weights differ only slightly, and only 1 mole of retinol is bound per mole of protein. The UV absorption, fluorescence, excitation, and emission spectra also show similar characteristics to the corresponding ones for HRBP. It is interesting that the molecular weight of HRBP appears to be significantly greater than those of the pig, ox, and rat in turn, and this is borne out by the amino acid analyses (Table V) the further study of which, along with others, should provide useful information on evolutionary trends among these key proteins which are important for the survival of the species.

REFERENCES

Alvsaker, J. D., Haugli, F. B., and Laland, S. G. (1967). *Biochem. J.* **102**, 362.
Andrews, P. (1964). *Biochem. J.* **91**, 222.
Andrews, P. (1965). *Biochem. J.* **96**, 595.

Blombäck, B., Blombäck, M., Edman, P., and Hessel, B. (1966). *Biochim. Biophys. Acta* **115**, 371.

Boller, R., and Brunner, O. (1936). *Klin. Wochenschr.* **16**, 441.

Campbell, D. A., Harrison, R., and Tonks, E. H. (1964). *Exp. Eye Res.* **3**, 374.

Catel, W. (1937). *Klin. Wochenschr.* **16**, 52.

Cejka, J., and Poulik, M. D. (1971). *Arch. Biochem.* **144**, 775.

Chamberlain, M. J., and Stimmler, L. (1967). *J. Clin. Invest.* **46**, 911.

Chin, H. P. (1970). "Cellulose Acetate Electrophoresis," p. 20. Ann Arbor-Humphrey Sci. Publ., London.

Clausen, S. W., and McCoord, A. B. (1938). *J. Pediat.* **13**, 635.

Clausen, S. W., Baum, W. S., McCoord, A. B., Rydeen, J. O., and Breese, B. B. (1942). *J. Nutr.* **24**, 1.

Conrad, D. H., and Wirtz, G. H. (1973). *Immunochemistry* **10**, 273.

Di Prisco, G., and Strecker, H. J. (1970). *FEBS (Fed. Eur. Biochem. Soc.), Lett.* **6**, 89.

Duke-Elder, S., and Dobree, J. H. (1967). "System of Ophthalmology," Vol. 10, p. 602. Kimpton, London.

Edelstein, S. J., and Schachman, H. K. (1967). *J. Biol. Chem.* **242**, 306.

Edman, P. (1950). *Acta Chem. Scand.* **4**, 283.

Flatmark, T. (1966). *Acta Chem. Scand.* **20**, 1487.

Futterman, S., and Heller, J. (1972). *J. Biol. Chem.* **247**, 5168.

Ganguly, J., Krinsky, N. I., Mehl, J. W., and Deuel, H. J. (1952). *Arch. Biochem. Biophys.* **38**, 275.

Garbers, C. F., Gillman, J., and Peisach, M. (1958). *S. Afr. J. Med. Sci.* **23**, 34.

Garbers, C. F., Gillman, J., and Peisach, M. (1960). *Biochem. J.* **75**, 124.

Glover, J., and Walker, R. J. (1964). *Exp. Eye Res.* **3**, 327.

Glover, J., Goodwin, T. W., and Morton, R. A. (1947). *Biochem. J.* **41**, 97.

Glover, J., Goodwin, T. W., and Morton, R. A. (1948). *Biochem. J.* **43**, 109.

Glover, J., Moxley, L., and Muhilal (1972). *Proc. Int. Congr. Nutr., 9th, Mexico City* Sum. p. 60.

Glover, J., Moxley, L., Muhilal, and Weston, S. M. (1973). *Clin. Chim. Acta* (in press).

Gonzalez, G., and Offord, R. E. (1971). *Biochem. J.* **125**, 309.

Goodman, DeW. S., and Leslie, R. B. (1972). *Biochim. Biophys. Acta* **260**, 670.

Goodman, DeW. S., and Raz, A. (1972). *J. Lipid Res.* **13**, 338.

Gotto, A. M., Lux, S. E., and Goodman, DeW. S. (1972). *Biochim. Biophys. Acta* **271**, 429.

Hack, M. H. (1956). *Proc. Soc. Exp. Biol. Med.* **91**, 92.

Harris, A. D., and Moore, T. (1947). *Brit. Med. J.* **1**, 553.

Haupt, V. H., and Heide, K. (1972). *Blut* **24**, 94.

Hoch, H., and Hoch, R. (1946). *Brit. J. Exp. Pathol.* **27**, 316.

Huang, C. C., Howarth, R. E., and Owen, B. D. (1972). *Comp. Biochem. Physiol.* **42B**, 57.

Johannesson, S., Alvsaker, N. D., and Laland, S. G. (1969). *FEBS (Fed. Eur. Biochem. Soc.), Lett.* **2**, 146.

Kanai, M., Raz, A., and Goodman, DeW. S. (1968). *J. Clin. Invest.* **47**, 2025.

Kimble, M. S. (1939). *J. Lab. Clin. Med.* **24**, 1055.

Kindler, U. (1972). *Deut. Med. Wochenschr.* **97**, 1821.

Kirby, W. (1971). Ph.D. Thesis, Univ. of Liverpool, Liverpool.

Kirby, W., White, G. H., and Glover, J. (1971). *Biochem. J.* **123**, 31P.

Krachmer, J. H., Smith, J. L., and Tocci, P. M. (1966). *Arch. Ophthalmol.* **75,** 661.
Krinsky, N. I., Cornwell, D. G., and Oncley, J. L. (1958). *Arch. Biochem. Biophys.* **73,** 233.
Laurence, P. A., and Sobel, A. E. (1953). *J. Clin. Endocrinol. Metab.* **13,** 1192.
Leitner, Z. A., Moore, T., and Sharman, I. M. (1952). *Brit. J. Nutr.* **6,** X.
McCullough, L. (1973). M.S. Thesis, Univ. of Liverpool, Liverpool.
McCullough, L., Jay, C., Kirby, W., and Glover, J. (1973). Unpublished observations.
McKerrow, J. H., and Robinson, A. B. (1971). *Anal. Biochem.* **42,** 565.
McLaren, D. S., Oomen, H. A. P. C., and Escapini, H. (1964). *Trop. Georgr. Med.* **16,** 271.
Mancini, G., Carbonara, A. O., and Heremans, J. F. (1965). *Immunochemistry* **2,** 235.
Mogielnicki, R. P., Waldmann, T., and Strober, W. (1971). *J. Clin. Invest.* **50,** 901.
Moore, T. (1957). "Vitamin A." Elsevier, Amsterdam.
Moore, T., and Sharman, I. M. (1950). *Biochem. J.* **34,** 355.
Moore, T., Sharman, I. M., and Ward, R. J. (1951). *Biochem. J.* **49,** xiii, xxxix.
Morgan, F. J., Canfield, R. E., and Goodman, DeW. S. (1971). *Biochim. Biophys. Acta* **236,** 798.
Muhilal, and Glover, J. (1973). *Eur. Conf. Nutr., Cambridge, Eng. Abs.,* p. 54.
Muto, Y., and Goodman, DeW. S. (1972). *J. Biol. Chem.* **247,** 2533.
Muto, Y., Smith, J. E., Milch, P. O., and Goodman, DeW. S. (1972). *J. Biol. Chem.* **247,** 2542.
Ouchterlony, O. (1962). *Progr. Allergy* **6,** 30.
Patek, A. J., and Haig, C. (1939). *J. Clin. Invest.* **18,** 609.
Peterson, P. A. (1971a). *J. Biol. Chem.* **246,** 34.
Peterson, P. A. (1971b). *J. Biol. Chem.* **246,** 44.
Peterson, P. A. (1971c). *Eur. J. Clin. Invest.* **1,** 437.
Peterson, P. A., and Berggard, I. (1971). *J. Biol. Chem.* **246,** 25.
Peterson, P. A., and Rask, L. (1971). *J. Biol. Chem.* **246,** 7544.
Pett, L. B., and LePage, G. A. (1940). *J. Biol. Chem.* **132,** 585.
Popper, H., Steigmann, F., and Zevin, S. (1943). *J. Clin. Invest.* **22,** 775.
Popper, H., Steigmann, F., Dubin, A., Dyniewicz, H. A., and Hesser, F. P. (1948). *Proc. Soc. Exp. Biol. Med.* **68,** 676.
Porath, J., and Fornstedt, N. (1970). *J. Chromatogr.* **51,** 479.
Rahi, A. H. S. (1971). *Brit. J. Ophthalmol.* **56,** 647.
Rask, L., Vahlquist, A., and Peterson, P. A. (1971). *J. Biol. Chem.* **246,** 6638.
Rask, L., Peterson, P. A., and Björk, J. (1972). *Biochemistry* **11,** 264.
Raz, A., and Goodman, DeW. S. (1969). *J. Biol. Chem.* **244,** 3230.
Raz, A., Shiratori, T., and Goodman, DeW. S. (1970). *J. Biol. Chem.* **245,** 1903.
Schultze, H. E., Heimburger, N., and Frank, G. (1962). *Biochem. Z.* **336,** 388.
Smith, F. R., and Goodman, DeW. S. (1971). *J. Clin. Invest.* **50,** 2426.
Smith, F. R., Raz, A., and Goodman, DeW. S. (1970). *J. Clin. Invest.* **49,** 1754.
Smith, F. R., Underwood, B. A., Denning, C. R., Varma, A., and Goodman, DeW. S. (1972). *J. Lab. Clin. Med.* **80,** 423.
Smith, J. E., Milch, P. O., Muto, Y., and Goodman, DeW. S. (1973). *Biochem. J.* **132,** 821.
Spackman, D. H., Stein, W. H., and Moore, S. (1958). *Anal. Chem.* **30,** 1190.
Sure, B., and Buchanan, K. S. (1937). *J. Nutr.* **13,** 521.
Thompson, J. N., Erdody, P., Brien, R., and Murray, T. K. (1971). *Biochem. Med.* **5,** 67.

Vahlquist, A. (1972). *Scand. J. Clin. Lab. Invest.* **30**, 349.

Vahlquist, A., and Peterson, P. A. (1972). *Biochemistry* **11**, 4526.

Vahlquist, A., Nilsson, S. E., and Peterson, P. A. (1971). *Eur. J. Biochem.* **20**, 160.

Weber, K., and Osborn, M. (1969). *J. Biol. Chem.* **244**, 4406.

Week, E. F., and Sevigne, F. J. (1950). *J. Nutr.* **40**, 563.

White, G. H. (1973). Ph.D. Thesis, Univ. of Liverpool, Liverpool.

White, G. H., Weston, S. M., Kirby, W., and Glover, J. (1971). *Biochem. J.* **126**, 10P.

White, G. H., Weston, S. M., and Glover, J. (1972). *FEBS (Fed. Eur. Biochem. Soc.), Lett.* **27**, 107.

Wiese, C. E., Mehl, J. W., and Deuel, H. J. (1948). *J. Biol. Chem.* **175**, 21.

Vitamin D, Calcium, and Protein Synthesis

R. H. WASSERMAN AND R. A. CORRADINO

*Department of Physical Biology, New York State Veterinary College,
Cornell University, Ithaca, New York*

I. GENERAL INTRODUCTION

Vitamin D, discovered some 50 years ago, was early shown to affect the growth and general health of animals. Its specific effects on calcium absorption and metabolism were also apparent early in its history. A significant question is whether the more general manifestations of vitamin D activity are mediated indirectly through an improved metabolism of calcium, or whether vitamin D per se elicits direct effects on growth, protein synthesis, and so forth. No clear-cut answer is available, but in this review several different aspects of the problem of vitamin D action and the function of calcium are approached.

The first part (I) is concerned primarily with the more specific effects of vitamin D on calcium metabolism, with emphasis on its proposed role in the synthesis of particular proteins thought to be involved in calcium translocation. The second part (II) deals with the broader aspects of the function of calcium and possibly vitamin D, including the available evidence implicating calcium and calcium-binding proteins in inter-cellular communication, cell aggregation, differentiation, and proliferation and an examination of a possible unifying mechanism underlying the role of calcium, parathyroid hormone, cyclic AMP, and, at least in-directly, vitamin D on cell and tissue growth.

Certain of the more obvious roles of the ubiquitous calcium ion in biological processes have been extensively covered in other recent reports, reviews and monographs; this justifies their exclusion from consideration here. These areas include: (1) calcification of bones and other tissues (Urist, 1966; Neuman, 1969; Comar and Bronner, 1969; Talmage, 1970; Baylink et al., 1970; Vaughan, 1970; Eanes and Posner, 1970; Nichols and Wasserman, 1971; Talmage and Munson, 1972); (2) muscle con-traction, i.e., excitation–contraction coupling, in skeletal muscle (Wine-grad, 1969; Martonosi et al., 1971; Katz and Repke, 1973), cardiac muscle (Reddy and Honig, 1972; Langer, 1973) and smooth muscle (Andersson, 1972); (3) nerve excitation, i.e., depolarization–secretion coupling, at the motor nerve terminal (Rahaminoff, 1970; Cooke et al., 1973), at sympathetic nerve endings (Kirpekai et al., 1968), and in the brain (Blaustein et al., 1972); (4) glandular secretion, i.e., stimulus–secretion coupling, in acetylcholine release from the adrenal medulla (Douglas, 1968; Poisner and Hava, 1970; Poisner, 1973), protein (Heisler et al., 1972) and amylase (Kanno, 1972) release from the pancreas, follicle-stimulating hormone release from the pituitary (Jutisz and de la Llosa, 1970), calcitonin release from the thyroid (Bell, 1970), PTH release from the parathyroid (Targovnik et al., 1971) and numerous other sites (Rubin, 1970); (5) synthesis of nucleic acids (Kaplan and Richman, 1973), proteins, most prominently PTH (Au et al., 1970; Cohn et al., 1972), but also ACTH-stimulated protein synthesis in the adrenal gland (Farese, 1971) and vitamin D-induced CaBP synthesis in organ-cultured chick intestine (Corradino and Wasserman, 1971a), phospho-lipids (Abdel-Latif and Smith, 1972), and adrenal steroids (Birmingham and Bartova, 1973). (6) activation or regulation of enzymes including lipoxidase (Koch, 1968), pyruvate carboxylase (Kimmich and Rasmus-sen, 1969), glutamic dehydrogenase (LeJohn et al., 1969), lipoprotein lipase (Posner and Morales, 1972), pyruvate kinase (Meli and Bygrave, 1972), and parathyroid hormone peptidase (Fischer et al., 1972); (7) membrane structure and function (Manery, 1969); (8) substrate uptake by mitochondria (Scarpa and Azzone, 1968; Harris and Berent, 1969; Mela and Chance, 1969; Carafoli and Crovetti, 1973). This listing is by no means all-inclusive but should lead the interested reader to other pertinent literature. Most of all, it should impress the reader with the pervasive nature and vital importance of calcium's role in diverse physiological processes, obviously prerequisites for growth, maintenance, and the good health of the individual.

PART I

VITAMIN D, PROTEIN SYNTHESIS, AND CALCIUM TRANSPORT

II. INTRODUCTION, PART I

Vitamin D is required for the optimal absorption of calcium. It also elicits effects on the skeleton (Wasserman et al., 1973; Omdahl and DeLuca, 1973) and kidney (Taylor and Wasserman, 1972). With regard to the intestine, vitamin D appears to increase both the active transport of calcium and the diffusional permeability of the intestinal membranes to this cation (Wasserman and Taylor, 1969). The movement of calcium out of bone is certainly enhanced by vitamin D, but its exact direct role on bone formation remains unclear at present (Omdahl and DeLuca, 1973). Whether vitamin D enhances the transfer of calcium across the kidney tubule is also not yet clear (see below).

The problems of the physiological effect of vitamin D on calcium metabolism are still enormous, and considerable effort is being dissipated in this direction. The tack of this section of the chapter is to emphasize the role of vitamin D on protein synthesis as related to calcium translocation. The next section emphasizes the more general effects of vitamin D and/or calcium on growth, mitosis, replication, cell aggregation, and so forth.

III. BIOCHEMICAL TRANSFORMATIONS OF VITAMIN D

Recent work of considerable significance has clearly demonstrated that the vitamin D molecule is metabolized in the body to more biologically active forms. The first of note is the 25-hydroxylation reaction which occurs in the liver, to produce 25-hydroxycholecalciferol ($25\text{-}OHD_3$) (Omdahl and DeLuca, 1973). Although initially championed as the active metabolite, $25\text{-}OHD_3$ was shown to be the forerunner of another biologically active derivative, 1,25-dihydroxycholecalciferol [$1,25\text{-}(OH)_2D_3$] (Haussler et al., 1971; Lawson et al., 1969a,b; Cousins et al., 1970; Myrtle et al., 1970). The $1,25\text{-}(OH)_2D_3$, produced in the kidney (Fraser and Kodicek, 1970), acts more rapidly than either D_3 or $25\text{-}(OH)D_3$ (Haussler et al., 1971; Myrtle and Norman, 1971; Omdahl et al., 1971) and localizes in cells of established target tissues, i.e., intestine and bone (Kodicek, 1973). Although the antirachitic activity of $1,25\text{-}(OH)_2D_3$ is no greater than that of D_3 or 25-OHD_3 (McNutt and Haussler, 1973), it potently enhances calcium translocation in tissue culture of intestine (Corradino and Wasserman, 1971a; Corradino, 1973a) and of bone (Raisz et al., 1972; Reynolds, 1973), and is now considered to be the active form of the vitamin.

As will be discussed subsequently, the formation of 1,25-$(OH)_2D_3$ by the kidney is feedback regulated. Since it acts on tissues remote from its production site, 1,25-$(OH)_2D_3$ meets the criteria and definition of a hormone. It was also reported that the hydroxylation of D_3 by liver enzymes is product inhibited (Bhattacharyya and DeLuca, 1973), although there is disagreement on this point (Tucker et al., 1973). Tucker et al. (1973) also gave evidence for the presence of the 25-hydroxylase enzyme in kidney and intestinal tissue.

Two other prominent metabolites that have been uncovered are 24,25-dihydroxycholecalciferol, produced in the kidney under conditions in

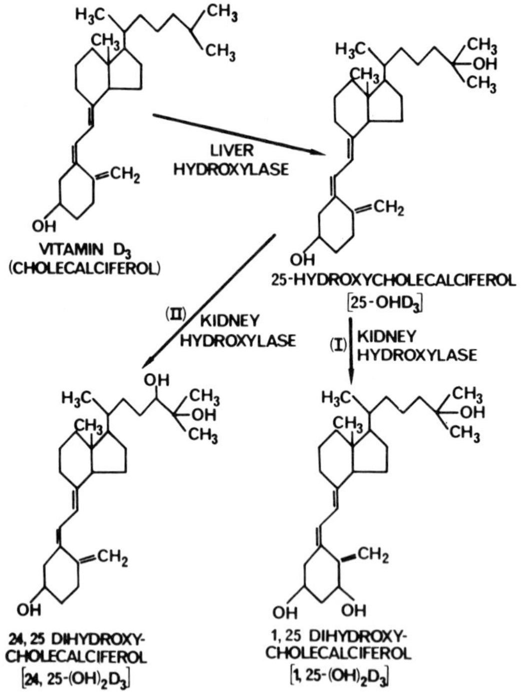

Fig. 1. Primary metabolism of vitamin D_3. The conversion of cholecalciferol to 25-OHD_3 occurs in the liver. The hydroxylation of 25-OHD_3 in kidney can yield 1,25-$(OH)_2D_3$ by reaction (I) or 24,25-$(OH)_2D_3$ by reaction (II). Reaction (I) appears to predominate in calcium deficiency and under conditions of a greater physiological need for calcium, and reaction (II) predominates when reaction (I) is depressed, as under high levels of dietary calcium or strontium, according to Omdahl and DeLuca (1973).

which the formation of $1,25\text{-}(OH)_2D_3$ is depressed or impaired (Omdahl and DeLuca, 1973), and 25,26-dihydroxycholecalciferol, identified in plasma of pigs given large doses of vitamin D_3 (Suda et al., 1970).

Other forms of vitamin D with biological activity are $5,6\text{-}trans\text{-}D_3$, $5,6\text{-}trans\text{-}25\text{-}OHD_3$, $1\text{-}\alpha\text{-}OHD_3$, dihydrotachysterol$_3$ (DHT$_3$), and 25-OHDHT$_3$ (Omdahl and DeLuca, 1973). Some of these show specificity with regard to the particular target tissue affected.

Vitamin D esters, glucuronides, and a sulfate have been identified and examined in detail by various groups (cf. Wasserman and Corradino, 1971, for summary).

A scheme of vitamin D metabolism is given in Fig. 1.

IV. PROTEIN SYNTHESIS AND VITAMIN D ACTION ON CALCIUM METABOLISM

The early suggestion that a protein synthetic event was required for vitamin D action dates back to the studies of Lindquist (1952). It was noted that the administration of vitamin D to rats did not yield an immediate effect on calcium metabolism but that a certain lag period was required. This lag period is now known to be comprised of several events. These include the translocation of vitamin D_3 from source (skin, diet) to liver and then to kidney, with their concomitant hydroxylation reactions. The dihydroxy derivative is next transported to the target tissue. After the tissue-active form $[1,25\text{-}(OH)_2D_3]$ localizes in the target site, there is still a significant latent period before the onset of the physiological effect (Haussler et al., 1971; Frolik and DeLuca, 1972). The evidence given below indicates that the synthesis of a specific protein or proteins is the final event before the expression of vitamin D action.

A. INHIBITORS OF PROTEIN SYNTHESIS

Eisenstein and Passavoy in 1964 reported that actinomycin D prevented the hypercalcemic effects of large doses of vitamin D (10,000 IU) in rats and mice. This was followed by several papers which indicated that actinomycin D, puromycin, and cycloheximide thwarted the response of the animal to vitamin D (Schachter and Kowarski, 1965; Zull et al., 1965; Norman, 1965). The responses measured were calcium absorption in vivo and in vitro and changes in blood calcium levels. Whereas the aforementioned reports were concerned with acute effects of the protein inhibitors, Bosmann and Chen (1966) administered actinomycin D chronically (about 2 μg/day for 14 days) to chicks fed vitamin D-deficient (rachitic) or vitamin D-supplemented diets. Calcium absorption was depressed by actinomycin D in the vitamin D-replete chicks but was unaffected in the rachitic animals.

There was general concurrence with the hypothesis that vitamin D action must be preceded by a protein synthetic event at the DNA–RNA transcription level. Recently, it was observed that the blockade of vitamin D effect on calcium absorption imposed by actinomycin D could be circumvented if 1,25-$(OH)_2D_3$ were injected into rats; 25-OHD_3 was inactive (Tanaka et al., 1971). It was proposed that DNA–RNA transcription at the intestinal site was not required, but that the induction step occurred in kidney cells where 25-OHD_3 causes the formation of the appropriate enzymes for the conversion of 25-OHD_3 to 1,25-$(OH)_2D_3$ (Tanaka and DeLuca, 1971a). This proposal was difficult to accept since Fraser and Kodicek (1970) showed that rachitic chick kidney homogenates could rapidly and immediately form 1,25-$(OH)_2D_3$ from the precursor, i.e., no evidence for a transcriptional time lag. The actinomycin D sensitivity of the rat kidney conversion mechanism now seems to be a consequence of the rapid turnover of 25-hydroxycholecalciferol-1-hydroxylase and its messenger, and the continual need for renewal of these factors (Tanaka et al., 1972).

Despite the difficulty in demonstrating an effect of actinomycin D on 1,25-$(OH)_2D_3$ action in the rat intestine, this has not been the case in chick intestine. In embryonic chick intestine maintained in organ culture (see Section V, A, 1, b), the presence in the culture medium of either actinomycin D or α-amanitin, a specific inhibitor of nuclear RNA polymerase, prevented the activity of 1,25-$(OH)_2D_3$ in the culture medium on the induction of CaBP and the stimulation of radiocalcium accumulation (Corradino, 1973c). In later studies, Lawson and Emtage (1973) and Tsai et al. (1973) reported that actinomycin D, when given to chicks prior to 1,25-$(OH)_2D_3$, inhibited the calcium absorptive process. In the Tsai et al. (1973) experiment, the protein inhibitor was given 4 times at 2-hour intervals. These latter investigators also showed that, in the chick, actinomycin D did not affect kidney 25-hydroxycholecalciferol-1-hydroxylase activity but that cycloheximide significantly reduced the concentration of this kidney enzyme.

The apparent disparity of the response of rats and chicks to actinomycin D might indicate a fundamental difference due to species. This would be surprising but not entirely unexpected because of other differences in vitamin D metabolism by the two species, such as the absoluteness of the requirement for exogenous sources of the vitamin.

B. RNA Labeling and DNA Template Activity

The incorporation of labeled uridine and orotic acid into RNA of intestinal mucosa was shown to be stimulated by administering vitamin D to rachitic animals (Norman, 1966; Stohs et al., 1967; Lawson et al., 1969c). Template activity for DNA-dependent RNA synthesis was significantly increased in vitamin D-deficient rats after they had received vitamin D (Hallick and DeLuca, 1969). These earlier observations were consistent with the involvement of *de novo* protein synthesis in the action of vitamin D. However, Lawson *et al.* (1969c) and Iotoyo *et al.* (1971) were unable to demonstrate an effect of vitamin D on the DNA-stimulated RNA polymerase.

C. LOCALIZATION OF THE ACTIVE FORM, 1,25-DIHYDROXYCHOLECALCIFEROL

Perhaps a more direct indication of a protein synthetic effect of vitamin D_3 would be the localization of the tissue active form [1,25-$(OH)_2D_3$] in the nuclear region. After the administration of labeled 25-OHD$_3$ or 1,25-$(OH)_2D_3$ to chicks, the intestinal nucleus accumulated the highest concentration of radioactivity, and chromatographic analysis indicated that the nuclear radioactivity was associated only with 1,25-$(OH)_2D_3$ (Tsai *et al.*, 1972). Further, the metabolite binds to the chromatin complex (Lawson *et al.*, 1969b; Haussler *et al.*, 1968). Evidence for the existence of a macromolecular receptor in chromatin material for vitamin D_3 metabolite has been given (Haussler and Norman, 1969), and Lawson and Emtage (1973) indicate that the receptor is not chromatin per se since, the purer the chromatin preparation, the lower its content of 1,25-$(OH)_2D_3$. Further, binding to the receptor was resistant to DNase, RNase, phospholipase, and hyaluronidase but inhibited by proteolytic enzymes (Lawson and Emtage, 1973). High salt concentrations also released bound 1,25-$(OH)_2D_3$ from the complex.

Evidence is also accumulating for the presence of a 1,25-$(OH)_2D_3$ receptor in the cytosol of the intestinal cell (Lawson and Emtage, 1973). The recent report on this matter by Brumbaugh and Haussler (1973) is of considerable interest. Chick intestinal tissues were incubated *in vitro* in a bathing solution containing labeled 1,25-$(OH)_2D_3$ at 0°C for 15 minutes. After rinsing, the labeled tissues were either incubated for an additional 40 minutes at 0°C or incubated for 40 minutes at 37°C. Labeled 1,25-$(OH)_2D_3$, after incubation at 0°C, was found associated primarily with the cytosol and that, in the tissue subsequently incubated at 37°C, was primarily in the chromatin fraction. This and additional information aided in establishing the presence of the cytoplasmic binder, and suggested that the function of the cytosol receptor, probably a protein, was to transport 1,25-$(OH)_2D_3$ from cytoplasm to nucleus.

D. *In Vitro* PROTEIN SYNTHESIS BY ISOLATED INTESTINAL POLYSOMES

Protein synthesis by polysomes derived from rachitic and vitamin D-replete chick intestine, in the presence of exogenous factors, was successfully and recently carried out by Lawson and Emtage (1973). The polysomes from the vitamin D-treated animals had the capacity to synthesize the vitamin D-dependent calcium-binding protein (CaBP) whereas those from the rachitic animal did not. No other difference was observed. The essence of this important experiment will be detailed subsequently.

E. Comment

The studies briefly reviewed in this section, all-in-all, are still consonant with the view that a protein synthetic event (or events) is a prerequisite for the action of vitamin D, 25-OHD$_3$ or 1,25-(OH)$_2$D$_3$. This concept was based on observations with inhibitors of protein synthesis, labeling experiments with RNA precursors, and studies on the localization of the tissue active form of the vitamin, 1,25-(OH)$_2$D$_3$. But perhaps the most significant evidence comes from the Lawson and Emtage investigations with intestinal ribosomes and their unique capacity to synthesis CaBP only *if* the donor animal were previously replete with respect to vitamin D.

Other studies done in rats have tended to question the protein synthesis hypothesis on the basis of observations with inhibitors of protein synthesis (Tanaka *et al.*, 1971). In addition, there is evidence, in intestine of rachitic rats, for a precursor of CaBP, implying that CaBP synthesis is not *de novo* but at the ribosomal or postribosomal stage (Drescher and DeLuca, 1971a). In the chick, the existence of a pre-CaBP has not been shown, and certainly the vitamin D-dependent calcium absorptive mechanism appears to be actinomycin D-sensitive (Lawson and Emtage, 1973; Tsai *et al.*, 1973). Until these matters are resolved, it might be necessary to assume the unlikely occurrence of a basic difference in the molecular action of vitamin D in these two species.

V. Specific Proteins Synthesized in the Presence of Vitamin D

A. Intestine

The syntheses of four intestinal proteins are affected by vitamin D. These are the calcium-binding protein and three phosphatases—alkaline phosphatase, a calcium-sensitive adenosine triphosphatase, and phytase —and these will be discussed below in turn. Specific protein synthesis in bone and other tissues will be described in later sections.

1. *Vitamin D-Induced Calcium-Binding Protein*

a. Synthesis in Vivo. The formation of an intestinal calcium-binding protein (CaBP) by rachitic chicks in response to vitamin D treatment was shown several years ago (Wasserman and Taylor, 1966). The synthesis of the protein was inhibited, or at least considerably depressed, by the prior administration of actinomycin D (Corradino and Wasserman, 1968), an observation consistent with *de novo* synthesis of CaBP. This view was substantiated by amino acid-labeling experiments done both *in vivo* and with an embryonic intestinal tissue culture system. In the former approach, MacGregor *et al.* (1970) maintained chicks on a nutritionally deficient level of vitamin D_3 (2–3 IU/day). A curative amount of vitamin D_3 (20 IU) was administered at zero time and, at 1 hour before sacrifice, leucine-^{3}H was injected. The intestinal CaBP was then purified and the amount of ^{3}H incorporated into the protein was determined. Total leucine-^{3}H incorporation into newly synthesized CaBP was evident at 8 hours after D_3 and maximizing at 12 hours (Fig. 2). *Net* synthesis of CaBP was first detectable at 12 hours, the same time period

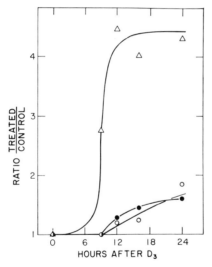

FIG. 2. Time course of vitamin D action in marginally vitamin D-deficient chicks. Three-week-old chicks received orally 20 IU of vitamin D_3 at zero hour. Calcium transport (●—●) was measured by the oral assay after Coates and Holdsworth (1961). Calcium-binding activity (○—○) was assayed in the 60°C supernatant fractions by the ion exchange procedure described by Wasserman and Taylor (1966). ^{3}H incorporation into CaBP (△—△) was determined by injecting leucine-^{3}H into the animals 1 hour before killing and measuring ^{3}H in polyacrylamide-purified CaBP from heat-treated intestinal homogenates. All parameters are shown as the ratio of treated:control. Each point represents an average of 2 or 3 separate experiments. In each experiment 15 chicks were used per time period for assay of calcium transport. The isolation and analysis of CaBP was performed on extracts from the pooled tissue of 5–8 chicks per time period. From MacGregor *et al.* (1971); reproduced with permission.

at which ^{45}Ca absorption was enhanced. After 12 hours, the net increase in CaBP paralleled the vitamin D-dependent increase in calcium absorption. A similar situation was apparent when 25-OHD$_3$ was given instead of vitamin D$_3$ (Fig. 3). This study certainly emphasizes the point that the CaBP synthetic mechanism is activated before the physiological response occurs, and that the net formation of CaBP goes hand-in-hand with enhanced calcium absorption. The uptake of the labeled amino acid into total mucosa protein was not affected by vitamin D.

Ebel *et al.* (1969) and Wasserman *et al.* (1973) also demonstrated that, after vitamin D, 25-OHD$_3$ or 1,25-(OH)$_2$D$_3$, the formation of intestinal CaBP occurred at the same time that the vitamin D-enhanced absorption of calcium was first detectable.

b. Synthesis in Tissue Culture. Intestinal segments, taken from 20-day chick embryos, have been successfully cultured *in vitro* for 2–3-day periods (Corradino and Wasserman, 1971a). The embryonic chick intestine does not contain CaBP and the protein appears only after hatching in the normal situation. However, the cultured intestinal tissue *in vitro* is capable of synthesizing CaBP in the presence of vitamin D$_3$ or a vitamin D-related steroid. This vitamin D$_3$-induced synthesis of CaBP is accompanied by an increase in ^{45}Ca uptake by tissue and increased translocation of ^{45}Ca across the epithelial membrane. In leucine-^{3}H

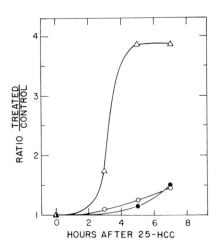

FIG. 3. Time course of 25-hydroxycholecalciferol (25-OHD$_3$) action in marginally vitamin D-deficient chicks. Chicks 3 weeks old received 80 IU of 25-hydroxycholecalciferol at zero hour. The data are the result of one experiment. All other conditions were identical to those described in the legend of Fig. 2. From MacGregor *et al.* (1971); reproduced with permission.

labeling experiments, the CaBP that was formed had a considerably higher specific activity than the bulk of the other intestinal proteins (Corradino and Wasserman, 1971a). Further, the inclusion of protein inhibiting antibiotics, including actinomycin D, inhibited the production of CaBP in response to vitamin D_3.

The evidence is strong that the embryonic tissue responds to the direct addition of vitamin D_3 or 25-OHD_3 to the culture medium, and a search for the local formation of 25-OHD_3 or 1,25-$(OH)_2D_3$ from labeled vitamin D_3 by the intestine proved negative (Corradino, 1973a). However, in terms of the synthesis of CaBP, 1,25-$(OH)_2D_3$ was by far the most potent of the vitamin D-related steroids investigated. It was interesting to also note that CaBP synthesis was dependent upon the concentration of calcium in the medium (Corradino and Wasserman, 1971c).

c. Synthesis by Isolated Polysomes. The investigation of Lawson and Emtage (1973) on protein synthesis by isolated polysomes from chick intestine was alluded to before, and will be described in more detail below.

Mucosa from jejunum and ileum of rachitic or vitamin D-repleted chicks was homogenized in rat-liver cell sap and the supernatant therefrom layered over a discontinuous sucrose gradient. Polysome profiles

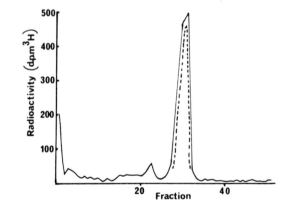

FIG. 4. Sodium dodecyl sulfate (SDS) acrylamide gel of immunologically precipitated calcium-binding protein. Intestinal slices from deficient or vitamin D-dosed chicks were incubated for 2 hours at 37°C in basal Eagle's medium containing leucine-^{14}C or leucine-^{3}H, respectively. After incubation, the slices were homogenized and the homogenate was centrifuged. Aliquots of the supernatant were pooled and the CaBP was immunoprecipitated with specific antiserum. The precipitate, after washing, was dissolved in SDS and dithiothreitol and electrophoresed on SDS gels containing 10% acrylamide. No ^{14}C was detected in the precipitate, and the labeled protein (—) gave a single ^{3}H peak with a mobility identical to reference CaBP (- - -). From Lawson and Emtage (1973); reproduced with permission.

indicated the presence of large aggregates of ribosomes. Rat liver cell sap had a stabilizing effect on the preparation. In the protein synthetic phase of the study, the polysomes were incubated in the presence of ATP, GTP, creatine phosphate, creatine kinase, amino acids including leucine-^{3}H and rat liver cell sap. The formation of CaBP was detected by using a precipitin reaction between CaBP and specific antiserum. A comparison was made of the capacity of polysomes from rat liver (as a control for nonspecific absorption of radioactivity to the immunoprecipitate), from rachitic chick intestine, and from treated chicks to synthesize CaBP; only polysomes from the vitamin D-dosed chicks had this capability (Fig. 4).

Further, to assess the specificity of the vitamin D effect on the synthesis of protein, polysomes from D_3-repleted chicks were incubated in the presence of leucine-^{3}H whereas polysomes from untreated animals were incubated in the presence of leucine-^{14}C. After the incubation period, the fluids containing the released polypeptide chains from each incubation series were mixed, and the proteins therein were separated by

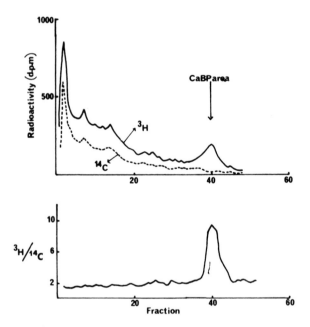

FIG. 5. Acrylamide gel electrophoresis of polypeptide chains released from polysomes after *in vitro* incubation. (—) ^{3}H-Labeled protein obtained from polysomes from intestine of vitamin D-replete chicks incubated in the presence of leucine-^{3}H. (- - - -) ^{14}C-labeled protein obtained from polysomes from intestine of rachitic chicks, incubated in the presence of leucine-^{14}C (Lawson and Emtage, 1973).

polyacrylamide gel electrophoresis. The distribution of ^{3}H and ^{14}C along the gel was determined and plotted as the ratio of ^{3}H:^{14}C (Fig. 5). Only one ^{3}H:^{14}C peak was noted and this corresponded to reference CaBP. This elegant experiment indicated that, under the conditions used, only one unique protein was synthesized in response to vitamin D, this being CaBP. It should be cautioned, however, that the system probably would not detect the synthesis of membrane-bound components and that only one time period after vitamin D dosing was used (72 hours). Alteration of conditions or timing might reveal the formation of another vitamin D-dependent protein.

  d. Properties. The vitamin D-induced CaBP was first isolated from chick intestine, and several of its properties were uncovered (Wasserman *et al.*, 1968; Ingersoll and Wasserman, 1971; Wasserman, 1970; Bredderman, 1971). CaBP is soluble in aqueous medium, is readily released from intestinal cells by simple homogenization procedures, and was isolated in high purity by a three-step procedure (Wasserman *et al.*, 1968). Some of its properties are summarized in Table I. Its molecular weight is about 28,000 by gel filtration and about 25,000 by sedimentation equilibrium, and the binding capacity of the high affinity sites ($\sim$4) is about 2 $\times$ 10^6 M^{-1}. A number of low affinity sites are also associated with the protein. No prosthetic groups have been detected, and binding of members of the alkaline earth series follows the sequence: Ca > Sr > Ba > Mg. These and other properties of chick CaBP have been detailed in recent reviews (Wasserman, 1973; Wasserman and Taylor, 1973a; Wasserman *et al.*, 1973).

  Analogous intestinal calcium-binding proteins have been identified in

TABLE I
SOME PROPERTIES OF CHICK CaBP[a]

1. Molecular weight	
Gel filtration	28,000
Sedimentation equilibrium	25,000
2. Ca-binding activity	
High affinity sites	
Number	4
Apparent k_a	$\sim$2 $\times$ 10^6 M^{-1}
Low affinity sites	
Number	$\sim$30
Apparent k_a	10–100 M^{-1}
3. Alkaline earth selectivity series	Ca > Sr > Ba > Mg
4. Prosthetic groups	None detected

  [a] Data from Wasserman *et al.* (1968), Wasserman and Taylor (1968), and Bredderman (1971).

other species, and these include amphibians, reptiles, a variety of avian species, and several different mammals (Table II). The mammalian CaBPs studied thus far range from rat to bovine to man and, as summarized in Table II, it appears that the molecular weight of the mammalian proteins is about 10,000–13,000 and therefore less than one-half the molecular weight of chick CaBP. The formation constants of the various CaBPs analyzed to date are in the range of 10^5–10^6 M^{-1}. Other differences between chick and mammalian CaBPs have been noted, such as their amino acid composition (see below) and their sensitivity to the proteolytic action of trypsin.

  e. *Amino Acid Composition of the Chick and Bovine CaBP.* The amino acid content of highly purified CaBP from bovine and chick in-

TABLE II
SPECIES SHOWN TO CONTAIN INTESTINAL CALCIUM-BINDING PROTEINS

Species	Molecular weight	Reference
Frog, toad	—	d
Turtle	—	d
Chick	25,000[a]; 28,000[b]	Wasserman *et al.* (1968)
Japanese quail, duck	—	d
Rat	—	Kallfelz *et al.* (1967)
	13,000[b]	Schachter (1970)
	24,000[b]	Ooizumi *et al.* (1970)
	8000–9000[a]; 13,000[b]	Drescher and DeLuca (1971b)
	12,000–13,000[b]	Hitchman and Harrison (1972)
Guinea pig	—	Chapman *et al.* (1972)
	10,000–12,000[b]	Fullmer and Wasserman (1973a)
Golden hamster	—	Schachter (1970)
	—	Kallfelz and Wasserman (1972)
Dog	—	Taylor *et al.* (1968)
Bovine	11,000[b]	Fullmer and Wasserman (1973[b])
Porcine	—	Forsyth *et al.* (1972)
	12,000–13,000[b]	Hitchman and Harrison (1972)
Horse	10,000–12,000[b]	Fullmer and Wasserman (1973a)
Monkey	—	Wasserman and Taylor (1971)
Human	12,000–13,000[b]	Hitchman and Harrison (1972)
	21,000[b]	Alpers *et al.* (1972)
	>21,500[b,c]	Piazolo *et al.* (1971)
	—	Menczel *et al.* (1971)

  [a] By ultracentrifugation.
  [b] By gel filtration.
  [c] From human kidney tissue.
  [d] Evidence for the existence of a vitamin D-dependent CaBP in these species was obtained by means of cross-reactivity studies with the specific antibody against chick CaBP, done in this laboratory.

testine is given in Table III (Bredderman, 1971; Fullmer and Wasserman, 1973a). The similarities and differences should be apparent. Both proteins have a large number of dicarboxylic amino acid residues, which explains their acidic character. Both also have a large content of lysine and leucine residues. Whereas chick CaBP contains a minimum of 3 of each of the residues, bovine CaBP is devoid of arginine, half-cysteine, and methionine. Tryptophan has also not been detected in the bovine protein. Preliminary analysis of highly purified CaBPs from guinea pig, horse, and pig intestine indicate these to be similar to that of the cow (Fullmer and Wasserman, 1973a).

There is no evidence that chick CaBP represents a polymer with subunits equivalent to the mammalian CaBP.

f. Tissue Distribution. In the avian species, CaBPs apparently identical to the intestinal CaBP have been identified in kidney (Taylor and Wasserman, 1967) and the uterine shell gland of the laying hen (Corradino *et al.*, 1968; Bar and Hurwitz, 1973a). In the bovine, there is evidence for CaBPs in the kidney (Fullmer and Wasserman, 1973b)

TABLE III

AMINO ACID COMPOSITION OF CHICK AND BOVINE CaBP

Residue	Chick[a]	Bovine[b]
Lysine	24	12–13
Histidine	3	0
Arginine	5	0
Aspartic acid	34	7
Threonine	9	2
Serine	9	6
Glutamic acid	44	17–18
Proline	3	5
Glycine	13	5
Alanine	17	3
Half-cysteine	3	0
Valine	5	3
Methionine	8	0
Isoleucine	11	2
Leucine	31	12
Tyrosine	8	1
Phenylalanine	13	5
Tryptophan	2	0
Amide nitrogen	17	6–7
Total:	242	80–82

[a] From Bredderman (1971).
[b] Fullmer and Wasserman (1973a).

and the mammary gland (Taylor, 1973), in addition to the intestine. Piazolo *et al.* (1971) have identified CaBP in human kidney.

g. Cellular Localization. By immunofluorescent antibody techniques, intestinal CaBP was shown to be highly concentrated in goblet cells and in the brush border region (Taylor and Wasserman, 1970a). The latter corresponds to a physiological site of action of vitamin D; the goblet cell localization might represent a site of synthesis. Recent work also places CaBP on the brush border of kidney tubule cells of the chick (Lippiello *et al.*, 1973).

h. Correlation between CaBP and Calcium Transport. A number of studies were undertaken in this laboratory and elsewhere to assess the relationship of CaBP to calcium translocation. From previously given information, it was already shown that CaBP is associated only with tissues and organs across which appreciable amounts of calcium move,

TABLE IV

SUMMARY OF SOME CORRELATIONS BETWEEN INTESTINAL CaBP
AND CALCIUM ABSORPTION

1. Simultaneous appearance of CaBP and increased Ca absorption after vitamin D_3 to rachitic chicks (Ebel *et al.*, 1969)
2. Simultaneous appearance of CaBP and increased Ca absorption after 25-hydroxy-D_3 to rachitic chicks (Wasserman *et al.*, 1973)
3. Simultaneous appearance of CaBP and increased Ca absorption after 1,25-dihydroxy D_3 to rachitic chicks (Wasserman *et al.*, 1973)
4. Enhanced CaBP levels and calcium absorption in animals adapted to a low calcium diet (Wasserman and Taylor, 1968; Bronner, 1969; Schachter, 1970; Morrissey and Wasserman, 1971; Bar and Hurwitz, 1972; Omdahl and Thornton, 1972a; Hurwitz *et al.*, 1973)
5. Enhanced CaBP levels and calcium absorption in animals adapted to a low-phosphorus diet (Morrissey and Wasserman, 1971; Bar *et al.*, 1972; Hurwitz *et al.*, 1973)
6. Enhanced CaBP levels and calcium absorption in hens during egg-laying cycle (Wasserman and Taylor, 1968; Bar and Hurwitz, 1971, 1972)
7. Depression of CaBP levels and calcium absorption by dietary stable strontium (Corradino and Wasserman, 1970; Corradino *et al.*, 1971a,b)
8. Decrease in CaBP levels and calcium absorption with age (Wasserman and Taylor, 1968; Schachter, 1970)
9. Correspondence between CaBP levels and effectiveness of various vitamin D-related steroids to affect calcium absorption; e.g., 5,6-*trans*-vitamin D_3, ergocalciferol, dihydrotachysterol, 25-hydroxy D_3 (Wasserman and Taylor, 1968; Omdahl and Thornton, 1972b; Kodicek, 1973)
10. Correspondence between CaBP levels and efficiency of calcium absorption from different intestinal segments (duodenum > jejunum > ileum) (Taylor and Wasserman, 1967; Schachter, 1970)
11. Correspondence between relative capacity of CaBP to bind alkaline earth cations (Ca > Sr > Ba > Mg) and the efficiency of absorption of these metals (Taylor and Wasserman, 1969)

these being the intestine, kidney, shell gland, and mammary gland. Physiological and other anatomical correlates are summarized in Table IV. Direct evidence of a role of CaBP in calcium transport has also been obtained utilizing the organ-cultured embryonic chick duodenum. When everted duodena were cultured in medium containing purified CaBP, but no vitamin D_3 to induce endogenous *de novo* synthesis of CaBP, increased uptake and mucosal to serosal transport of radio-calcium were observed (Corradino and Wasserman, 1971b).

i. CaBP in Adaptation. Chicks and other animal species have the capacity to alter their efficiency of calcium absorption in response to calcium intake (Nicolaysen *et al.*, 1953). When the diet is low in calcium, the efficiency of the physiological process increases and, with this and as shown in Fig. 6, there is an increase in the concentration of intestinal CaBP (Wasserman and Taylor, 1968; Morrissey and Wasserman, 1971; Hurwitz *et al.*, 1973). Experimental animals respond to a low phosphorus intake in the same way in that both calcium absorption and

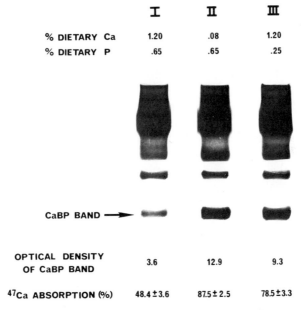

	I	II	III
% DIETARY Ca	1.20	.08	1.20
% DIETARY P	.65	.65	.25
OPTICAL DENSITY OF CaBP BAND	3.6	12.9	9.3
^{47}Ca ABSORPTION (%)	48.4±3.6	87.5±2.5	78.5±3.3

FIG. 6. Alteration in CaBP content of duodenal mucosa and ^{47}Ca absorption as a consequence of the calcium and phosphorus content of the diet. CaBP was quantitated by determining the optical density of the CaBP band, the values given represent the relative area under the density profile. Note that either a calcium-deficient or a phosphorus-deficient diet results in an increased amount of CaBP and an enhanced absorption of calcium. (from Wasserman and Taylor, (1973a); reproduced with permission; modified from Morrissey and Wasserman, 1971).

CaBP levels are also elevated (Fig. 6) (Morrissey and Wasserman, 1971; Bar and Hurwitz, 1973a).

The question of considerable importance is the control mechanism involved in adaptation. What is the detector of the low calcium or phosphorus status, and from where does the "message" arise? Nicolaysen *et al.* (1953) originally proposed that the skeleton had the capacity of elaborating an "endogenous factor" (so called) that affected calcium absorption and that the secretion of this factor was an inverse function of the mineralized state of bone. The experiments showing that either a calcium deficiency or a phosphorus deficiency causes adaptation were taken as supporting evidence for the bone hormone idea (Morrissey and Wasserman, 1971), since the common denominator between these two deficiency states is an undermineralized skeleton. Others have also voiced this view (Benson *et al.*, 1969; Stanbury *et al.*, 1973; Bar and Hurwitz, 1973a). Unfortunately, there has never been any direct evidence for the existence of the "endogenous factor."

The current version of the adaptation story has now placed considerable emphasis on the metabolic pathway of vitamin D, and there is substantial evidence that the point of control involves the 25-cholecalciferol-1-hydroxylase system of the kidney. The degree of formation of $1,25\text{-}(OH)_2D_3$ apparently can be modulated in order to increase the rate of synthesis of the active metabolite under deficiency conditions. Modulators that have been proposed are serum calcium (Boyle *et al.*, 1971), parathyroid hormone (Garabedian *et al.*, 1972; Rasmussen *et al.*, 1972a; Fraser and Kodicek, 1973; Galante *et al.*, 1972a), calcitonin (Rasmussen *et al.*, 1972a; Galante *et al.*, 1972b), and serum phosphate (Tanaka and DeLuca, 1973). There is some disagreement as to the polarity of the response of the 1-hydroxylase system to parathyroid hormone and calcitonin. A recent unifying suggestion is that the ultimate controlling condition in $1,25\text{-}(OH)_2D_3$ synthesis is the concentration of phosphate in the kidney tissue (Omdahl and DeLuca, 1973). A low kidney phosphate level stimulates $1,25\text{-}(OH)_2D_3$ production, and this situation can occur either directly through a low phosphate intake or indirectly through parathyroid hormone action. Parathyroid hormone, secreted in response to a low serum calcium level, depresses phosphate reabsorption by the kidney, which supposedly leads to a reduced level of phosphate in the kidney cell.

Since, according to the kidney conversion hypothesis, the intestine is responding only to modulating levels of $1,25\text{-}(OH)_2D_3$ via kidney production, animals should not adapt to a low-calcium or low-phosphorus diet if the only source of vitamin D activity were $1,25\text{-}(OH)_2D_3$ or dihydroxytachysterol (DHT_3) or some vitamin D-like steroid already hydroxylated in the 1 position. Recent evidence (Bar and Wasserman,

1973) indicates that chicks, receiving DHT_3 as their only source of vitamin D activity, cannot adapt to a low calcium diet (Table V). This result is in accordance with the kidney 1-hydroxylase thesis. However, when chicks on DHT_3 were fed a low-phosphorus diet, they did demonstrate appreciable adaptation in terms of enhanced calcium absorption and intestinal CaBP levels (Table V). This result was *not* expected in terms of the aforementioned hypothesis, and indicates that a modification of the hypothesis is required. The low-phosphorus state might affect the intestine directly or there might be a modification of the steroid-25-hydroxylase enzyme in liver.

j. *Dietary Stable Strontium and CaBP.* The ingestion of diets containing a high content of stable strontium causes skeletal defects somewhat analogous to vitamin D-deficiency rickets (Shipley *et al.*, 1922; Sobel, 1954). A possible relation between strontium rickets and a defect in calcium absorption was suggested from the observations of Bartley and Reber (1961), who noted an increased fecal excretion of oral radiostrontium in pigs fed stable strontium. It was later shown that, in chicks fed a diet containing 2.62% Sr and 0.1% Ca, the intestinal absorption of calcium decreased within a few days, accompanied by a similar decrease in intestinal CaBP (Corradino and Wasserman, 1970; Corradino *et al.*, 1971a). When the Sr-containing diet was replaced by a normal Ca-containing diet, the intestinal absorption of calcium tended to return to normal after a transient overshoot; intestinal CaBP also returned to normal after a similar transient overshoot (Corradino *et al.*, 1971b). The mechanism of inhibition by stable strontium, according to Omdahl and

TABLE V

ADAPTATION TO LOW-CALCIUM OR LOW-PHOSPHORUS DIETS IN
PRESENCE OF VITAMIN D_3 OR DHT_3[a]

Vitamin D source	⁴⁷Ca Absorption (Control = 100)[b]	CaBP
	Low-calcium diet	
D_3	183[c]	245[c]
DHT_3	104	98
	Low-phosphorus diet	
D_3	150[c]	232[c]
DHT_3	130[c]	150[c]

[a] Modified from Bar and Wasserman (1973).

[b] Control groups received normal Ca, P diet and either D_3 or DHT_3. Their respective values taken as equal to 100.

[c] Significantly different from control at $p < 0.001$.

DeLuca (1972), may involve an inhibition of conversion of 25-hydroxy-cholecalciferol to 1,25-dihydroxycholecalciferol by the kidney hydroxylating enzymes.

k. *CaBP and Corticosteroids.* Glucocorticoids from the adrenal glands elicit an effect thought to be antagonistic to the action of vitamin D, one manifestation being the reduction of the intestinal absorption of calcium (Harrison and Harrison, 1960; Williams *et al.*, 1961; Kimberg *et al.*, 1961; Sallis and Holdsworth, 1962). Investigations were undertaken to determine whether the synthesis of CaBP could be prevented if rachitic chicks were predosed with cortisone. It was shown that the administration of cortisone to the rachitic animals did not inhibit CaBP synthesis in response to vitamin D, whereas the vitamin D stimulation of intestinal absorption of calcium did not occur (Wasserman and Taylor, unpublished data). Kimberg *et al.* (1971) noted also that CaBP levels in rat intestine were not reduced by cortisone. Additional experiments by Kimberg *et al.* (*loc. cit.*) showed that cortisone did not reduce the assayable vitamin D activity in intestinal mucosa, and that the absorption of substances not dependent on vitamin D (galactose, iron) was similarly reduced. It was suggested that cortisone directly affected the absorptive mechanism, but not by a direct interaction with vitamin D_3 or 25-OHD$_3$. Favus *et al.* (1973) were unable to restore intestinal calcium transport by administering 1,25-$(OH)_2D_3$ to cortisone-injected rats. This observation was taken as further support for the contention that the cortisone inhibition occurred at the end organ and did not represent a direct interaction between the adrenal corticoid and vitamin D (or metabolite).

Kimberg *et al.* (1971) noted that, in fact, CaBP levels in intestinal mucosa were greater in cortisone-treated, vitamin D-replete animals than in the vitamin D-replete controls. Since there is no evidence that cortisone alters the metabolism of vitamin D, this result is expected because of the depressed absorption of calcium. The insufficient absorption of calcium, being comparable to the ingestion of a low-calcium diet, presumably would provide the stimulus for enhancing kidney 25-OHD$_3$ to 1,25-$(OH)_2D_3$ conversion and thereby cause an enhancement of CaBP synthesis.

Krawitt (1972) reported that cortisone treatment of rats did not interfere with CaBP synthesis but did suppress brush border alkaline phosphatase activity.

l. *CaBP and Anticonvulsants.* Anticonvulsant therapy with diphenylhydantoin and phenobarbitol has been recently associated with the occurrence of hypocalcemia, rickets, and osteomalacia in the human (Schmid, 1967; Kruse, 1968; Hunter *et al.*, 1970; Dent *et al.*, 1970). Several studies with anticonvulsant-treated individuals have not yielded a clear-cut indication of an aberration in the metabolism of vitamin D (Schaefer et al., 1972; Hahn et al., 1972; Tolman et al., 1972; Omdahl and DeLuca, 1973). It was instructive, though, that Stamp et al. (1972) were able to counteract the effect of the anticonvulsants by administering 25-OHD$_3$ or higher levels of vitamin D$_3$, and thereby induce bone healing in patients.

Both Caspary (1972) and Koch et al. (1972), in studies with the rat, were unable to show any significant change in intestinal calcium-binding activity due to anticonvulsant treatment, whereas a depression in calcium absorption was observed. A recent investigation in chicks, however, showed that diphenylhydantoin fed to chicks causes a reduction in both calcium absorption and intestinal CaBP (Fig. 7) (Villareale et al., 1973). The correlation coefficient between CaBP and Ca absorption in this study was 0.99. These results are consonant with the view that the anticonvulsant interferes with the metabolism of vitamin D, or the responsiveness of the tissue to the active form of the vitamin. The reason why Caspary (1972) and Koch et al. (1972) could not show a change in calcium-binding activity in the rat is not known, but this may be another example of species variation in the handling of the vitamin.

2. Calcium-Dependent Adenosine Triphosphatase

Brush borders isolated from rat and chick intestinal mucosa were found to contain an ATPase stimulated by the presence of Ca^{2+} (Martin et al., 1969; Melancon and DeLuca, 1970). The amount of enzyme activity was greater in material obtained from vitamin D-replete as compared to vitamin D-deficient animals. The brush border Ca-dependent ATPase was also stimulated by Ba^{2+} and Sr^{2+}, had a pH optimum of about 7.7, and was not inhibited by ouabain, oligomycin, mersalyl acid, or 4-mercuribenzoate. The assessment of the time course of increase in CaATPase, after vitamin D was given to rachitic chicks, revealed no change at 15 hours whereas a significant increase was noted at 16–16.5 hours (Melancon and DeLuca, 1970). An adjunct experiment purported to show a similar change in calcium absorption (Melancon and DeLuca, 1970).

If CaATPase is closely involved in calcium transport, it would be suspected that the enzyme should increase in animals adapted to a low calcium diet, as does CaBP (Wasserman et al., 1973). However, Taylor and Wasserman (1970b) and Krawitt et al. (1973) noted no change in intestinal brush border CaATPase activity obtained from either chicks or rats. Further, Parkinson and Radde (1971) indicated that only about 20% of the CaATPase in the rat intestinal cell is associated with the brush border and 80% with mitochondrial and nonluminal surfaces.

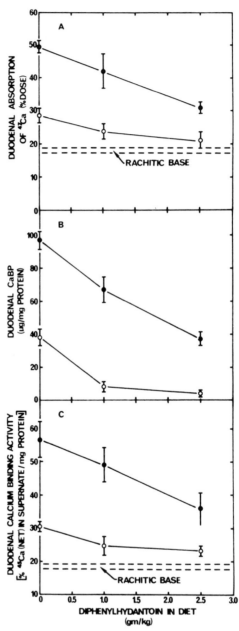

FIG. 7. Effect of diphenylhydantoin and vitamin D_3 on calcium absorption CaBP, and calcium-binding activity. Six chicks per group; values = mean ± standard error of the mean. Duodenal calcium absorption (panel A) was determined by the

According to Holdsworth (1970), L-phenylalanine, which inhibits CaATPase and alkaline phosphatase activities of isolated brush borders, was incapable of inhibiting Ca transport by everted gut sacs. This suggested that these phosphatases were not involved in the Ca^{2+} translocation process, although there is always a question of penetration of inhibitor in sufficient quantities to the active site.

3. Alkaline Phosphatase

An alteration by vitamin D of alkaline phosphatase activity in various tissues, including the intestine, was noted several times in the past (Motzok, 1950). More recently, Holdsworth (1970) and Norman et al. (1970) clearly demonstrated that, indeed, the brush border alkaline phosphatase enzyme was increased when vitamin D was administered to rachitic animals. The data of Norman et al. (1970) suggested to them that alkaline phosphatase activity in the brush border preparation increased at a rate comparable to the increase in calcium absorption after vitamin D was given to vitamin D-deficient chicks. In a more recent investigation, Spielvogel et al. (private communication, 1973) revealed that, after $1,25-(OH)_2D_3$ was given to rachitic chicks, alkaline phosphatase activity did not change until several hours after calcium absorption was enhanced. This suggested that the alteration of the activity of this enzyme might be an indirect consequence of the change in calcium metabolism by the intestinal cell. A similar experiment in which CaATPase was measured would be of considerable interest.

Krawitt et al. (1973) measured the alkaline phosphatase activity in brush borders isolated from various intestinal segments of rats adapted to a low calcium diet. A significant increase was noted in material from the duodenum, but not from the jejunum or ileum. Taylor and Wasserman (1970b), in chicks, could detect no difference in duodenal brush border alkaline phosphatase activity in the adapted animal.

4. Identity of Alkaline Phosphatase and CaATPase?

When the presence of a vitamin D-stimulated Ca-dependent ATPase was initially reported in intestinal brush borders, the question immediately arose as to whether CaATPase and alkaline phosphatase represented different manifestations of the same protein molecule. The results of several studies have not provided an unequivocal answer.

---

in situ ligated loop technique (Corradino and Wasserman, 1970), CaBP (panel B) by radial immunoassay (Corradino and Wasserman, 1971a), and calcium-binding activity (panel C) by the ion-exchange resin assay using Chelex 100 (Wasserman and Taylor, 1966). ●, 6 IU of vitamin D_3 per day; ○, 3 IU of vitamin D_3 per day. From Villareale et al. (1973).

Both phosphatases are similarly inhibited by L-phenylalanine, beryllium, and zinc (Haussler et al., 1970; Holdsworth, 1970), and a definite parallelism between the temperature denaturation of CaATPase and alkaline phosphatase was noted by Russell et al. (1972). Furthermore, the administration of ethane-1-hydroxyl-1,1-diphosphonate (EHDP) to rats caused a reduction in intestinal levels of alkaline phosphatase, CaATPase, and calcium-binding protein (Bonjour et al., 1973). Russell et al. (1972) also noted a reasonable correspondence between the two phosphatases in rats raised either on a high-calcium or low-calcium diet.

On the other hand, Krawitt et al. (1973) found a disparity between the levels of the phosphatases in animals subjected to a low-calcium diet. Whereas duodenal alkaline phosphatase activity increased in the adapted animal, no such increase was apparent for CaATPase. Butanol extraction procedures, which solubilized alkaline phosphatase from the intestinal mucosa, did not contain CaATPase activity (Russell et al., 1972), providing chemical evidence that the two phosphatases are not molecularly identical or that a part of the complex that confers Ca sensitivity is lost during the extraction procedure. These and other data indicate that alkaline phosphatase and CaATPase are not exactly the same molecule. There is the possibility that the enzyme is a multicomponent complex containing a basic phosphatase and that other moieties are required to modify its function with regards to Ca sensitivity and/or pH optima.

5. Phytase

Another phosphatase uncovered several years ago in intestinal tissue is a phytase, an enzyme capable of hydrolyzing phosphorus from phytins, i.e., meso-inositol hexaphosphate (Spitzer and Phillips, 1945). The level of intestinal phytase is dependent upon vitamin D and other dietary factors (Steenbock et al., 1953; Davies et al., 1970), and a detailed evaluation suggested that alkaline phosphatase and phytase are isoenzymes (Davies and Motzok, 1972). The evidence was derived from elution profiles of the activities from a gel filtration column. Both activities were eluted in the same fractions.

B. KIDNEY

The calcium ions in the glomerular filtrate are almost quantitatively reabsorbed by the kidney tubules, and any change in this reabsorptive capacity would be readily reflected in a considerable increase in urinary calcium levels. Therefore, the kidney has the potential of being the primary controlling point in calcium homeostasis, and such a role is advocated by Peacock and Nordin (1973) through the action of parathyroid hormone. The kidney is also an efficient reabsorber of filtered phosphate ions, a function also prone to control by circulating parathyroid hormone levels. It is well documented that the hormone decreases phosphate reabsorption, an effect that confounds interpretation of responses of the kidney to other substances, including vitamin D, unless the animal was previously parathyroidectomized.

Harrison and Harrison in 1941 suggested that vitamin D, in rats, increased tubular reabsorption of phosphate, and Bordier et al. (1969) noted a similar response in human patients to vitamin D. Bordier et al. (loc. cit.) considered this effect to be direct, not through secondary hyperparathyroidism. More recently, Puschett et al. (1972) observed that in thyroparathyroidectomized dogs the administration of vitamin D or 25-OHD$_3$ increased the tubular reabsorption of calcium, phosphate, and sodium ions. Unfortunately the dogs used in the above study were not vitamin D deficient.

Gran (1960) had earlier examined tubular reabsorption of calcium in vitamin D-deficient dogs and suggested an effect of vitamin D on the reabsorptive process, but Gran's dogs were not parathyroidectomized. Because of the readily demonstrable effect of parathyroid hormone on kidney function, it is imperative that these effects be absolutely dissociated from possible responses to vitamin D. Required, therefore, is a careful study in which the experimental animal is both vitamin D-deficient and devoid of the parathyroid glands. A response to vitamin D in such a circumstance would provide a clearer indication of an effect on kidney function, provided that other secondary complications, such as the magnitude of the filtered load and volume expansion, can be eliminated.

Peacock and Nordin (1973) have reported that hypervitaminosis D is associated with an increase in the tubular reabsorption of phosphate, and this study was performed in human patients with hypoparathyroidism. However, the small amounts of circulating hormone could conceivably complicate precise interpretation.

Perhaps the clearest evidence of a direct effect of vitamin D on kidney metabolism comes from an investigation of the vitamin D-dependent calcium-binding protein (Taylor and Wasserman, 1967, 1972). Chick kidney was found to contain a CaBP immunologically identical to, and of the same molecular size, as the intestinal CaBP. The concentration of kidney CaBP was shown to decrease slowly in chicks fed a vitamin D-deficient diet (Fig. 8A), and rapidly increased when vitamin D was administered to rachitic chicks (Table VI). Certainly these observations indicate that vitamin D does directly effect one aspect of the kidney, the induction of CaBP formation.

An important outcome of the above study on kidney CaBP was that

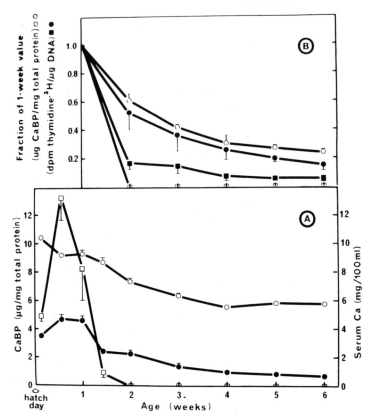

FIG. 8. (A) Serum Ca (○), duodenal mucosa (□), and kidney CaBP (●) concentration as a function of age of chick raised from day of hatch on a rachitogenic diet. Purified CaBP of known concentration was employed as a standard in the immunoassay of samples. Each point represents mean ± SE of 5–10 chicks.

(B) Fractional concentration of CaBP and thymidine-³H-labeled DNA of intestine and kidney from chicks raised on a rachitogenic diet. For comparative purposes, the 1-week value of all measured parameters was set at 1.0, and for subsequent weeks the fraction of that value was plotted. CaBP concentration was determined by same method as above. One-day-old chicks were injected with 100 μCi of thymidine-methyl-³H (10 Ci/mmole), and both total DNA and ³H-labeled DNA were determined at indicated times. Each point represents mean ± SE of 4 chicks. ○, ●, Kidney; □, ■, duodenal mucosa. From Taylor and Wasserman (1972), with permission of the publishers.

the turnover of the protein appears to be a direct function of the turnover of the cells in a given tissue (Taylor and Wasserman, *loc. cit.*). Day-old chicks were injected with tritiated thymidine at day 1 and placed immediately on a vitamin D-deficient diet. The concentration of ³H in DNA, and CaBP levels in intestinal mucosa and kidney, were

TABLE VI

RESPONSE OF INTESTINE AND KIDNEY OF RACHITIC CHICKS TO VITAMIN D_3[a]

| Treatment | Serum Ca (mg/100 ml) | CaBP | |
| | | Duodenum | Kidney |
		(μg/mg total protein)	
Rachitic	6.6 ± 0.3	0	1.20 ± 0.02
Rachitic + D_3	9.8 ± 0.3	28.6 ± 1.1	2.88 ± 0.08

[a] Chicks were raised on a rachitogenic diet for 4 weeks. Vitamin D_3 (500 IU) was given intramuscularly 72 hours before sacrifice. From Taylor and Wasserman (1972).

followed with time. A parallelism between DNA-^{3}H and CaBP concentrations was evident in both intestine and kidney (Fig. 8B) and, as expected, the turnover of intestinal cells was considerably faster than that of kidney cells, providing support for the concept of the relationship between the turnover of tissue cells and CaBP. A corollary of this concept is that CaBP per se is a long-lived protein and its turnover is dictated by the turnover of the tissue in which it resides.

We are not aware of reports implicating vitamin D on the synthesis or maintenance of kidney CaATPase; however, Motzok (1950) found no relationship between chick kidney phosphatase activity and the vitamin D content of the diet.

C. SKELETON

1. Bone Formation; Matrix Metabolism

Despite the historical contention that rickets and osteomalacia are caused primarily by a lack of an adequate supply of mineral ions, considerable effort has been given to uncovering a direct effect of vitamin D on the mineralization process (Neuman and Neuman, 1958; McLean and Urist, 1968). The usual concept has been that the osteoid matrix synthesized by the bone cells is essentially normal and does not calcify because of the insufficient availability of precursor calcium and/or phosphorus ions in the fluids bathing the bone. Considerable evidence supports this idea, as summarized recently by Omdahl and DeLuca (1973). However, it is also apparent that the rachitic condition is associated with a quantitative change in the enzymes in bone cells. As an example, Balough and Kunin (1968) observed that lactic dehydrogenase and glyceraldehyde-3-phosphate dehydrogenase in hypertrophic cells and in the zone of provisional calcification were *increased* in vitamin D-deficient, phosphate-deficient rats, possibly reflecting a disturbance in the maturation of cartilage cells. Lactate production was also greater in rachitic bone (Meyer and Kunin, 1969), and reversal of these effects was brought about by supplementing the diet with either phosphate or vitamin D. Others have also noted differences in bone alkaline phosphatase, proteases, peptidases, dehydrogenases, and acid β-glycerophosphatase levels as a function of the vitamin D status of the animal (Kunin and Krane, 1965; Dixit, 1969; Wergedal, 1969; Cipera and Willmer, 1963). Wergedal and Baylink (1971) measured a series of enzymes in bone from vitamin D-deficient rats fed either a diet containing 1.2% Ca or 0.6% Ca. When on the higher calcium intake, the rats were normocalcemic and displayed little or no change in the measured enzymes as compared to the vitamin D-replete controls. Those animals given the low calcium diet were markedly hypocalcemic and had significantly altered bone enzyme levels. The hypocalcemia preceded the enzyme changes in bone and, thus, no direct effect of vitamin D on bone enzyme levels was apparent.

Collagen is the main organic component of bone matrix, is intimately involved in the calcification process, and is characterized by its high content of glycine, proline, and hydroxyproline, with hydroxylysine also present (Schmitt, 1959). The hydroxyproline component can be labeled by the injection of proline-^{14}C or proline-^{3}H into the animal; the hydroxylation occurs after the proline is incorporated into protocollagen (Peterkofsky and Udenfriend, 1963). A principal role of collagen in the nucleation of mineral crystals from ions in the interstitial fluid has been advocated for many years (cf. Bachra, 1972). Other ideas concerning the calcification mechanism include the involvement of calcium-accumulating vesicles from bone cells (Anderson, 1973; Bonucci, 1970) and the formation of intracellular micropackets of a calcium-phosphate precipitate that are extruded toward the bone surface (Nichols *et al.*, 1971; Lehninger, 1970). There is, in addition, evidence for the existence of a bone cell membrane that functions to control the passage of ions and other substances between the bone surface and its bathing fluid (Thomas and Howard, 1964; Neuman, 1969; Neuman *et al.*, 1973).

The response of the collagen synthetic system to vitamin D has been evaluated, with two differing points of view being disclosed. Patterson and Fourman (1968), using chicks, and Rohr (1965), using rats, noted that the incorporation of labeled proline into collagen was greater in rachitic than in normal animals. Canas *et al.* (1969), on the other hand, observed an increased incorporation of proline-^{3}H into collagen of rachitic chicks after vitamin D repletion. This change occurred 12 hours before any change in serum calcium, therefore suggesting that vitamin D directly affects collagen synthesis.

Recent attention has been given to the possible involvement of vitamin D on two other aspects of the metabolism of collagen: (a) the hydroxylation of lysine residues of the collagen molecule (Barnes, 1973; Barnes *et al.*, 1973; Toole *et al.*, 1972) and (b) the degree of cross-linking between adjacent microfibrils in the collagen maturation process (Mechanic *et al.*, 1972). The cross-linking reaction involves at least two steps (Piez, 1971). First, the ϵ-amino group of lysine or hydroxylysine residue is converted to an aldehyde, catalyzed by an amine oxidase. Second, the aldehyde condenses with an aldehyde or ϵ-amino group on adjacent chains via a Schiff base or aldol reaction. Mechanic *et al.* (1972) compared the quantity and character of reducing groups in collagen from rachitic and vitamin D-replete chicks, using ^{3}H-labeled sodium borohydride (NaB^3H_4) as reducing reagent. Differences in reducing groups were noted between the two groups and suggested that, in the rachitic chick, lesser amounts of α-aminoadipic-ζ-semialdehyde were being synthesized. The decreased quantity of this lysine oxidation product most likely contributed to the lack of maturation of rachitic collagen. Mechanic *et al.* (1972) suggested that vitamin D might stimulate the synthesis of lysyl oxidase, the enzyme which catalyzes the conversion of lysyl residues to the semialdehyde cross-link precursor.

Both Toole *et al.* (1972) and Barnes (1973) reported that rachitic collagen in rats and chicks contains a higher content of hydroxylysine than that of the vitamin D-replete controls. Otherwise, the collagen synthesized by the two groups was similar. The reason for this difference in degree of hydroxylation is not yet apparent but could influence cross-linking capability.

Rats with imposed chronic renal insufficiency also displayed a less mature collagen as compared to their pair-fed controls (Russell and Avioli, 1972). The reason for the possible deficiency in cross-linking of collagen microfibrils is yet to be disclosed, but could be related to the decreased production of $1,25-(OH)_2D_3$ by the kidney conversion enzymes in the uremic state.

2. Bone Resorption

The process of resorption of bone goes on continuously in the young and the mature individual alike, and is of considerable importance in bone remodeling. One of the first and uncontested effects of vitamin D on the skeleton was shown to be an enhancement of bone resorption (Lindquist, 1952; Carlsson and Lindquist, 1955). The extensive studies *in vitro* and with organ culture systems, such as those of Au and Bartter (1966), Morova *et al.* (1971), Raisz and Trummel (1971), and Reynolds (1973), emphasize that the skeletal response to vitamin D or metabolite is directly on the tissue and not mediated via some other hormonal factor, such as parathyroid hormone. It has also been shown that 1,25-$(OH)_2D_3$ is extremely more potent than 25-OHD_3 or vitamin D_3 in causing bone resorption by fetal bone in organ culture (Raisz et al., 1972).

The involvement of vitamin D in a protein synthetic event in bone is not as clear as for intestine. The first study on protein inhibitors and vitamin D effects did show that vitamin D-stimulated bone resorption was inhibited by actinomycin D (Eisenstein and Passavoy, 1964). The hypercalcemia produced in mice with 10,000 IU of vitamin D did not occur when actinomycin D was administered at about the same time. Actinomycin D also inhibits the action of 25-OHD_3 and 1,25-$(OH)_2D_3$ on bone (Tanaka and DeLuca, 1971b). Weber et al. (1972) have indicated that 1,25-$(OH)_2D_3$ localizes specifically in the nuclei of bone cells.

The specific protein induced in bone by vitamin D, if this is the case, has not been identified. Despite several attempts, there is no evidence that CaBP occurs in this tissue.

D. Uterine Shell Gland of the Laying Hen

The shell gland (the uterus) of the laying hen is a remarkable organ in that considerable quantities of calcium are secreted during the formation of the egg shell. This amounts to about 2.2 gm of calcium per 15 hours or 100–150 mg of Ca per hour. Together with cosecreted carbonate, calcium deposits in the egg shell as $CaCO_3$.

The uterus is comprised of two main cell types, the tubular gland cells and the epithelial lining cells, the latter categorized as either apical or basal depending upon the geometric locality of the nucleus. It is not yet clear which cell type is concerned with calcium transport and which with carbonate transfer, and arguments and evidence in both directions are available (Wasserman, 1973).

CaBP was early identified as being present in the shell gland by Corradino et al. (1968), and current evidence shows it to be electrophoretically and immunologically identical to the intestinal protein, and of the same molecular size.

Recent fundamental work on the uterine protein has been carried out by Bar and Hurwitz (1973a). With advent of laying in the hen, CaBP began to appear in the uterus and increased in concentration to a steady-state level. CaBP in the intestinal mucosa was also followed and similarly shown to increase in concentration as the egg-laying cycle was initiated. When laying hens were fed a diet low in calcium, the CaBP concentration in the intestine increased, in accordance with the operation of the adaptation mechanism. However, the CaBP content of the uterus remained un-

TABLE VII

EFFECT OF CALCIUM RESTRICTION ON CALCIUM-BINDING ACTIVITY OF
INTESTINAL AND UTERINE MUCOSA OF LAYING HENS[a]

Dietary Ca (%)	Calcium-binding activity[b] (cpm $\times 10^{-3}$ per ml)	
	Intestine	Uterus
3.7	9.0 ± 0.8[c]	6.4 ± 0.8
1.7	18.3 ± 1.5	6.7 ± 0.5

[a] From Bar and Hurwitz (1973a).
[b] By ion exchange method after Wasserman and Taylor (1966).
[c] Values = mean $\pm$ SE of 7 hens.

changed (Table VII). This finding can be rationalized when it is recognized that the precursor calcium for the egg shell is plasma calcium, and this changes little during calcium deprivation (Bar and Hurwitz, 1973b). What is difficult to fathom is the differential response of the CaBP synthesizing system in the intestine and uterus to the adaptation factor, presumably $1,25\text{-}(OH)_2D_3$. Why does the intestine respond, whereas the uterus does not? This question has important bearing on the mechanisms of control and adaptation with respect to CaBP synthesis and vitamin D metabolism.

VI. SUMMARY, PART I

It is clear that vitamin D affects the formation of specific proteins that appear to be concerned with calcium metabolism. In intestine, calcium-binding protein has been identified in several species and the synthesis of this protein is absolutely dependent upon the presence of vitamin D. The majority of the evidence indicates CaBP to arise by *de novo* synthesis and via the action of a specific messenger RNA, at least in the chick. The situation in the rat is less clear because of the possible presence of a pre-CaBP in intestinal mucosa and the inability (at present) to block the action of $1,25\text{-}(OH)_2D_3$ by actinomycin D. Whatever the way that the protein is formed, there is little question that it plays a significant role in calcium transport.

The other proteins that increase as a consequence of vitamin D are the phosphatases—alkaline phosphatase, CaATPase, and phytase—and each of these may represent different manifestations of the same macromolecular complex. The important result of Spielvogel and Norman (private communication, 1973) that alkaline phosphatase does not increase until after calcium absorption increases with $1,25\text{-}(OH)_2D_3$ as the vitamin D source suggests this enzyme to be indirectly involved in the action of vitamin D. Whether this pertains to the other phosphatases is yet to be shown but, if alkaline phosphatase and CaATPase are the same molecule, the same result would be expected. After $1,25\text{-}(OH)_2D_3$, CaBP does appear in intestinal mucosa at the same time that Ca absorption increases (Wasserman et al., 1973); however, there was a disparity at later times. When calcium absorption had returned to the rachitic base line, CaBP could still be detected by radial immunoassay. This latter finding indicates that another vitamin D-dependent factor is involved, or that the CaBP measured immunologically has the immunological determinants but is functionally "dead" or that it is located in a nonfunctional site.

Filipin, one of the polyene antibiotics, was shown by the Norman group (Adams et al., 1970) to elicit interesting effects on everted gut sacs in vitro. It was shown that the addition of filipin to the mucosal incubation fluid selectively affected calcium transport by the rachitic tissue without having an effect on that from vitamin D-treated animals. The transport capacity of the rachitic everted sac was about equivalent to that of the vitamin D tissue. This study suggests that the active transport mechanism is reasonably intact in the absence of vitamin D and that filipin either "activates" the system or modifies the permeability characteristics of the membrane. It may be that the protein synthesized in response to vitamin D, in a sense, duplicates the effect of filipin. However, filipin is effective only in vitro and elicits no response in vivo.

In the kidney, the only clear-cut effect of vitamin D shown thus far on this organ is the induction of CaBP synthesis. Physiological studies have tended to show also a response of the calcium reabsorptive mechanism to the steroid, but there are difficulties in precise interpretation.

In bone, vitamin D repletion was shown to have important effects on collagen synthesis and metabolism, particularly on the cross-linking reaction and hydroxylation of lysyl residues. The molecular changes accompanying vitamin D-stimulated bone resorption remains unknown.

Little emphasis was placed herein on a description of the nature of the calcium translocation process and the physiological consequences of vitamin D thereon. This was the subjects of previous reviews by us (Wasserman and Taylor, 1969; Wasserman and Kallfelz, 1970; Wasserman, 1972) and another in progress (Wasserman, 1974).

PART II

GENERAL EFFECTS OF VITAMIN D AND CALCIUM ON CELL
METABOLISM AND GROWTH

VII. INTRODUCTION, PART II

One point made clear from the foregoing is that vitamin D, or an active metabolite, via a mechanism involving specific protein synthesis, regulates the availability of calcium to the animal from the diet. The fate of the absorbed calcium in diverse physiological processes has already been alluded to.

No single mechanism has been shown to underlie all the various known actions of calcium, nor is a single mechanism likely. However, an attempt to link calcium with the equally ubiquitous cyclic AMP in a single hypothesis, at least as regards the action of hormonal and certain other stimuli, has been made (Rasmussen et al., 1972b). As will be discussed below, a very plausible mechanism involving calcium, cyclic AMP and PTH in the regulation of cell proliferation (growth) has been postulated (Whitfield et al., 1973). The purpose of this section is to discuss calcium's role in maintaining communication between cells and the relationship of this communication to cell aggregation, differentiation, and proliferation. We will also present evidence which suggests an additional link in the chain of regulation of cell proliferation (growth), namely, vitamin D.

VIII. CALCIUM AND INTERCELLULAR COMMUNICATION

In a variety of epithelial tissues, the permeability of the cell membranes in close contact is markedly greater—as much as 3–4 orders of magnitude—than at the free cell surfaces (Loewenstein et al., 1965; Penn, 1966; Loewenstein and Penn, 1967). On the basis of electrical conductivity measurements and tracer diffusion studies, Loewenstein described a hypothetical structural model of the membrane junction which accounted for this differential permeability (Loewenstein, 1966). A membrane junction, according to a recent reiteration (Loewenstein, 1972): "consists of a system of passageways connecting adjoining cells. Each passageway unit consists of a matched pair of membrane regions of high permeability (junctional membranes), one region on either side of the cell junction, and a seal (junctional seal) insulating the interior of the connected cell system from the exterior." This original description was essentially verified by recent electron microscopic observations in which the movement of horseradish peroxidase was followed in a row of three cells of *Chironomus* salivary gland (Loewenstein, 1973). One of the end cells was deliberately injured and exposed to the 10^{-3} M calcium bathing medium—a condition resulting in impermeability of the membrane junction between it and the middle cell (see below). The peroxidase, 30 minutes after injection into the middle cell, had its highest density in passageways in the cell-to-cell junction of the two intact cells and was undetectable in the membrane junction between the middle and injured cells.

The essential features of the structure of a membrane junction are the junctional membrane (J), which is much more permeable than the nonjunctional membrane, and the impermeable junctional seals (S). Such membrane junctions form extremely rapidly when isolated cells capable of making them come into contact. For example, individual early embryonic newt cells (macromeres) were micromanipulated together while cell-to-cell conductance was continuously monitored. Within seconds of cell contact, the conductance was increased, indicating a change in membrane permeability (Ito and Loewenstein, 1969).

Calcium (and magnesium) ion was early shown to be essential both in the formation and stabilization of membrane junctions and in determining junctional permeability. Sponge cells are readily dissociated and can then be reassembled in pairs with a consequent increase in cell permeability within minutes of contact. This occurs, however, only in the presence of Ca^{2+} in the medium ($10^{-2} M$ Ca) (Loewenstein, 1967a). Once formed, the stability of the membrane junction depends on the continued attachment of calcium ions. Thus, when the joined sponge cells were placed in calcium-free medium, the cells remained in close contact, but the permeability of the junction decreased. Detailed electrical measurements of the junctional complex in studies of *Chironomus* salivary gland cells revealed that this Ca^{2+} requirement is in the formation of the S element (Loewenstein *et al.*, 1967).

The cytoplasmic faces of junctional membranes are in contact with a low Ca^{2+} medium, i.e., cytoplasmic free $[Ca^{2+}]$ is below $10^{-5} M$. Normal extracellular concentration is in the order of $10^{-3} M$. If the intracellular calcium concentration is altered, by injection, or by breaking the nonjunctional membrane of the cell in media of differing calcium ion concentrations, the permeability of the junctional membrane undergoes a transformation. Under the latter conditions, so long as the concentration of Ca^{2+} in the external bathing medium was $10^{-5} M$ or less, there was no change in junctional membrane permeability. However, at higher concentration, about $10^{-4} M$, permeability decreased and at $10^{-3} M$, the junctional membranes became impermeable (Loewenstein *et al.*, 1967).

IX. CALCIUM, CALCIUM-BINDING PROTEINS, AND CELL AGGREGATION

Other work has implicated organic factors in the formation of membrane junctions. From the surface of the sponge cells, a sugar- and protein-containing material has been obtained which is essential to cell adhesion (Humphreys, 1965; Margoliash *et al.*, 1965). When this material was washed off the cells, and the cells were prevented from making it, the cells failed to adhere. When the material was added to the medium, the cells did adhere and junctional communication ensued (Loewenstein, 1967b). Again, detailed electrical measurements indicated that the organic material was involved in the S-element formation. Loewenstein hypothesized from these observations (1967b) that junction formation begins when the organic factor, which has a high affinity for Ca^{2+} and Mg^{2+} (Humphreys, 1965; Margoliash *et al.*, 1965), sequesters Ca^{2+} and Mg^{2+} on the surface membrane. The Ca^{2+} and Mg^{2+} activities in the junction are thereby, reduced. They are reduced still further as the junction is sealed off by the driving force of the low intracellular divalent cation concentrations as the junction, in effect, becomes an intracellular component. The end result is a junction of very low Ca^{2+} and Mg^{2+} concentration facing equally low intracellular concentrations of these ions, conditions favoring high permeability.

Several protein factors have now been discovered that are essential to the reaggregation of disaggregated cells. Thus, reaggregation of dissociated chick embryonic retinal cells has been shown to be dependent on a protein removed from the cells during disaggregation (Daday and Creaser, 1970). Similarly, a protein substance immunologically and chromatographically identical to hyalin (Stephens and Kane, 1970), a calcium-insoluble protein of the hyaline layer of the sea urchin egg, was extractable from sea urchin embryos during dissociation in urea-EDTA and was necessary for reaggregation of the embryonic cells (Kondo and Sakai, 1971).

Two separate factors were isolated from medium "conditioned" with a large number of chick embryo fibroblasts by Sephadex G-25 gel filtration. One factor, in the high molecular weight fraction (approximately 200,000 daltons) and the second in the low molecular weight fraction, stimulated plating efficiency and growth rate of sparsely cultured cells, respectively (Takahashi and Okada, 1971). Reaggregation of dissociated cells in the presence of the high molecular weight factor was rapid. The low molecular weight factor had no effect on aggregation by itself but introduced a transient lag in aggregation after pretreatment of the cells with the cells with the high molecular weight factor. The low molecular weight growth-promoting factor apparently inhibited cell aggregation during the lag period, but its specific role in normal cell contact is unknown.

Cyclic AMP was shown to influence the aggregation of the cellular slime mold, and this process was calcium-dependent (Mason *et al.*, 1971). Whether or not cyclic AMP-mediated cell aggregation is important in the proliferation of cells in multicellular organisms is unknown, but as will be discussed below, calcium and cyclic AMP are central to the mitotic process. A link between cyclic AMP-induced mitosis and cell aggregation is certainly an attractive hypothesis.

X. Cell Aggregation and Control of Growth and Differentiation

Membrane junctions are permeable not only to small ions, but also to relatively large molecules of the order 10^4 molecular weight (Loewenstein and Kanno, 1964; Kanno and Loewenstein, 1966). The possibility exists, therefore, that substances controlling cellular function, including perhaps some small informational macromolecules, might be transferred from cell-to-cell via membrane junctions. Likely areas for the study of such phenomena would be in growing or differentiating cells. Normal development requires that specific cell growth stop at the right time in the right place. It is known from tissue culture studies that cells growing on a surface stop moving and growing upon contact with each other. The term "contact inhibition" was introduced to describe this phenomenon (Abercrombie and Heaysman, 1954), and it is likely that some sort of signal is transmitted upon contact. Cancerous cells, on the other hand, continue to grow in culture even after contact and high cell densities can be reached (Abercrombie et al., 1957). Specific signal substances have not yet been identified but Loewenstein and colleagues have found a correlation between defective junctional connection in cells with uncontrolled cancerous growth. In early studies, liver cancer cells were shown to have no detectable communication (very high junctional resistance to electrical flow) whereas normal liver cells displayed very little resistance (Loewenstein and Kanno, 1966). Hepatoma cells in tissue culture were also shown to be incapable of junctional communication (Azarnia and Loewenstein, 1971). The availability of noncoupled (defective junctional connection) cells capable of uncontrolled growth in culture provides an eminently suitable system for the evaluation of a possible relationship between uncontrolled growth and noncoupling. An important breakthrough was made when it was shown that rat hepatoma cells (noncoupling) would fuse with normal rat fibroblasts (coupling). Unlike the parent cancer cell the multinucleated cancer cell-fibroblast hybrids formed communicating junctions with each other, were contact-inhibited and did not produce fatal tumors when injected into rats (Loewenstein, 1973). These characteristics of the hybrid were retained by several generations. These findings provide strong evidence for a genetic link between junctional noncoupling and uncontrolled growth.

An indication of biochemical differentiation controlled by cell contact was obtained in the recent study of isolated cells from *Xenopus* blastulae. Alkaline phosphatase activity was measured as a function of time in cells allowed to aggregate and was shown to increase at a far greater rate than in cells prevented from aggregating (Abe et al., 1972). The initial rapid increase in alkaline phosphatase activity (the first 3 hours of aggregate formation) was unaffected by actinomycin D in the medium although DNA synthesis was almost completely blocked. However, cycloheximide in the medium immediately inhibited the rise in alkaline phosphatase activity during aggregate formation. Protein synthesis was 80%

inhibited. Previous studies had shown that ribosomal RNA synthesis proceeded normally in isolated *Xenopus* cells. Nucleoside and amino acid incorporation also proceeded normally. On the basis of these findings, it is likely that alkaline phosphatase biosynthesis is dependent on cell contact and that the signal transferred exercises translational control. Thus, cell-to-cell contact may not be necessary for DNA transcription but appears to be essential to RNA translation.

An apparently similar relationship between cell contact and enzyme activity during differentiation exists in retinal cells of the chick embryo and glutamine synthetase (GS), an enzyme inducible by 11β-hydroxycorticosteroids (Morris and Moscona, 1971). During normal development in the intact retina, glutamine synthetase increases very rapidly from day 16 of incubation. This rapid rise can be induced precociously both *in vivo* and *in vitro* by hydrocortisone several days before normal onset. *In vitro*, the induction has a less than 2-hour lag period and involves *de novo* synthesis of GS (Alescio and Moscona, 1969). Inducibility increases with embryonic age and depends on cell association, i.e., it is lowest in isolated retinal cells, intermediate in aggregates of freshly isolated cells, and highest in intact retina. The ability of isolated cells to reaggregate was inversely related to the age of the embryo from which they were obtained. Thus, inducibility and the ability to reaggregate were directly correlated. It was shown that reaggregation reflected the state of differentiation at the time of dissociation, i.e., the older the embryo from which derived, the more highly differentiated were the cells and the smaller the aggregate that could form. This could reflect irreversible changes in the properties of cell surfaces and in the mechanisms regulating the biosynthesis of cell surface components.

XI. Calcium and Mitosis

It has been known for some time that the calcium ion concentration of the bathing medium can regulate the mitotic rate of isolated cells. For example, St. Amand *et al.* (1960) showed that increased medium calcium concentration hastened the passage of grasshopper neuroblasts through metaphase. In the most thoroughly studied system, suspensions of lymphocytes isolated from rat thymus glands, the mitotically competent lymphoblasts have been shown to progress through mitosis at an accelerated rate when bathed in medium containing greater than 1 mM calcium (Whitfield *et al.*, 1969a). This acceleration of mitotic activity by calcium followed stimulation of the entry of the cells into the DNA-synthetic (S) phase of the growth-division cycle.

The mitogenic action of calcium has also been seen *in vivo*. When blood calcium concentration was raised directly, by repeated intraperitoneal injections of $CaCl_2$ solution, the mitotic rate of thymic cells was increased (Perris and Whitfield, 1967a). When blood calcium concentration was raised indirectly, by injection of parathyroid extract, the mitotic rate of bone marrow cells was increased (Perris et al., 1967). Calcium also counteracted the transient mitotic inhibition in these tissues following ^{60}Co gamma irradiation (Whitfield and Youdale, 1966). If the calcium level of blood was lowered by parathyroidectomy, mitotic rate was lowered (Rixon, 1968). These in vivo observations were fully reproducible in vitro, i.e., high calcium concentration results in a high mitotic rate plus irradiation protection (Whitfield and Youdale, 1966).

When attempts were made to lower blood calcium concentrations of rats by intraperitoneal injection of EDTA, there was a rapid, but transient, decrease in blood calcium. However, isolated thymus and bone marrow cells showed an increase in mitotic rate (Perris and Whitfield, 1967b). This apparent discrepancy was resolved when it was found that the enhanced mitotic rate followed an abnormally elevated ionized calcium concentration in blood after the initial rapid lowering by EDTA. Mitotic activity, therefore, was regulated by the level of ionized rather than total or bound calcium in the cell's environment. This strongly suggested that those hormones regulating calcium homeostasis in the animal, such as parathyroid hormone (PTH) and calcitonin (CT) may be involved in the control of cellular proliferation at least in lymphatic and erythropoietic tissues.

Indeed, it was later found that several peptide hormones affected the mitotic rate of isolated thymocyte suspensions. Growth hormone (STH), parathyroid hormone, prolactin, vasopressin, and oxytocin were all found to stimulate mitosis, but each was found to have brought about its action by sensitizing the cells to calcium, the primary stimulant; i.e., none of these hormones had any mitotic effect on cells maintained in calcium-free medium (Whitfield et al., 1969b). The similarity of action between these chemically and functionally different hormones suggested that they might stimulate calcium-dependent, intracellular production of a common mitogenic agent. All these hormones are known to stimulate cyclic AMP production in their respective target tissues (Major and Kilpatrick, 1972). In fact, it is now known that STH (MacManus and Whitfield, 1969), PTH (Whitfield et al., 1970a), and vasopressin (Whitfield et al., 1970b) all stimulate proliferation in thymocyte suspensions via mediation of cyclic AMP. This conclusion was based on three findings: first, the mitogenic action of all three hormones was potentiated by caffeine, an inhibitor of a phosphodiesterase which catalyzes conversion of cyclic AMP to the inactive 5'-AMP (Robison et al., 1968); second, in the cases of PTH and vasopressin, their mitogenic action was inhibited by imidazole, an activator of phosphodiesterase (Robison *et al.*, 1968) ; and, third, cyclic AMP itself, at typical intracellular concentrations ($\sim 10^{-7}\,M$) was mitogenic and its action was potentiated by caffeine and inhibited by imidazole.

Interestingly, CT, which is considered to oppose, and thereby regulate, PTH action on calcium homeostasis *in vivo*, blocked the mitogenic action of both PTH (MacManus and Whitfield, 1970) and vasopressin (Whitfield *et al.*, 1970b) on rat thymocytes *in vitro*. In addition, porcine CT blocked the mitogenic action of cyclic AMP itself (MacManus and Whitfield, 1970), and it was speculated that calcitonin may act like imidazole in stimulating phosphodiesterase activity.

Epinephrine is a very potent stimulator of endogenous cyclic AMP production in a variety of tissues including heart, liver, and muscle (Robison *et al.*, 1968). Again, in rat thymus cells *in vitro*, epinephrine stimulated cell proliferation involving the endogenous production of cyclic AMP (MacManus *et al.*, 1971a). This stimulatory action of epinephrine was also inhibited by low concentrations of porcine calcitonin (Whitfield *et al.*, 1971).

The above observations, taken together, strongly suggest that (1) since cyclic AMP is the common mediator of the mitogenic action of the several hormones tested, (2) since, with the exception of epinephrine (see below), calcium ion is essential to their mitogenic action, and (3) since calcium ion itself is mitogenic, calcium ion also brings about its action by increasing intracellular levels of cyclic AMP. Recent experiments have confirmed this suggestion. Merely raising the calcium ion concentration of the medium bathing rat thymocytes to between 1.2 and 2.4 mM increased intracellular cyclic AMP levels, DNA synthesis and cell proliferation (MacManus and Whitfield, 1971). The mitogenic and cyclic AMP-stimulating activity of ionic calcium was inhibited by imidazole but potentiated by caffeine. Caffeine itself was mitogenic, as expected, since it inhibits phosphodiesterase, thereby raising cyclic AMP content. Calcium, too, inhibited phosphodiesterase activity in the thymocytes, and it is likely that this action is central to the mitogenic action of calcium (MacManus and Whitfield, 1971). This conclusion is based on the finding that neither calcium ion nor PTH stimulated endogenous production of cyclic AMP in thymic lymphocytes (MacManus *et al.*, 1972). On the other hand, epinephrine stimulated adenyl cyclase activity and, thus, DNA-synthesis and mitosis, in the complete absence of calcium although calcium potentiated its action (MacManus *et al.*, 1971a).

Whitfield *et al.* (1973) have recently speculated on possible mechanisms whereby calcium, PTH, and cyclic AMP bring about their actions on DNA synthesis and cell proliferation in rat thymocytes. Calcium in the extracellular fluid (or in the bathing medium) at a level greater than 1.0 mM, may inhibit the degradation of cyclic AMP by a membrane-bound phosphodiesterase. The higher endogenous level of cyclic AMP, produced by adenyl cyclase in the membrane, is seen as stimulating the mitogenic and DNA synthetic parts of an activation site in the membrane. This stimulation, in turn, leads to entry into the cell of initiators of DNA synthesis and mitosis. Several lines of evidence were cited to support this proposed mechanism. It is known that adenyl cyclase and, in some cases, cyclic nucleotide phosphodiesterase, are membrane bound in the target cells of hormones known to act via cyclic AMP (Robison et al., 1968). In the case of thymic lymphocytes, cyclic AMP has been shown to reversibly bind to the cell surface (MacManus and Whitfield, 1972) and bring about its mitogenic response without entering the cell (MacManus et al., 1971b). Likewise, the inhibition of cyclic AMP's mitogenic effect on isolated thymocytes by caffeine and its stimulation by imidazole suggest a membrane localization for the calcium-inhibited phosphodiesterase. Calcium itself probably does not stimulate cyclic AMP production by thymocyte adenyl cyclase since mitogenic levels of calcium ion actually inhibit adenyl cyclase activity in broken cell preparations (Whitfield et al., 1971). Similarly, phosphodiesterase activity is inhibited by calcium in broken cell preparations (MacManus and Whitfield, 1971).

As has already been mentioned, PTH stimulates thymic cell proliferation via a cyclic AMP-mediated process. PTH is known to stimulate adenyl cyclase activity in its classical target organs, bone (Chase and Aurbach, 1970) and kidney (Melson et al., 1970). However, the mitogenic action of PTH in isolated thymocytes does not proceed via stimulation of adenyl cyclase: this enzyme is unaffected by PTH in broken cell preparations (Whitfield et al., 1971). Likewise, phosphodiesterase activity is unaffected by PTH in similar preparations (Whitfield et al., 1971). The reason for this apparent discrepancy is that PTH action on thymocyte cyclic AMP is indirect, via calcium ion. Thus, in calcium-free medium, PTH had no effect on thymocyte proliferation; however, when these cells were transferred to a PTH-free medium containing a nonmitogenic calcium concentration (0.6 mM), cyclic AMP content rose rapidly, followed by cell proliferation (Whitfield et al., 1971). PTH is known to increase calcium influx into isolated monkey kidney cells (Borle, 1972), and it seems possible that, in isolated thymocytes, PTH is merely enhancing calcium permeation into the membrane wherein it inhibits phosphodiesterase activity. This in turn raises the endogenous cyclic AMP level which then stimulates the membranous activation site. The calcium mediation of action of STH, prolactin, vasopressin and oxytocin, as well as PTH, suggests that these hormones also may facilitate calcium's access to the phosphodiesterase of the cell membrane.

It should be reiterated at this point that there are agents that do directly stimulate adenyl cyclase activity in thymocyte suspensions, namely, epinephrine (MacManus et al., 1971a), as already mentioned, and prostaglandin E_1 (Whitfield et al., 1972a). These agents can induce DNA synthesis and mitosis in the complete absence of calcium from the medium. Through the use of the latter agent, insight was gained into another role of calcium in the proliferative process. It had been previously observed that the PTH effect on cellular cyclic AMP and cell proliferation was dependent on calcium level (Whitfield et al., 1971): at zero calcium in the medium, PTH was ineffective; at 0.6 mM calcium, cyclic AMP content increased and mitosis ensued; and, at 1 mM calcium, PTH still raised the cyclic AMP level, but cell proliferation was not stimulated. Thus, it appeared that calcium could not only stimulate cyclic AMP in the hormone-treated cell, but could then regulate the mitogenic reaction. By using prostaglandin E_1, which produces a powerful stimulation of adenyl cyclase activity, and therefore, greatly increases cellular cyclic AMP level in the complete absence of calcium, the action of calcium on cell proliferation could be studied independently of its action on cyclic AMP. In the presence of prostaglandin E_1 in the medium bathing the thymocytes, there is a short burst of cyclic AMP production: at 0.1 μg/ml, cyclic AMP rose 15-fold whereas at 5 μg/ml it rose almost 70-fold (Whitfield et al., 1972a,b). At 0.1 μg of prostaglandin E_1 per milliliter, cell proliferation did not proceed unless the calcium concentration was greater than 0.2 mM. However, at 5 μg of prostaglandin E_1, cell proliferation was prevented by calcium concentrations greater than 0.2 mM. At both concentrations of prostaglandin E_1, DNA synthesis was stimulated. To explain this dual action of calcium on mitogenesis, Whitfield et al. (1973) have proposed that cyclic AMP stimulates DNA synthesis and mitogenesis at the same time but that the latter process is not needed until, nor does it necessarily follow, stimulation of DNA synthesis. Since it was shown that calcium's effect on low levels of exogenous cyclic AMP, which did not enter the cell, was similar to the action of prostaglandin E_1 at low concentrations (0.1 μg/ml), namely, that there was a marked potentiation of the cyclic AMP effect on cell proliferation (Whitfield et al., 1971), it was hypothesized that cyclic AMP produced endogenously may interact at the surface activation site. These considerations led to the conclusion that, at low exogenous or endogenous cyclic AMP levels, the DNA-synthesis–mitogenic activator site is continuously operative but that calcium ion is essential to production of the mitogenic initiator.

The inhibition by calcium of mitosis, but not DNA synthesis, at high prostaglandin E_1 levels—and, consequently, high endogenous cyclic AMP production—was probably not due to inhibition of the surface activator site. This is so because relatively high exogenous cyclic AMP levels, which do not enter the cell, stimulate DNA-synthesis and mitosis even in the presence of 1 mM calcium (Whitfield *et al.*, 1971). Therefore, the inhibitory action must take place within the cell and may be the result of entry of some of the endogenously produced cyclic AMP into the cell wherein it may mobilize previously stored calcium from intracellular sites (mitochondria?), inhibiting mitogenesis. Borle (1972) has shown that such intracellular calcium shifts, especially efflux from mitochondria to cytoplasm, indeed occurred after bathing monkey kidney cells in a solution containing dibutyryl cyclic AMP ($10^{-3} M$).

With this hypothesis of the complex interaction of cyclic AMP and calcium in mind, the effects of CT and PGE_1 and their interaction, might be explained (Whitfield *et al.*, 1972c). As already mentioned, porcine CT at low concentrations, inhibited the cyclic AMP mediated action of both epinephrine and PTH as well as exogenous cyclic AMP itself (Whitfield *et al.*, 1971; MacManus and Whitfield, 1970). Low concentrations of salmon CT were shown to lower the PGE_1 stimulation of cyclic AMP production in thymocyte populations *in vitro* by a calcium-mediated process. Nonetheless, initiation of DNA synthesis was not inhibited. If the initial burst of cyclic AMP was high (5 μg of PGE_1/ml), CT (1 ng of CT/ml) completely blocked cell proliferation with the addition of as little as 0.05 μM calcium to the bathing medium, whereas it had no effect in "calcium-free" medium (0.2 mM residual calcium). By contrast, if the initial burst of cyclic AMP was low (0.1 μg of PGE_1/ml), CT (1 ng of CT/ml) stimulated cell proliferation between 0.2 and 0.4 mM calcium but inhibited mitosis at higher calcium concentration. Very high CT (100 ng of CT/ml) actually stimulated cyclic AMP production by a calcium-independent mechanism, but this level of cyclic AMP was incapable of stimulating thymoblast proliferation in the absence of calcium. These complex, but fascinating, results tend to support the contention that cyclic AMP and calcium are very closely related in the control of DNA synthesis and cell proliferation.

The authors contend that all these effects are explicable on the basis of calcium fluxes mediated by calcitonin and cyclic AMP. The action of dibutyryl cyclic AMP on the mitochondrial calcium flux of isolated kidney cells (Borle, 1972) has already been mentioned. In addition, porcine CT has been shown to increase cellular calcium concentration by reducing calcium efflux from kidney cells *in vitro* (Borle, 1969). Thus, the action of CT on lymphoblasts in low calcium medium (<0.2 mM),

after a small surge of cyclic AMP induced by 0.1 μg of PGE_1 per milliliter, was to convert a DNA-synthesizing but nonproliferating cell into a
proliferating cell due to an increase in the intracellular calcium level.
The calcium efflux-inhibiting action of CT on lymphoblasts in the same
low calcium medium after a large surge of cyclic AMP induced by 5 μg
of PGE_1 per milliliter would combine with the intracellular calcium-
mobilizing capacity of the endogenous cyclic AMP to inhibit cell proliferation. The fact that PGE_1-induced cyclic AMP production was reduced by CT was also explained on the basis of intracellular calcium
inhibition of cyclic AMP production, via inhibition of adenyl cyclase
activity, since CT itself has no effect on either adenyl cyclase or phosphodiesterase activity in broken-cell preparations. The stimulatory
action of a very high CT level (100 ng of CT/ml) on cyclic AMP production in the absence of calcium remains unexplained.

Although the Whitfield et al. (1973) models of calcium, PTH, and
cyclic AMP action on DNA-synthesis and cell proliferation have considerable justification, there remain some questions of detail and, of
course, more work to further elucidate the proliferative process and calcium's role in it. For example, Burgoyne et al. (1970) found that DNA
synthesis was directly stimulated by calcium, but not by cyclic AMP,
in nuclei isolated from rat thymus cells. This would suggest that calcium
ion itself may be the ultimate regulator of DNA synthesis, not a calcium-
dependent, cyclic AMP-mediated initiator of DNA synthesis produced
by an activator site in the cell membrane. Also the fact that calcium can
inhibit both enzymes—adenyl cyclase, which catalyzes production of
cyclic AMP, and phosphodiesterase, which catalyzes its breakdown—in
broken-cell preparations makes it difficult to reconcile the action of calcium in its many apparent manifestations, for example, in the case of
CT induction of cyclic AMP. It is possible, however, that calcium does
not have equal access to both enzymes in the intact cell or inhibits dif-
ferentially. Finally, clarification of the biochemical mechanisms involved
in the action of calcium and cyclic AMP, plus identification of the hypothetical activation site and initiators, remain.

Important strides in these directions have been made, however. With
regard to the role of calcium and/or cyclic AMP in stimulating DNA
synthesis, it is known that nuclear, lysine-rich histones are phosphoryl-
ated by cyclic AMP-dependent histone kinases in mitotically competent
thymic lymphoblasts (Langan, 1969a). This phosphorylation necessarily
precedes progression of cells into the S phase of their cell cycle (Ord
and Stocken, 1969). It is likely that histone phosphorylation would
weaken, or break, histone-DNA bonds and lead to DNA transcription
followed by cell proliferation (Whitfield and Perris, 1968; Langan, 1969b).

Besides thymus and bone marrow cells, as already discussed, calcium has been shown to stimulate proliferation of several other isolated cell types including strain L mouse cells (Yang and Morton, 1971) and normal chicken fibroblasts (Balk, 1971) *in vitro*. In the latter case, calcium did not regulate the proliferation of chicken fibroblasts after they were infected by Rous sarcoma virus. In later studies, Balk *et al.* (1973) showed that the proliferative inactivity of normal chicken fibroblasts at very low calcium ion concentration was not due to contact inhibition, because the inactivity was independent of culture density. The results suggested that calcium regulates a cellular function initiating mitosis in normal cells but not in the virus-transformed cells. This may be the result either of the transformed cell's being independent of the calcium-mediated mechanism or of its being able to accumulate a greater proportion of the available calcium in the medium. Radiocalcium uptake studies could decide between these alternatives, but such have not yet been reported.

Another cell type, the normally nonproliferating blood lymphocyte, in the presence of phytohemagglutinin (PHA), a potent mitogenic mucoprotein extract from the bean plant, *Phaseolus vulgaris,* transforms into large cells capable of intensive nucleic acid and protein synthesis and, eventually, mitosis. This action of PHA has now been shown to be calcium dependent (Whitney and Sutherland, 1972a). During PHA-induced transformation, there is a rapid stimulation of calcium influx into the cells (Whitney and Sutherland, 1972b). Earlier studies had established that PHA markedly stimulated lymphocyte adenyl cyclase activity (Smith *et al.*, 1971). Calcium probably initiates the mitogenic response since PHA attachment to the cells was unaffected by complexation of the culture medium's calcium by EGTA but DNA synthesis was completely blocked. Removal of calcium after initial exposure to PHA-induced transformation had no effect on DNA synthesis during a subsequent measurement period.

In summary, it is now well established that calcium is a specific initiator of mitosis in a number of isolated cell types. The adenyl cyclase system of the cell membrane is involved in the calcium effect. Hormones and agents which alter the cyclic AMP level of cells either stimulate or inhibit mitosis, depending on the ambient calcium concentration. A cogent mechanism for these actions and relationships has been postulated (Whitfield *et al.*, 1973).

XII. CALCIUM AND GROWTH

The mitogenic action of calcium in isolated cell systems suggests a possible role of calcium, and, therefore, of the hormones controlling calcium homeostasis, in growth of the whole organism. In examining the average daily increase in body weight of male rats, Perris *et al.* (1968) noted that growth rate increased to a maximum between 70 and 120 gm of body weight; after this, although the rats continued to grow, the growth rate rapidly declined. Following the growth rate curve to its maximum value was a similar curve showing a marked and progressive increase in mitotic activity of the bone marrow and thymus gland. During the decline in growth rate, mitotic rates declined to a minimum in these tissues and, thereafter, remained constant. At any stage during this growth period, the mitotic rate of cells in bone marrow or thymus could be artificially raised by exogenous calcium administration.

It was of interest to determine whether there exists any natural variation in blood calcium level as a function of growth and what effect this might have on the mitotic activity of these two tissues. It was discovered that, indeed, during the very stage of most rapid body growth, there was an equally marked rise in the level of blood calcium, most particularly, the ionic calcium fraction (Perris *et al.*, 1968). These observations strongly suggested involvement of the calcium homeostatic mechanism in early body growth.

Confirmation of this suggestion with respect to certain organs followed. In thyroparathyroidectomized rats, mitotic activity and weight of the thymus were markedly reduced (Perris *et al.*, 1970). Thymic involution also followed parathyroidectomy. The degree of involution could be lessened by PTH injections or by providing calcium in the drinking water. Reticulocyte loss from both bone marrow and peripheral blood were also noted following thyroparathyroidectomy and PTH injections restored levels to normal (Perris and Whitfield, 1971).

Following acute hemorrhage, there was a rapid, but transient, hypocalcemia followed by hypercalcemia after 24 hours (Perris *et al.*, 1971). Corresponding to the period of hypercalcemia, there was an increase in bone marrow proliferation. These responses were not seen after acute hemorrhage in thyroparathyroidectomized rats, again implicating the parathyroid hormone. The transient hypocalcemia probably sufficed to stimulate PTH-secretion in excess resulting in the later hypercalcemia. The point is that PTH and/or calcium mediated alterations could account not only for reticulocyte proliferation during active growth, when presumably the increasing body mass has an increasing oxygen requirement, but following injury, resulting in blood loss, to restore the erythrocyte level.

Further work has established a PTH-calcium involvement in the action of erythropoietin on bone marrow mitosis (Hunt and Perris, 1973). Injection of ovine erythropoietin into rats resulted in parallel increases in plasma calcium concentration and the mitotic activity of bone marrow cells. This erythropoietin effect was not observed in parathyroidectomized animals. Unlike acute hemorrhage, there was no transient hypocalcemia to trigger PTH release. One possible explanation is that erythropoietin directly stimulates the parathyroid gland.

Both cell proliferation and enlargement account for the increasing mass of other tissues of the growing animal. It is tempting to suppose that PTH, and/or calcium may be involved in the proliferative processes of tissues other than thymus or bone marrow.

In this connection, it is instructive to consider the specific case of liver regeneration following subtotal hepatectomy. The liver tissue remaining undergoes a compensatory hyperplasia which may be under extrahepatic humoral control (Fisher et al., 1971). In recent experiments, parathyroidectomized (PTX) rats were subjected to partial hepatectomy (median and left lateral lobes removed) after all PTH had disappeared from the circulation (Rixon and Whitfield, 1972). In sham-PTX animals, there was a striking increase in both DNA synthesis and liver cell proliferation beginning 18–24 hours after partial hepatectomy, reflecting the classical regenerative phenomenon. In PTX rats, by contrast, DNA synthesis and mitotic activity, after partial hepatectomy, were reduced about 50% and were delayed 12–14 hours. Of course, in the PTX rats, the plasma calcium was also reduced—to about half normal values. Of interest was a transient hypocalcemia which occurred within a few hours of partial hepatectomy in sham-PTX rats, a situation favoring PTH secretion. Coincident with this hypocalcemia, liver cyclic AMP content increased, declined, and increased again to a peak shortly before initiation of DNA synthesis (Whitfield et al., 1973).

Although circulating PTH was not actually measured, these experiments clearly implicate PTH and/or calcium and cyclic AMP in liver regeneration. Whether or not the action of PTH on liver cell proliferation after hepatectomy is direct or, as in the case of thymoblasts in vitro, is indirect via calcium and cyclic AMP is not certain. However, reminiscent of Borle's (1972) work on isolated kidney cells, there is evidence that PTH administered to rats stimulates calcium influx into liver slices in vitro (Chausmer et al., 1972). The increased calcium influx correlated well with the PTH-enhanced binding of calcium by supernatants of rat liver homogenates in a competitive binding assay using Chelex 100 (Bio-Rad) cation exchange resin. It was speculated that this PTH-enhanced binding, which might reflect production of specific binding factor(s) within liver cells could account for the increased influx of calcium. It was shown by others that PTH stimulated adenyl cyclase activity in liver in vivo (Chase et al., 1969), and the increase in cyclic AMP production could account for the increase in calcium accumulation by liver slices *in vitro* (Wallach *et al.*, 1966). These observations seem fully compatible with the Whitfield *et al.* (1973) model of PTH action on cell proliferation based on studies of thymocytes *in vitro:* PTH causes increased calcium uptake, some of which may be sequestered intracellularly, and some of which causes a rise in cellular cyclic AMP levels leading to stimulation of DNA synthesis and, finally, cell proliferation.

Another case was provided by the finding that adrenal hypertrophy followed bilateral nephrectomy in rats, but only if they had not been previously thyroparathyroidectomized (Canas *et al.*, 1967).

Cyclic AMP is likely involved in kidney cell proliferation *in vivo* (Malamud and Malt, 1971). Cyclic AMP also seems to be involved in proliferation in parotid gland (Malamud, 1969) and heart (Kizer and Howell, 1971) although calcium involvement is not known.

XIII. VITAMIN D AND GROWTH

The action of vitamin D in stimulating intestinal calcium transport is now firmly established. Starting with the early observations of Nicolaysen (1937), a number of workers have investigated this phenomenon and considerable insight has been obtained (Wasserman and Taylor, 1969). However, one aspect of vitamin D physiology has received very little attention, namely, the role of the vitamin as a growth factor. It is now well known that animals fed an otherwise normal but vitamin D-deficient diet exhibit reduced growth rates. This is true with chicks (Migicovsky and Emslie, 1947; Corradino *et al.*, 1971b), and mammals, including rats (Steenbock and Herting, 1955), dogs (Mellanby, 1919; Ney *et al.*, 1965), foxes (Harris *et al.*, 1951), sheep (Duckworth, 1943), calves (Bechtel *et al.*, 1936), monkeys (Hunt *et al.*, 1967), and humans (Richards *et al.*, 1968). With the exception of the rat, in these animals, vitamin D deficiency also results in rickets, a bone disease characterized histologically, by the accumulation of unmineralized hypertrophic cartilage and osteoid in the zones of preparatory calcification, radiographically, by the partial to complete absence of mineralization of the skeletal tissue, and grossly, by severe deformation of the weight-bearing bones, swelling of the joints, and beading of the ribs.

Rodents, such as the rat, which has been most studied, are not as prone to rickets as these other animals, and vitamin D deficiency alone is insufficient to produce rickets. It has been necessary to feed a low-phosphorus vitamin D-deficient diet with a high calcium to phosphorus ratio to produce rickets in the rat (Steenbock and Herting, 1955; Harrison *et al.*, 1958). Thus, it was possible to separate the antirachitic activity of vitamin D from its growth-promoting effect. When rats were fed an otherwise normal (0.7% Ca; 0.56% P) but vitamin D-deficient diet, there was a decrease in growth while their bones showed no evidence of rickets (Harrison et al., 1958). Of interest to the present discussion was the finding of a severe hypocalcemia in the nonrachitic, vitamin D-deficient rats, and, consequently, enlarged parathyroids (Harrison, 1966).

Hypocalcemia and hyperparathyroidism are consistent findings in other vitamin D-deficient animals as well, ranging from chicks (Bar et al., 1972) to humans (Joffe et al., 1972). The association of parathyroid hyperplasia with human rickets has been known for over 50 years (Pappenheimer and Minor, 1921). The functional hyperactivity of the parathyroids of vitamin D-deficient chicks (Bar et al., 1972), rats (Au and Raisz, 1965), and humans (Joffe et al., 1972) has been verified.

When hypocalcemic, hyperparathyroid rats were given vitamin D (100 IU of vitamin D_2 3 days prior to killing), normalization of serum calcium occurred (Harrison, 1966). The finding of hypocalcemia in vitamin D-deficient rats with normal bones suggested that the bone was refractory to PTH. Indeed, even administration of parathyroid extract, sufficient to cause hypercalcemia in normal rats, to such animals had no effect on serum calcium unless the rats were previously given vitamin D (Harrison et al., 1958). Parathyroidectomy of vitamin D-deficient rats had no further effect on the already established hypocalcemia (Rasmussen et al., 1963). These studies led to the conclusion that vitamin D exerts a permissive action on PTH function in bone mineral resorption and that it is a necessary cofactor for PTH action (Harrison et al., 1958; Rasmussen et al., 1963). This view required some modification, however, since it was found possible to restore PTH effectiveness in vitamin D-deficient rats by multiple injections of calcium or by adding lactose—which enhances calcium absorption—to the diet (Au and Raisz, 1967). A more likely explanation is that vitamin D and PTH exert separate but synergistic effects on bone calicum resorption (Raisz and Trummel, 1969). The restoration of responsiveness to PTH in vitamin D-deficient rats by parenteral calcium took the form of lower parathyroid functional activity (Au and Raisz, 1965), higher serum calcium, and a slightly higher body weight (Au and Raisz, 1967).

It is most tempting to speculate on the basis of the above findings that, as is the case in isolated thymic lymphocytes or regenerating liver, PTH and/or calcium are intimately involved in the total growth of the animal. It seems clear, moreover, that vitamin D is also vitally important to the growth process. This action on growth may be the result only of its stimulation of calcium absorption by the intestine, thus providing adequate levels of serum calcium and a reservoir of calcium in bone. However, in the aforementioned experiments of Au and Raisz (1967), a normal serum calcium and near normal bone calcium could be maintained in vitamin D-deficient rats merely by feeding lactose in the diet. As already mentioned, such animals had reduced parathyroid function (Au and Raisz, 1965). Even though these rats grew slightly better than rats given no lactose, their growth was only 75% of that achieved by rats given vitamin D. Therefore, it seems more likely that vitamin D has a direct action on growth over and above its action on calcium homeostasis.

There can be no doubt, however, that a vitamin D action on growth is dependent on calcium. In rats fed vitamin D-free diets of different calcium and phosphorus content, a 120% increase in body weight was achieved by raising the calcium level from 0.03 to 0.4%—phosphorus in these diets was 0.1 and 0.3%, respectively (Au and Raisz, 1965). (Serum phosphate was unchanged, but serum calcium increased 63%.) Adding vitamin D to the low calcium diet resulted in a 65% increase in body weight and a near normalization of serum calcium–serum phosphorus was normal—but growth was still only 65% of that achieved by rats fed normal calcium (0.4% of diet) and vitamin D. Thus, it is apparent that optimal growth requires both vitamin D and calcium; the full growth effect of the vitamin is not produced at lower than normal blood calcium, nor is full growth achieved in the absence of vitamin D even though blood calcium is normal or near normal.

Although PTH involvement in growth is suggested by these same experiments, direct experimental proof is lacking. The appropriate experiment has not yet been done. Such an experiment would involve relatively long term (a week to a few weeks) maintenance of vitamin D deficient, parathyroidectomized animals on varying dietary lactose. These animals could then be administered vitamin D and/or PTH and relative effects on growth assessed.

The effect of vitamin D on whole body growth may be the direct result of a calcium-mediated action on cell proliferation, similar to that of PTH on isolated thymus cells or on liver regeneration, involving cyclic AMP. Alternatively, vitamin D may stimulate growth indirectly by facilitating absorption of many nutrients, much as vitamin D stimulates absorption of calcium. There is some evidence in support of both mechanisms. In support of the former proposal, vitamin D is known to result in increased adenyl cyclase activity in the chick intestine (Neville and Holdsworth, 1969). Embryonic chick intestine maintained in organ culture (Corradino, 1973a,b) in the presence of vitamin D in the culture medium contained more cyclic AMP than intestines cultured in the absence of vitamin D_3 (Corradino, 1973d). Dibutyryl cyclic AMP *in vitro* stimulated calcium absorption across everted intestinal sacs, but, accord-

ing to one report, the action occurred only in intestine from vitamin
D-deficient chicks (Neville and Holdsworth, 1969); according to another
report, the action occurred only in vitamin D-repleted rats (Harrison
and Harrison, 1970). In recent experiments with embryonic chick intestine in organ culture, both dibutyryl cyclic AMP and theophylline
stimulated radiocalcium uptake in guts cultured in the complete absence
of vitamin D (Corradino, 1973d). In these experiments, vitamin D alone
stimulated calcium accumulation and the effects of dibutyryl cyclic AMP
and theophylline were additive either alone or in combination. Of great
interest in these experiments was the finding that, although radiocalcium
accumulation was stimulated by any one or all of these agents, stimulation of dibutyryl cyclic AMP and/or theophylline was associated with a
decline in intestinal content of the vitamin D induced calcium-binding
protein (CaBP), a protein involved in calcium transport (Taylor and
Wasserman, 1969; Corradino and Wasserman, 1971b, also see pp. 50–63).
The organ culture experiments clearly implicate a complex interaction
between the adenyl cyclase system, calcium, and vitamin D in the calcium absorptive mechanism of the intestine.

Support for an involvement of vitamin D in intestinal cell proliferation
has been produced. First, within 48 hours of treating vitamin D-deficient
rats with vitamin D, there was an increase in the duodenal mucosal
weight as a function of dry weight of duodenum (Urban and Schedl,
1969). Ileal mucosal weight was not significantly affected. Second, the
villous length of intestine from normal chicks and rachitic chicks given
vitamin D for 5 days prior to sacrifice was markedly greater than in
untreated rachitic chicks (Spielvogel et al., 1972). The migration rate of
cells up the villous was also greater in normal or vitamin D-treated
rachitic chicks than in rachitic chicks. Insofar as transit time of cells
from the crypts to the villous tips is a function of proliferative pressure
of cells in the crypts, these data strongly suggest that cell proliferation
in the intestine is increased by vitamin D, although the authors of that
work did not state that conclusion. STH, which was shown to stimulate
thymic cell proliferation by a calcium-dependent, cyclic AMP-mediated
mechanism (Whitfield et al., 1969b), is known to stimulate mitosis in
duodenal mucosal cells of the rat (Leblond and Carriere, 1955). These
observations taken in toto are suggestive of a vitamin D action on intestinal cell mitosis which may be mediated via calcium and cyclic AMP.
The end result, an action of vitamin D on soft tissue (intestinal) growth,
may be a specific example of the general growth effect of vitamin D.

As already suggested, however, the vitamin D action on growth may
be indirectly due to enhanced intestinal absorption of growth-promoting
nutrients. The actions of the vitamin on the intestinal adenyl cyclase

system and intestinal growth might then be viewed as functioning to increase the efficiency of nutrient absorption by the intestine. It is known that normal animals, or vitamin D-deficient animals given vitamin D, not only absorb calcium more efficiently, but also absorb glucose (Corradino et al., 1968), amino acids, e.g., alanine (Corradino et al., 1971b) and histidine (Corradino et al., 1971b; Sugai and Matsuda, 1968, 1971), and minerals, e.g., iron, cobalt (Wasserman, 1962), and phosphate (Wasserman and Taylor, 1973b) more efficiently than untreated, vitamin D-deficient animals. Embryonic chick intestine when maintained in organ culture in the presence of vitamin D in the medium also accumulates more iron, cobalt, and phosphorus, as well as calcium, than does intestine cultured in the absence of vitamin D (Corradino, 1973a). The activities of certain intestinal enzymes are enhanced by vitamin D (also see pp. 63–66). Administration of vitamin D to rachitic chicks (Norman et al., 1970)—or culturing embryonic chick intestine in the presence of vitamin D (Corradino, 1973a)—results in increased activity of intestinal alkaline phosphatase, an enzyme that may be linked to phosphate transport in the intestine (Moog and Glazier, 1972). Vitamin D also stimulates the activity of a calcium-dependent ATPase (CaATPase) in the intestine (Melancon and DeLuca, 1970), an enzyme that may function in calcium translocation in the intestine. At present, CaATPase and alkaline phosphatase appear to be the same enzyme (Haussler et al., 1970; Holdsworth, 1970). There is also evidence that vitamin D stimulates leucine aminopeptidase activity in chick intestine (Taylor and Wasserman, 1970b). Vitamin D induces de novo synthesis of calcium-binding protein (CaBP) in the intestinal mucosa of many species, and its implication in calcium transport in the intestine seems certain (see pp. 50–63).

There can be little doubt that vitamin D stimulates a variety of intestinal functions which may be ramifications of a primary action and which may contribute to the general adequacy of nutrient supply to the animal. Further experiments should shed some light on these possibilities. However, it is virtually certain that vitamin D promotes growth of other bodily tissues in a more direct fashion, by a calcium-dependent mechanism, perhaps involving cyclic AMP. This aspect of vitamin D physiology deserves more attention.

XIV. SUMMARY, PART II

An attempt has been made to review the evidence establishing a role of calcium in intercellular communication, cell aggregation, differentiation, and growth. There seems to be little doubt that calcium is central to these processes, and theoretical mechanisms of calcium action have been advanced. An additional attempt has been made to suggest an involvement of vitamin D in the process of growth in the animal independent of its action on intestinal calcium absorption. Whether or not this latter suggestion proves valid remains to be seen, but perhaps this review will provide some impetus in that direction.

ACKNOWLEDGMENTS

Part of the work mentioned herein was supported by NIH Grants AM-04652 and AM-15355 and USAEC Contract AT(11-1)-3167. We thank Mrs. Norma Jayne and Mrs. Karen Ni for their helpful assistance in the preparation of the manuscript.

REFERENCES

Abdel-Latif, A. A., and Smith, J. P. (1972). *Biochem. Pharmacol.* **21**, 436.
Abe, H., Miyahara, E., and Yamana, K. (1972). *Nature New Biol.* **235**, 254.
Abercrombie, M., and Heaysman, E. M. (1954). *Exp. Cell Res.* **6**, 293.
Abercrombie, M., Heaysman, E. M., and Karthauser, M. (1957). *Exp. Cell Res.* **13**, 176.
Adams, T. H., Wong, R. G., and Norman, A. W. (1970). *J. Biol. Chem.* **245**, 4432.
Alescio, T., and Moscona, A. A. (1969). *Biochem. Biophys. Res. Commun.* **34**, 176.
Alpers, D. H., Lee, S. W., and Avioli, L. V. (1972). *Gastroenterology* **62**, 559.
Anderson, H. C. (1973). *In* "Hard Tissue Growth, Repair and Remineralization," *Ciba Found. Symp. No. 11,* pp. 213–226. Elsevier, Amsterdam.
Andersson, R. (1972). *Acta Physiol. Scand.* **85**, 312.
Au, W. Y. W., and Bartter, F. C. (1966). *Endocrinology* **78**, 1100.
Au, W. Y. W., and Raisz, L. G. (1965). *Amer. J. Physiol.* **209**, 637.
Au, W. Y. W., and Raisz, L. G. (1967). *J. Clin. Invest.* **46**, 1572.
Au, W. Y. W., Poland, A. P., Stern, P. H., and Raisz, L. G. (1970). *J. Clin. Invest.* **49**, 1639.
Azarnia, R., and Loewenstein, W. R. (1971). *J. Membrane Biol.* **6**, 368.
Bachra, B. N. (1972). *Calcif. Tissue Res.* **8**, 287.
Balk, S. D. (1971). *Proc. Nat. Acad. Sci. U. S.* **68**, 271.
Balk, S. D., Whitfield, J. F., Youdale, T., and Braun, A. C. (1973). *Proc. Nat. Acad. Sci. U. S.* **70**, 675.
Balough, K., Jr., and Kunin, A. S. (1968). *Lab Invest.* **18**, 782.
Bar, A., and Hurwitz, S. (1971). *Is. J. Med. Sci.* **7**, 382.
Bar, A., and Hurwitz, S. (1972). *Comp. Biochem. Physiol.* **41B**, 735.
Bar, A., and Hurwitz, S. (1973a). *Comp. Biochem. Physiol.* **45A**, 579.
Bar, A., and Hurwitz, S. (1973b). *Comp. Biochem. Physiol.* **45A**, 571.
Bar, A., and Wasserman, R. H. (1973). *Biochem. Biophys. Res. Commun.* **54**, 191.
Bar, A., Hurwitz, S., and Cohen, I. (1972). *Comp. Biochem. Physiol.* **43A**, 519.
Barnes, M. J. (1973). *In* "Hard Tissue Growth, Repair and Remineralization," *Ciba Found. Symp. 11,* pp. 247–259. Elsevier, Amsterdam.
Barnes, M. J., Constable, B. J., Morton, L. F., and Kodicek, E. (1973). *Biochem. J.* **132**, 113.
Bartley, J. C., and Reber, E. F. (1961). *J. Dairy Sci.* **44**, 1754.
Baylink, D., Stauffer, M., Wergedal, J., and Rich, C. (1970). *J. Clin. Invest.* **49**, 1122.
Bechtel, H. E., Hallman, E. T., Huffman, C. F., and Duncan, C. W. (1936). *Mich. Agr. Exp. Sta., Spec. Bull.* **150**.

Bell, N. H. (1970). *J. Clin. Invest.* **49**, 1368.

Benson, J. D., Emery, R. S., and Thomas, J. W. (1969). *J. Nutr.* **97**, 53.

Bhattacharyya, M. H., and DeLuca, H. F. (1973). *J. Biol. Chem.* **248**, 2974.

Birmingham, M. K., and Bartova, A. (1973). *Endocrinology* **93**, 743.

Blaustein, M. P., Johnson, E. M., Jr., and Needleman, P. (1972). *Proc. Nat. Acad. Sci. U. S.* **69**, 2237.

Bonjour, J.-P., Russell, R. G. G., Morgan, D. B., and Fleisch, H. A. (1973). *Amer. J. Physiol.* **224**, 1011.

Bonucci, E. (1970). *Z. Zellforsch. Mikrosk. Anat.* **103**, 192.

Bordier, P., Hioco, D., Ronquier, M., Hepner, G. W., and Thompson, G. R., (1969). *Calcif. Tissue Res.* **4**, 78.

Borle, A. B. (1969). *Endocrinology* **85**, 194.

Borle, A. (1972). *In* "Calcium, Parathyroid Hormone and the Calcitonins" (R. V. Talmage and P. L. Munson, eds.), pp. 484–491. Excerpta Medica, Amsterdam.

Bosmann, H. B., and Chen, P. S., Jr. (1966). *J. Nutr.* **90**, 405.

Boyle, I. T., Gray, R. W., and DeLuca, H. F. (1971). *Proc. Nat. Acad. Sci. U. S.* **68**, 2131.

Bredderman, P. J. (1971). Ph.D. Thesis, Cornell University, Ithaca, New York.

Bronner, F. (1969). *In* "Membrane Proteins" (Symp. N. Y. Heart Assn.), pp. 134–135. Little, Brown, Boston, Massachusetts.

Brumbaugh, P. F., and Haussler, M. R. (1973). *Biochem. Biophys. Res. Commun.* **51**, 74.

Burgoyne, L. A., Wagar, M. A., and Atkinson, M. R. (1970). *Biochem. Biophys. Res. Commun.* **39**, 918.

Canas, F. M., Bergstrom, W. H., and Churgin, S. J. (1967). *Metab. Clin. Exp.* **16**, 670.

Canas, F. M., Brand, J. S., Neuman, W. F., and Terepka, A. R. (1969). *Amer. J. Physiol.* **216**, 1092.

Carafoli, E., and Crovetti, F. (1973). *Arch. Biochem. Biophys.* **154**, 40.

Carlsson, A., and Lindquist, B. (1955). *Acta Physiol. Scand.* **35**, 53.

Caspary, W. F. (1972). *Arch. Pharmacol.* **275**, 146.

Chapman, M., Pond, W., Taylor, A. N., Krook, L., and Rivers, J. (1972). *J. Anim. Sci.* **35**, 283.

Chase, L. R., and Aurbach, G. D. (1970). *J. Biol. Chem.* **245**, 1520.

Chase, L. R., Fedak, S., and Aurbach, G. D. (1969). *Endocrinology* **84**, 761.

Chausmer, A. B., Sherman, B. S., and Wallach, S. (1972). *Endocrinology* **90**, 663.

Cipera, J. D., and Willmer, J. S. (1963). *Can. J. Biochem. Physiol.* **41**, 1490.

Coates, M. E., and Holdsworth, E. S. (1961). *Brit. J. Nutr.* **15**, 131.

Cohn, D. V., MacGregor, R. R., Chu, L. L. H., and Hamilton, J. W. (1972). *In* "Calcium, Parathyroid Hormone and the Calcitonins" (R. V. Talmage and P. L. Munson, eds.), pp. 173–182. Excerpta Medica, Amsterdam.

Comar, C. L., and Bronner, F., eds. (1969). "Mineral Metabolism. An Advanced Treatise," Vol. III. Academic Press, New York.

Cooke, J. D., Okamoto, K., and Quastel, D. M. J. (1973). *J. Physiol. (London)* **228**, 459.

Corradino, R. A. (1973a). *J. Cell Biol.* **58**, 64.

Corradino, R. A. (1973b). *Science* **179**, 402.

Corradino, R. A. (1973c). *Nature (London)* **243**, 41.

Corradino, R. A. (1973d). *Proc. 55th Meet., Endocrine Soc., Chicago.*

Corradino, R. A., and Wasserman, R. H. (1968). *Arch. Biochem. Biophys.* **126**, 957.

Corradino, R. A., and Wasserman, R. H. (1970). *Proc. Soc. Exp. Biol. Med.* **133,** 960.

Corradino, R. A., and Wasserman, R. H. (1971a). *Science* **172,** 731.

Corradino, R. A., and Wasserman, R. H. (1971b). *Biophys. Soc. Abstr.* **11,** 276a.

Corradino, R. A., and Wasserman, R. H. (1971c). *Fed. Proc., Fed. Amer. Soc. Exp. Biol.* **30,** 407.

Corradino, R. A., Wasserman, R. H., Pubols, M. H., and Chang, S. I. (1968). *Arch. Biochem. Biophys.* **125,** 378.

Corradino, R. A., Ebel, J. G., Craig, P. H., Taylor, A. N., and Wasserman, R. H. (1971a). *Calcif. Tissue Res.* **7,** 81.

Corradino, R. A., Ebel, J. G., Craig, P. H., Taylor, A. N., and Wasserman, R. H. (1971b). *Calcif. Tissue Res.* **7,** 93.

Cousins, R. J., DeLuca, H. F., Suda, T., Chen, T., and Tanaka, Y. (1970). *Biochemistry* **9,** 1453.

Daday, H., and Creaser, E. H. (1970). *Nature (London)* **226,** 970.

Davies, M. I., and Motzok, I. (1972). *Comp. Biochem. Physiol.* **42B,** 345.

Davies, M. I., Ritcey, G. M., and Motzok, I. (1970). *Poultry Sci.* **49,** 1280.

Dent, C. E., Richens, A., Rowe, D. J. F., and Stamp, T. C. B. (1970). *Brit. Med. J.* **4,** 69.

Dixit, P. K. (1969). *J. Histochem. Cytochem.* **17,** 411.

Douglas, W. W. (1968). *Brit. J. Pharmacol.* **34,** 451.

Drescher, D., and DeLuca, H. F. (1971a). *Biochemistry* **10,** 2308.

Drescher, D., and DeLuca, H. F. (1971b). *Biochemistry* **10,** 2302.

Duckworth, J., Godden, W., and Thomson, W. (1943). *J. Agr. Sci.* **33,** 190.

Eanes, E. D., and Posner, A. S. (1970). *In* "Biological Calcification: Cellular and Molecular Aspects" (H. Schraer, ed.), pp. 1–26. Appleton, New York.

Ebel, J. G., Taylor, A. N., and Wasserman, R. H. (1969). *Amer. J. Clin. Nutr.* **22,** 431.

Eisenstein, R., and Passavoy, M. (1964). *Proc. Soc. Exp. Biol. Med.* **117,** 77.

Farese, R. V. (1971). *Science* **173,** 447.

Favus, M. J., Walling, M. W., and Kimberg, D. V. (1973). *J. Clin. Invest.* (in press).

Fischer, J. A., Oldham, S. B., Sizemore, G. W., and Arnaud, C. D. (1972). *Proc. Nat. Acad. Sci. U. S.* **69,** 2341.

Fisher, B., Szuch, P., Levine, M., and Fisher, E. R. (1971). *Science* **171,** 575.

Forsyth, D. M., Pond, W. G., Wasserman, R. H., and Krook, L. (1972). *J. Nutr.* **102,** 1623.

Fraser, D. R., and Kodicek, E. (1970). *Nature (London)* **228,** 764.

Fraser, D. R., and Kodicek, E. (1973). *Nature New Biol.* **241,** 163.

Frolik, C. A., and DeLuca, H. F. (1972). *J. Clin. Invest.* **51,** 2900.

Fullmer, C. S., and Wasserman, R. H. (1973a). Unpublished data.

Fullmer, C. S., and Wasserman, R. H. (1973b). *Biochim. Biophys. Acta* **317,** 172.

Galante, L., MacAuley, S. J., Colston, K. W., and MacIntyre, I. (1972a). *Lancet* **I,** 985.

Galante, L., Colston, K. W., MacAuley, S. J., and MacIntyre, I. (1972b). *Nature (London)* **238,** 271.

Garabedian, M., Holick, M. F., DeLuca, H. F., and Boyle, I. T. (1972). *Proc. Nat. Acad. Sci. U. S.* **69,** 1673.

Gran, F. C. (1960). *Acta Physiol. Scand.* **50,** 132.

Hahn, T. J., Hendin, B. A., Scharp, C. S., and Haddad, J. G. (1972). *N. Engl. J. Med.* **287,** 900.

Hallick, R. B., and DeLuca, H. F. (1969). *Proc. Nat. Acad. Sci. U. S.* **63**, 528.

Harris, E. J., and Berent, C. (1969). *Biochem. J.* **115**, 645.

Harris, L. E., Bassett, C. F., and Wilke, C. F. (1951). *J. Nutr.* **43**, 153.

Harrison, H. E. (1966). *Yale J. Biol. Med.* **38**, 393.

Harrison, H. E., and Harrison, H. C. (1941). *J. Clin. Invest.* **20**, 47.

Harrison, H. E., and Harrison, H. C. (1960). *Amer. J. Physiol.* **199**, 265.

Harrison, H. C., and Harrison, H. E. (1970). *Endocrinology* **86**, 756.

Harrison, H. C., Harrison, H. E., and Park, E. A. (1958). *Amer. J. Physiol.* **192**, 432.

Haussler, M. R., and Norman, A. W. (1969). *Proc. Nat. Acad. Sci. U. S.* **62**, 155.

Haussler, M. R., Myrtle, J. F., and Norman, A. W. (1968). *J. Biol. Chem.* **243**, 4055.

Haussler, M. R., Nagode, L. A., and Rasmussen, H. (1970). *Nature (London)* **228**, 1199.

Haussler, M. R., Boyce, D. W., Littledike, E. T., and Rasmussen, H. (1971). *Proc. Nat. Acad. Sci. U. S.* **68**, 177.

Heisler, S., Fast, D., and Tenenhouse, A. (1972). *Biochim. Biophys. Acta* **279**, 561.

Hitchman, A. J. W., and Harrison, J. E. (1972). *Can. J. Biochem.* **50**, 758.

Holdsworth, E. S. (1970). *J. Membrane Biol.* **3**, 43.

Humphreys, T. (1965). *Exp. Cell Res.* **40**, 539.

Hunt, N. H., and Perris, A. D. (1973). *J. Endocrinol.* **56**, 47.

Hunt, R. D., Garcia, F. G., and Hegsted, D. M. (1967). *Lab. Anim. Care* **17**, 222.

Hunter, J., Maxwell, J. D., Stewart, D. A., Parsons, V., and Williams, R. (1970). *Brit. Med. J.* **4**, 202.

Hurwitz, S., Bar, A., and Cohen, I. (1973). *Amer. J. Physiol.* **225**, 150.

Ingersoll, R. J., and Wasserman, R. H. (1971). *J. Biol. Chem.* **246**, 2808.

Iotoyo, N., Moriuchi, S., Takase, S., and Hosoya, N. (1971). *J. Vitaminol. (Kyoto)* **17**, 73.

Ito, S., and Loewenstein, W. R. (1969). *Develop. Biol.* **19**, 228.

Joffe, B. I., Hackeng, W. H. L., Seftel, H. C., and Hartdegen, R. G. (1972). *Clin. Sci.* **42**, 113.

Jutisz, M., and de la Llosa, M. P. (1970). *Endocrinology* **86**, 761.

Kallfelz, F. A., and Wasserman, R. H. (1972). *Proc. Soc. Exp. Biol. Med.* **139**, 77.

Kallfelz, F. A., Taylor, A. N., and Wasserman, R. H. (1967). *Proc. Soc. Exp. Biol. Med.* **125**, 54.

Kanno, T. (1972). *J. Physiol.* **226**, 353.

Kanno, Y., and Loewenstein, W. R. (1966). *Nature (London)* **212**, 629.

Kaplan, E., and Richman, H. G. (1973). *Proc. Soc. Exp. Biol. Med.* **142**, 487.

Katz, A. M., and Repke, D. I. (1973). *Biochim. Biophys. Acta* **298**, 270.

Kimberg, D. V., Schachter, D., and Schenker, H. (1961). *Amer. J. Physiol.* **200**, 1256.

Kimberg, D. V., Baerg, R. D., Gershon, E., and Graudusius, R. T. (1971). *J. Clin. Invest.* **50**, 1309.

Kimmich, G. A., and Rasmussen, H. (1969). *J. Biol. Chem.* **244**, 190.

Kirpekai, S. M., Misu, Y., and Wakade, A. R. (1968). *J. Physiol.* **194**, 595.

Kizer, D. E., and Howell, B. A. (1971). *Fed. Proc., Fed. Amer. Soc. Exp. Biol.* **30**, 1178.

Koch, H. U., Kraft, D., Von Herrath, D., and Schaeffer, K. (1972). *Epilepsia* **13**, 829.

Koch, R. B. (1968). *Arch. Biochem. Biophys.* **125**, 303.

Kodicek, E. (1973). *In* "Hard Tissue Growth, Repair and Mineralization," *Ciba Found. Symp. 11*, pp. 359–367. Elsevier, Amsterdam.

Kondo, K., and Sakai, H. (1971). *Develop. Growth & Differentiation* **13**, 1.

Krawitt, E. L. (1972). *Biochim. Biophys. Acta* **274**, 179.
Krawitt, E. L., Stubbert, P. A., and Ennis, P. H. (1973). *Amer. J. Physiol.* **224**, 548.
Kruse, R. (1968). *Monatsschr. Kinderheilk.* **116**, 378.
Kunin, A. S., and Krane, S. M. (1965). *Biochim. Biophys. Acta* **107**, 203.
Langan, T. A. (1969a). *J. Biol. Chem.* **244**, 5763.
Langan, T. A. (1969b). *Proc. Nat. Acad. Sci. U. S.* **64**, 1276.
Langer, G. A. (1973). *Annu. Rev. Physiol.* **35**, 55.
Lawson, D. E. M., Wilson, P. W., and Kodicek, E. (1969a). *Nature (London)* **222**, 171.
Lawson, D. E. M., Wilson, P. W., and Kodicek, E. (1969). *Biochem. J.* **115**, 269.
Lawson, D. E. M., Wilson, P. W., Barker, D. C., and Kodicek, E. (1969c). *Biochem. J.* **115**, 262.
Lawson, D., and Emtage, J. S. (1973). *In* "Metabolism and Function of Vitamin D" (D. R. Fraser, ed.). Biochem. Soc. Special Publ. No. 3 (in press).
Leblond, C. P., and Carriere, R. (1955). *Endocrinology* **56**, 261.
Lehninger, A. L. (1970). *Biochem. J.* **119**, 129.
LeJohn, H. B., Jackson, S. G., Klassen, G. R., and Sawula, R. V. (1969). *J. Biol. Chem.* **244**, 5346.
Lindquist, B. (1952). *Acta Paediat. (Stockholm)* **41**, Suppl. 86, 1.
Lippiello, L., and Wasserman, R. H. (1973). Unpublished data.
Loewenstein, W. R. (1966). *Ann. N. Y. Acad. Sci.* **137**, 441.
Loewenstein, W. R. (1967a). *Develop. Biol.* **15**, 503.
Loewenstein, W. R. (1967b). *J. Colloid Interface Sci.* **25**, 34.
Loewenstein, W. R. (1972). *In* "Cell Interactions" (Luigi G. Silvestri, ed.), pp. 296–298. North-Holland Publ., Amsterdam.
Loewenstein, W. R. (1973). *Fed. Proc., Fed. Amer. Soc. Exp. Biol.* **32**, 60.
Loewenstein, W. R., and Kanno, Y. (1964). *J. Cell Biol.* **22**, 565.
Loewenstein, W. R., and Kanno, Y. (1966). *Nature (London)* **209**, 1248.
Loewenstein, W. R., and Penn, R. D. (1967). *J. Cell Biol.* **33**, 235.
Loewenstein, W. R., Socolar, S. J., Higashino, S., Kanno, Y., and Davidson, N. (1965). *Science* **149**, 295.
Loewenstein, W. R., Nakas, M., and Socolar, S. J. (1967). *J. Gen. Physiol.* **50**, 1865.
MacGregor, R. R., Hamilton, J. W., and Cohn, D. V. (1970). *Biochim. Biophys. Acta* **222**, 482.
MacGregor, R. R., Hamilton, J. W., and Cohn, D. V. (1971). *Clin. Orthop.* **78**, 83.
McLean, F. C., and Urist, M. R. (1968). "Bone, Fundamentals of the Physiology of Skeletal Tissue." Univ. of Chicago Press, Chicago, Illinois.
MacManus, J. P., and Whitfield, J. F. (1969). *Proc. Soc. Exp. Biol. Med.* **132**, 409.
MacManus, J. P., and Whitfield, J. F. (1970). *Endocrinology* **86**, 934.
MacManus, J. P., and Whitfield, J. F. (1971). *Exp. Cell Res.* **69**, 281.
MacManus, J. P., and Whitfield, J. F. (1972). *Life Sci. Part II*, **11**, 837. Pergamon, New York.
MacManus, J. P., Whitfield, J. F., and Youdale, T. (1971a). *J. Cell. Physiol.* **77**, 103.
MacManus, J. P., Whitfield, J. F., and Braceland, B. (1971b). *Biochem. Biophys. Res. Commun.* **42**, 503.
MacManus, J. P., Youdale, T., Whitfield, J. F., and Franks, D. J. (1972). *In* "Calcium, Parathyroid Hormone and the Calcitonins" (R. V. Talmage and P. L. Munson, eds.), pp. 338–350. Excerpta Medica, Amsterdam.
McNutt, K. W., and Haussler, M. R. (1973). *J. Nutr.* **103**, 681.
Major, P. W., and Kilpatrick, R. (1972). *J. Endocrin.* **52**, 593.

Malamud, D. (1969). *Biochem. Biophys. Res. Commun.* **35**, 754.

Malamud, D., and Malt, R. A. (1971). *Lab. Invest.* **24**, 140.

Manery, J. F. (1969). *In* "Mineral Metabolism. An Advanced Treatise" (C. L. Comar and F. Bronner, eds.), Vol. III, pp. 405–452. Academic Press, New York.

Margoliash, E., Schenck, J. R., Hargie, M. P., Burokas, S., Richter, W. R., Barlow, G. H., and Moscona, A. A. (1965). *Biochem. Biophys. Res. Commun.* **20**, 383.

Martin, D. L., Melancon, M. J., and DeLuca, H. F. (1969). *Biochem. Biophys. Res. Commun.* **35**, 819.

Martonosi, A., Pucell, A. G., and Halpin, R. A. (1971). *In* "Cellular Mechanisms for Calcium Transfer and Homeostasis" (G. Nichols, Jr., and R. H. Wasserman, eds.), pp. 175–193. Academic Press, New York.

Mason, J. W., Rasmussen, H., and Dibella, F. (1971). *Exp. Cell. Res.* **67**, 156.

Mechanic, G. L., Toverud, S. U., and Ramp, W. K. (1972). *Biochem. Biophys. Res. Commun.* **47**, 760.

Mela, L., and Chance, B. (1969). *Biochem. Biophys. Res. Commun.* **35**, 556.

Melancon, M. J., Jr., and DeLuca, H. F. (1970). *Biochemistry* **9**, 1658.

Meli, J., and Bygrave, F. L. (1972). *Biochem. J.* **128**, 415.

Mellanby, E. (1919). *Lancet* **I**, 407.

Melson, G. L., Chase, L. R., and Aurbach, G. D. (1970). *Endocrinology* **86**, 511.

Menczel, J., Eilon, G., Steiner, A., Karaman, C., Mor, E., and Ron, A. (1971). *Isr. J. Med. Sci.* **7**, 396.

Meyer, W. L., and Kunin, A. S. (1969). *Arch. Biochem. Biophys.* **129**, 438.

Migicovsky, B. B., and Emslie, A. R. G. (1947). *Arch. Biochem. Biophys.* **13**, 175.

Moog, F., and Glazier, H. S. (1972). *Comp. Biochem. Physiol.* **42A**, 321.

Morova, E., Winter, M., and Tarjan, R. (1971). *Nutr. Rep. Int.* **4**, 119.

Morris, J. E., and Moscona, A. A. (1971). *Develop. Biol.* **25**, 420.

Morrissey, R. L., and Wasserman, R. H. (1971). *Amer. J. Physiol.* **220**, 1509.

Motzok, I. (1950). *Biochem. J.* **47**, 193.

Myrtle, J. F., and Norman, A. W. (1971). *Science* **171**, 79.

Myrtle, J. F., Haussler, M. R., and Norman, A. W. (1970). *J. Biol. Chem.* **245**, 1190.

Neuman, W. F. (1969). *Fed. Proc., Fed. Amer. Soc. Exp. Biol.* **28**, 1846.

Neuman, W. F., and Neuman, M. W. (1958). "Chemical Dynamics of Bone Mineral." Univ. of Chicago Press, Chicago, Illinois.

Neuman, W. F., Mulryan, B. J., Neuman, M. W., and Lane, K. (1973). *Amer. J. Physiol.* **224**, 600.

Neville, E., and Holdsworth, E. S. (1969). *FEBS Lett.* **2**, 313.

Ney, R. L., Au, W. Y. W., Kelly, G., Radde, I., and Bartter, F. C. (1965). *J. Clin. Invest.* **44**, 2003.

Nichols, G., Jr., and Wasserman, R. H., eds. (1971). "Cellular Mechanisms for Calcium Transfer and Homeostasis." Academic Press, New York.

Nichols, G., Jr., Hirschmann, P., and Rogers, P. (1971). *In* "Cellular Mechanisms for Calcium Transfer and Homeostasis" (G. Nichols, Jr., and R. H. Wasserman, eds.), pp. 211–235. Academic Press, New York.

Nicolaysen, R. (1937). *Biochem. J.* **31**, 323.

Nicolaysen, R., Eeg-Larsen, N., and Malm, O. J. (1953). *Physiol. Rev.* **33**, 424.

Norman, A. W. (1965). *Science* **149**, 184.

Norman, A. W. (1966). *Biochem. Biophys. Res. Commun.* **23**, 335.

Norman, A. W., Mircheff, A. K., Adams, T. H., and Spielvogel, A. (1970). *Biochim. Biophys. Acta* **215**, 348.

Omdahl, J. L., and DeLuca, H. F. (1972). *J. Biol. Chem.* **247**, 5520.

Omdahl, J. L., and DeLuca, H. F. (1973). *Physiol. Rev.* **53**, 327.
Omdahl, J. L., and Thornton, P. A. (1972a). *Proc. Soc. Exp. Biol. Med.* **139**, 975.
Omdahl, J. L., and Thornton, P. A. (1972b). *Biochem. Pharmacol.* **21**, 231.
Omdahl, J. L., Holick, M., Suda, T., Tanaka, Y., and DeLuca, H. F. (1971). *Biochemistry* **10**, 2935.
Ooizumi, K., Moriuchi, S., and Hosoya, N. (1970). *J. Vitaminol. (Kyoto)* **16**, 228.
Ord, M. G., and Stocken, L. A. (1969). *Biochem. J.* **112**, 81.
Pappenheimer, A. M., and Minor, J. (1921). *J. Med. Res.* **42**, 391.
Parkinson, D. K., and Radde, I. C. (1971). *In* "Cellular Mechanisms for Calcium Homeostasis" (G. Nichols, Jr., and R. H. Wasserman, eds.), p. 506. Academic Press, New York.
Paterson, C. R., and Fourman, P. (1968). *Biochem. J.* **109**, 101.
Peacock, M., and Nordin, B. E. C. (1973). *In* "Hard Tissue Growth, Repair and Remineralization," *Ciba Found. Symp. 11*, pp. 409–428. Elsevier, Amsterdam.
Penn, R. D. (1966). *J. Cell Biol.* **29**, 171.
Ferris, A. D., and Whitfield, J. F. (1967a). *Nature (London)* **214**, 302.
Perris, A. D., and Whitfield, J. F. (1967b). *Nature (London)* **216**, 1350.
Perris, A. D., and Whitfield, J. F. (1971). *Physiol. Pharmacol.* **49**, 22.
Perris, A. D., Whitfield, J. F., and Rixon, R. H. (1967). *Radiat. Res.* **32**, 550.
Perris, A. D., Whitfield, J. F., and Tölg, P. K. (1968). *Nature (London)* **219**, 527.
Perris, A. D., Weiss, L. A., and Whitfield, J. F. (1970). *J. Cell. Physiol.* **76**, 141.
Perris, A. D., MacManus, J. P., Whitfield, J. F., and Weiss, L. A. (1971). *Amer. J. Physiol.* **220**, 773.
Peterkofsky, B., and Udenfriend, S. (1963). *Biochem. Biophys. Res. Commun.* **12**, 257.
Piazolo, P., Schleyer, M., and Franz, H. E. (1971). *Hoppe-Seyler's Z. Physiol. Chem.* **352**, 1480.
Piez, K. A. (1971). *Isr. J. Med. Sci.* **7**, 453.
Poisner, A. M. (1973). *Biochem. Pharmacol.* **22**, 469.
Poisner, A. M., and Hava, M. (1970). *Mol. Pharmacol.* **6**, 407.
Posner, I., and Morales, A. (1972). *J. Biol. Chem.* **247**, 2255.
Puschett, J. B., Moranz, J., and Kurnick, W. S. (1972). *J. Clin. Invest.* **51**, 373.
Rahaminoff, R. (1970). *In* "Calcium and Cellular Function" (A. W. Cuthbert, ed.), pp. 131–147. St. Martin's, New York.
Raisz, L. G., and Trummel, C. L. (1969). *In* "The Fat-Soluble Vitamins" (H. F. DeLuca and J. W. Suttie, eds.), pp. 93–99. Univ. of Wisconsin Press, Madison, Wisconsin.
Raisz, L. G., and Trummel, C. L. (1971). *In* "Cellular Mechanisms for Calcium Transfer and Homeostasis" (G. Nichols, Jr., and R. H. Wasserman, eds.), pp. 441–451. Academic Press, New York.
Raisz, L. G., Trummel, C. L., Holick, M. F., and DeLuca, H. F. (1972). *Science* **175**, 768.
Rasmussen, H., DeLuca, H. F., Arnaud, C., Hawker, C., and van Stediugk, M. (1963). *J. Clin. Invest.* **42**, 1940.
Rasmussen, H., Wong, M., Bikle, D., and Goodman, D. B. P. (1972a). *J. Clin. Invest.* **51**, 2502.
Rasmussen, H., Kurokawa, K., Mason, J., and Goodman, D. B. P. (1972b). *In* "Calcium, Parathyroid Hormone and the Calcitonins" (R. V. Talmage and P. L. Munson, eds.), pp. 492–501. Excerpta Medica, Amsterdam.

Reddy, Y. S., and Honig, G. R. (1972). *Biochim. Biophys. Acta* **275**, 453.

Reynolds, J. J. (1973). *In* "Hard Tissue Growth, Repair and Remineralization," *Ciba Found. Symp. 11*, pp. 315–326. Elsevier, Amsterdam.

Richards, I. D. G., Sweet, E. M., and Arneil, G. C. (1968). *Lancet* **I**, 803.

Rixon, R. H. (1968). *Curr. Mod. Biol.* **2**, 68.

Rixon, R. H., and Whitfield, J. F. (1972). *Proc. Soc. Exp. Biol. Med.* **141**, 93.

Robison, G. A., Butcher, R. W., and Sutherland, E. W. (1968). *Annu. Rev. Biochem.* **37**, 149.

Rohr, H. (1965). *Z. Gesamte Exp. Med.* **139**, 621.

Rubin, R. P. (1970). *Pharmacol. Rev.* **22**, 389.

Russell, J. E., and Avioli, L. V. (1972). *J. Clin. Invest.* **51**, 3072.

Russell, R. G. G., Monod, A., Bonjour, J.-P., and Fleisch, H. (1972). *Nature (London) New Biol.* **240**, 126.

St. Amand, G. A., Anderson, N. G., and Gaulden, M. E. (1960). *Exp. Cell Res.* **20**, 71.

Sallis, J. D., and Holdsworth, E. S. (1962). *Amer. J. Physiol.* **203**, 506.

Scarpa, A., and Azzone, G. F. (1968). *J. Biol. Chem.* **243**, 5132.

Schachter, D. (1970). *In* "The Fat-Soluble Vitamins" (H. F. DeLuca and J. W. Suttie, eds.), pp. 55–65. Univ. of Wisconsin Press, Madison, Wisconsin.

Schachter, D., and Kowarski, S. (1965). *Bull. N. Y. Acad. Med.* **41**, 241.

Schaefer, K., Flury, W. H., von Herrath, D., Kraft, D., and Schweingruber, R. (1972). *Schweiz. Med. Wochenschr.* **102**, 785.

Schmid, F. (1967). *Fortschr. Med.* **9**, 381.

Schmitt, F. O. (1959). *Rev. Mod. Phys.* **31**, 349.

Shipley, P. C., Park, E. Q., McCollum, E. V., Simmonds, N., and Kinney, E. M. (1922). *Bull. Johns Hopkins Hosp.* **33**, 216.

Smith, J. W., Steiner, A. L., Newberry, W. M., and Parker, C. W. (1971). *J. Clin. Invest.* **50**, 432.

Sobel, A. E. (1954). *Ann. N. Y. Acad. Sci.* **60**, 713.

Spielvogel, A. M., Farley, R. O., and Norman, A. W. (1972). *Exp. Cell Res.* **74**, 359.

Spitzer, R. R., and Phillips, P. H. (1945). *J. Nutr.* **30**, 183.

Stamp, T. C. B., Round, J. B., Rowe, D. J. F., and Haddad, J. G. (1972). *Brit. Med. J.* **4**, 9.

Stanbury, S. W., Hill, L. F., and Mawer, E. B. (1973). *In:* "Hard Tissue Growth, Repair and Mineralization," *Ciba Found. Symp. 11*, pp. 391–401. Elsevier, Amsterdam.

Steenbock, H., and Herting, D. C. (1955). *J. Nutr.* **57**, 449.

Steenbock, H., Krieger, C. H., Wiest, W. G., and Pileggi, V. J. (1953). *J. Biol. Chem.* **205**, 993.

Stephens, R. E., and Kane, R. E. (1970). *J. Cell Biol.* **44**, 611.

Stohs, S. J., Zull, J. E., and DeLuca, H. F. (1967). *Biochemistry* **6**, 1304.

Suda, T., DeLuca, H. F., Schnoes, H. K., Tanaka, Y., and Holick, M. F. (1970). *Biochemistry* **9**, 4776.

Sugai, M., and Matsuda, I. (1968). *Biochim. Biophys. Acta* **170**, 474.

Sugai, M., and Matsuda, I. (1971). *Experientia* **27**, 25.

Takahashi, K., and Okada, T. S. (1971). *Develop. Growth & Differentiation* **13**, 15.

Talmage, R. V. (1970). *Amer. J. Anat.* **129**, 467.

Talmage, R. V., and Munson, P. L., eds. (1972). "Calcium, Parathyroid Hormone and the Calcitonins." Excerpta Medica, Amsterdam.

Tanaka, Y., and DeLuca, H. F. (1971a). *Proc. Nat. Acad. Sci. U. S.* **68**, 605.
Tanaka, Y., and DeLuca, H. F. (1971b). *Arch. Biochem. Biophys.* **146**, 574.
Tanaka, Y., and DeLuca, H. F. (1973). *Arch. Biochem. Biophys.* **154**, 566.
Tanaka, Y., DeLuca, H. F., Omdahl, J. L., and Holick, F. M. (1971). *Proc. Nat. Acad. Sci. U. S.* **68**, 1286.
Tanaka, Y., Chen, T. C., and DeLuca, H. F. (1972). *Arch. Biochem. Biophys.* **152**, 291.
Targovnik, J. H., Rodman, J. S., and Sherwood, L. M. (1971). *Endocrinology* **88**, 1477.
Taylor, A. N. (1973). Unpublished observation.
Taylor, A. N., and Wasserman, R. H. (1967). *Arch. Biochem. Biophys.* **119**, 536.
Taylor, A. N., and Wasserman, R. H. (1969). *Fed. Proc., Fed. Amer. Soc. Exp. Biol.* **28**, 1834.
Taylor, A. N., and Wasserman, R. H. (1970a). *J. Histochem. Cytochem.* **18**, 107.
Taylor, A. N., and Wasserman, R. H. (1970b). *Fed. Proc., Fed. Amer. Soc. Exp. Biol.* **29**, 368.
Taylor, A. N., and Wasserman, R. H. (1972). *Amer. J. Physiol.* **223**, 110.
Taylor, A. N., Wasserman, R. H., and Jowsey, J. (1968). *Fed. Proc., Fed. Amer. Soc. Exp. Biol.* **27**, 675.
Thomas, W. C., Jr., and Howard, J. E. (1964). *In* "Mineral Metabolism" (C. L. Comar and F. Bronner, eds.), Vol. 2A, pp. 445–482. Academic Press, New York.
Tolman, K. G., Jubix, W., DeLuca, H. F., and Freston, J. W. (1972). *Clin. Res.* **20**, 414.
Toole, B. P., Kang, A. H., Treslad, R. L., and Gross, J. (1972). *Biochem. J.* **127**, 715.
Tsai, H. C., Wong, R. G., and Norman, A. W. (1972). *J. Biol. Chem.* **247**, 5511.
Tsai, H. C., Midgett, R. J., and Norman, A. W. (1973). *Arch. Biochem. Biophys.* **157**, 339.
Tucker, G., Gagnon, R. E., and Haussler, M. R. (1973). *Arch. Biochem. Biophys.* **155**, 47.
Urban, E., and Schedl, H. P. (1969). *Experientia* **25**, 1270.
Urist, M. R. (1966). *Clin. Orthop. Relat. Res.* **44**, 13.
Vaughan, J. M. (1970). "The Physiology of Bone." Oxford Univ. Press (Clarendon), London and New York.
Villareale, M., Gould, L. V., Wasserman, R. H., Bar, A., Chiroff, R. T., and Bergstrom, W. H. (1973). *Science* (in press).
Wallach, S., Reizenstein, D., and Bellavia, J. (1966). *J. Gen. Physiol.* **49**, 743.
Wasserman, R. H. (1962). *J. Nutr.* **77**, 69.
Wasserman, R. H. (1970). *Biochim. Biophys. Acta* **203**, 176.
Wasserman, R. H. (1972). *In* "Metabolic Transport" (L. E. Hokin, ed.), pp. 351–384. Academic Press, New York.
Wasserman, R. H. (1973). *Ciba Found. Symp. Hard Tissue Growth, Repair and Remineralization*, pp. 373–384. Elsevier, Amsterdam.
Wasserman, R. H. (1974). *In* "Handbook in Physiology" (G. Aurbach, ed.). In preparation.
Wasserman, R. H., and Corradino, R. A. (1971). *Annu. Rev. Biochem.* **40**, 501.
Wasserman, R. H., and Kallfelz, F. A. (1970). *In* "Biological Calcification—Cellular and Molecular Aspects" (H. Schraer, ed.), pp. 313–345. Appleton, New York.
Wasserman, R. H., and Taylor, A. N. (1966). *Science* **152**, 791.
Wasserman, R. H., and Taylor, A. N. (1968). *J. Biol. Chem.* **243**, 3987.

Wasserman, R. H., and Taylor, A. N. (1969). *In* "Mineral Metabolism: An Advanced Treatise" (C. L. Comar and F. Bronner, eds.), Vol. III, pp. 321–403. Academic Press, New York.

Wasserman, R. H., and Taylor, A. N. (1971). *Proc. Soc. Exp. Biol. Med.* **136,** 25.

Wasserman, R. H., and Taylor, A. N. (1973a). *Triangle* **12** (in press).

Wasserman, R. H., and Taylor, A. N. (1973b). *J. Nutr.* **103,** 586.

Wasserman, R. H., Corradino, R. A., and Taylor, A. N. (1968). *J. Biol. Chem.* **243,** 3978.

Wasserman, R. H., Taylor, A. N., and Fullmer, C. S. (1973). *In* "Metabolism and Function of Vitamin D," Biochemical Symposium (D. Fraser, ed.) (in press).

Weber, J. C., Pons, V., and Kodicek, E. (1972). *Biochem. J.* **125,** 147.

Wergedal, J. E. (1969). *Calcif. Tissue Res.* **3,** 67.

Wergedal, J. E., and Baylink, D. J. (1971). *Amer. J. Physiol.* **220,** 406.

Whitfield, J. F., and Perris, A. D. (1968). *Exp. Cell Res.* **49,** 359.

Whitfield, J. F., and Youdale, T. (1966). *Exp. Cell Res.* **43,** 602.

Whitfield, J. F., Rixon, R. H., Perris, A. D., and Youdale, T. (1969a). *Exp. Cell Res.* **57,** 8.

Whitfield, J. F., Perris, A. D., and Youdale, T. (1969b). *J. Cell. Physiol.* **73,** 203.

Whitfield, J. F., MacManus, J. P., and Rixon, R. H. (1970a). *J. Cell. Physiol.* **75,** 213.

Whitfield, J. F., MacManus, J. P., and Gillan, D. J. (1970b). *J. Cell. Physiol.* **76,** 65.

Whitfield, J. F., MacManus, J. P., Youdale, T., and Franks, D. J. (1971). *J. Cell. Physiol.* **78,** 355.

Whitfield, J. F., MacManus, J. P., Braceland, B. M., and Gillan, D. J. (1972a). *Horm. Metab. Res.* **4,** 304.

Whitfield, J. F., MacManus, J. P., Braceland, B. M., and Gillan, D. J. (1972b). *J. Cell. Physiol.* **79,** 353.

Whitfield, J. F., MacManus, J. P., Franks, D. J., Braceland, B. M., and Gillan, D. J. (1972c). *J. Cell. Physiol.* **80,** 315.

Whitfield, J. F., Rixon, R. H., MacManus, J. P., and Balk, S. D. (1973). *In Vitro* **8,** 257.

Whitney, R. B., and Sutherland, R. M. (1972a). *J. Cell. Physiol.* **80,** 329.

Whitney, R. B., and Sutherland, R. M. (1972b). *Cell. Immunol.* **5,** 137.

Williams, G. A., Bowser, E. N., Henderson, W. J., and Uzgiries, V. (1961). *Proc. Soc. Exp. Biol. Med.* **106,** 664.

Winegrad, S. (1969). *In* "Mineral Metabolism." (C. L. Comar and F. Bronner, eds.), Vol. III, pp. 191–233. Academic Press, New York.

Yang, D.-P., and Morton, H. J. (1971). *J. Nat. Cancer Inst.* **46,** 505.

Zull, J. E., Czarnowska-Misztal, E., and DeLuca, H. F. (1965). *Science* **149,** 182.

Erythropoietin*

ALBERT S. GORDON

*Laboratory of Experimental Hematology, Department of Biology,
Graduate School of Arts and Science, New York University,
New York, New York*

* The original work incorporated in this review has been supported by a research grant (5-R01-HL03357-16) and a training grant (5-T01-HL05645-08) from the National Heart and Lung Institute, National Institutes of Health, U. S. Public Health Service. Support was also derived in part from a National Institutes of Health Bio-Medical Science Support Grant to New York University.

I. Introduction

Erythropoietin (Ep),* a circulating glycoprotein hormone, is now acknowledged to be the prime regulator of erythropoiesis in higher organisms. In an earlier review (Gordon, 1959), it was pointed out that considerably more research was required on the physiology and biochemistry of this hormone before its true significance could be stated. This included work relating to improvements in assay methods, to a more complete elucidation of its chemical nature, its site(s) of action and of production, as well as its clinical significance and possible applications. It is the purpose of this chapter to review fundamental advances in this field in the last 14 years.

The indication based on preliminary evidence (Rambach et al., 1956) that Ep is glycoprotein in nature has been amply fortified in recent years (Krantz and Jacobson, 1970). It is detectable in elevated quantities in the plasma and serum (Gordon, 1959; Gordon and Zanjani, 1970a; Fisher and Roh, 1971; Fisher, 1972) and in the lymph (Keighley, 1962; Zivny et al., 1972b; Murphy and Gordon, unpublished observations) of animals subjected to diverse hypoxic stimuli as well as in different oxygen deficiency and tumorous states in man (Gordon and Zanjani, 1970a; Krantz and Jacobson, 1970; Fisher, 1972). It is of considerable significance that Ep is present in the plasma (Mirand et al., 1965b) and urine (Adamson et al., 1966; Alexanian, 1966; Van Dyke et al., 1966) of normal humans. These findings strengthen the conclusion that Ep plays a role not only in so-called "panic" or emergency erythropoiesis, but also in the normal daily replacement of red cells. A diurnal variation (Adamson et al., 1966) and a sex difference (Alexanian, 1966; Van Dyke et al., 1966) appears to

---

* The question whether Ep is to be considered a true hormone remains an arbitrary one. The criteria generally employed in distinguishing between a "factor" or "principle" and a "hormone" involves the relative state of purification and characterization of the substance under consideration. Ideally, a substance is designated as a hormone when it has been purified to a point where little or no contamination exists. In addition, the classic endocrine definition of a hormone as stated by Bayliss and Starling (1904) is that it be produced by specialized cells in some part of the body and carried by the blood stream to another organ or organs in which a particular function is enhanced. Ep is now acknowledged to be produced or activated by the kidney, is transported by the circulation to its target sites, the blood-forming tissues, where it stimulates erythropoiesis. This fact coupled with the high state of purity achieved for Ep by Goldwasser and Kung (1971) and by Espada and Gutnisky (1970a) would, in this reviewer's opinion, justify its categorization as a hormone. A similar situation prevails for the renin–angiotensin system. It is recommended, therefore, that the designation originally suggested (Gordon, 1959) of erythropoiesis-stimulating factor (ESF) be replaced by the term erythropoiesis-stimulating hormone (ESH), or simply Ep.

exist as determined from its normal daily excretion pattern. The impressive observation that administration of anti-Ep immune serum results in an almost complete suppression of erythropoiesis (Schooley and Garcia, 1962) lends additional weight to the concept that Ep is involved in supporting normal baseline levels of erythropoiesis.

II. METHODS OF ASSAY FOR ERYTHROPOIETIN (EP)

A. *In Vivo* ASSAYS

Earlier criteria for determining the Ep content of serum, plasma, urine, or fractions derived therefrom as well as tissue extracts included increases in peripheral red blood cell (RBC) indexes (RBC counts, hemoglobin, hematocrit, and reticulocyte levels), the numbers of nucleated RBC in the erythropoietic organs (Borsook *et al.*, 1954; Gordon *et al.*, 1954) and total circulating RBC volume (Garcia and Van Dyke, 1959) of intact rats. With the demonstration that the measurement of ^{59}Fe incorporation into newly formed RBC constituted a simpler, more sensitive and reproducible method of estimating erythropoiesis (Huff *et al.*, 1950; Plzak *et al.*, 1955), this criterion became widely used for determining the Ep content of body fluid and tissue extracts.

It soon became realized that the sensitivity of the assay procedures for Ep could be increased through the use of animals in which erythropoiesis had been inhibited. This led to the use of starved (Gurney *et al.*, 1957a) and hypophysectomized (Gordon *et al.*, 1955; Fried *et al.*, 1956) rats as recipients. In these animals, metabolism is depressed, erythropoiesis proceeds at a slower rate, and Ep levels are probably reduced, factors that result in a more sensitive response to Ep. However, limitations exist in the use of fasted and hypophysectomized animals for the assay of Ep in untreated body fluids or crude extracts prepared from these sources as well as in organ extracts. Thus the erythropoiesis-stimulating actions induced by plasma or serum may arise at least in part from their content of endocrine factors to which the hypophysectomized animal is highly sensitive. These include hormones of adenohypophyseal, adrenal cortical, and thyroidal origin (Gordon, 1968). Similarly, the starved animal may be responding with increased erythropoiesis to nonspecific nutrients, especially protein in the injected materials. The *in vivo* assays most commonly used at present measure the increases induced by Ep in the percentage of ^{59}Fe incorporation into the red cells of mice made plethoric by transfusion of homologous red cells or polycythemic by exposure to reduced oxygen tensions followed by return of the mice to normal pressures for several days (see reviews by Camiscoli *et al.*, 1968; Camiscoli and Gordon, 1970). In addition, erythro-

poietic depression in mice has been induced by hyperbaric hyperoxia
(Linman and Pierre, 1968) and by carbon monoxide-induced polycythemia (Fogh, 1966). Another method involves exposing mice to low
oxygen tensions in silicone rubber membrane enclosures, which display
a greater permeability to carbon dioxide than to oxygen (Lange *et al.*,
1966). Values of percent radioiron incorporation into RBC obtained in
the mice used in all the above assays may be converted into equivalent
Ep units by reference to the standard curve for the International Reference Preparation (IRP) of Ep (Cotes, 1970; Annable *et al.*, 1972).
These procedures permit quantitative detection of quantities of Ep as
small as 0.05–0.10 IU per sample administered.

Studies make it apparent that the exhypoxic polycythemic mouse is
more economical to prepare and more sensitive to small doses of Ep than
the hypertransfused mouse. This is probably the result of three features
of the exhypoxic mouse: (1) presence of greater numbers of Ep-
responsive precursor cells (Hurst *et al.*, 1969; OKunewick and Fulton,
1970); (2) a possible shortening of precursor cell cycle time (Kretchmar,
1966); and (3) the persistence, for at least 3 or 4 days after interruption
of the hypoxia, of small numbers of nucleated RBC in the erythropoietic
organs, which are also believed now to be responsive to Ep (Borsook
et al., 1968; Necheles *et al.*, 1968). However, the fact remains that a true
quantitative measurement of the reaction of Ep-responsive cells (ERC)
to Ep requires mice rendered severely plethoric by hypertransfusion. To
avoid the possibility that the occasional small response of the hypertransfused mouse to Ep is due in part to the presence of some nucleated
erythroid cells in the erythropoietic organs may require treatment with
anti-Ep serum or neuraminidase before the assay is run (Schooley and
Mahlmann, 1972a).

B. *In Vitro* Assays

Considerable effort has been applied in developing reproducible methods for assaying Ep in culture systems. Early reports (Erslev, 1962)
suggested the use of rabbit bone marrow cell cultures for assessing the
activity of Ep. Utilizing the criterion of ^{59}Fe incorporation into heme, a
dose-response relation was demonstrated between the amount of Ep
added to rat bone marrow cell cultures and the rate of synthesis of heme
(Krantz *et al.*, 1963; Gallien-Lartigue and Goldwasser, 1964). The
method is capable of detecting human or sheep Ep in quantities as low
as 0.05 IU in human bone marrow cell cultures (Krantz, 1968). Similar
results have been obtained employing dog bone marrow (Ward, 1967).
More recently, liver cells from 13-day mouse fetuses have been shown to
respond to Ep in culture by a linear increase in the rate of heme syn-

thesis with a logarithmic increase in Ep concentration (Stephenson and Axelrad, 1971a). The minimal amount of Ep detectable with this method is 0.01 IU per milliliter of culture medium. Since each pregnant mouse provides enough fetal liver tissue for 300–400 culture plates, this method provides greater economy than bone marrow cell culture techniques. When plasma specimens containing very small amounts of Ep are being assayed, difficulties may arise from the need to add large amounts of plasma to the culture system. Moreover, the presence of even small quantities of impurities in some Ep preparations may tend to falsify interpretation of the assay data. Thus, in at least this respect, the *in vivo* methods are more desirable since the liver, kidney, and other organs of the assay animal undoubtedly aid in the detoxification and removal of the contaminating agents. Of relevance here are observations that a number of Ep preparations, while exhibiting similar erythropoietic potencies in the polycythemic mouse assay, show different activities in marrow culture systems that utilize heme synthesis or glucosamine incorporation as the biochemical parameters (Dukes *et al.*, 1970). These findings, which indicate that results obtained with the *in vivo* and *in vitro* assays do not always concur, emphasize that estimates obtained in the two types of assay are not necessarily comparable.

Immunochemical methods have also been utilized for the assay of Ep. These include: (1) double diffusion techniques (Goudsmit *et al.*, 1967) for detecting Ep in human plasma, (2) inhibition of agglutination of tanned RBC that have been coated with Ep (Lange *et al.*, 1969, 1972; Lange, 1971), and (3) radioimmune assay techniques (Fisher *et al.*, 1971c, 1972; Garcia, 1972). With samples of plasma and urine obtained from anemic subjects, a good correlation is seen to exist between the levels of Ep determined by immunochemical methods and those derived from the *in vivo* assays in polycythemic mice (Lange *et al.*, 1972). The sensitivity afforded by the immunochemical methods exceeds greatly that of the conventional *in vivo* bioassays. Thus these procedures make possible the detection of Ep in samples of normal human body fluids. With the double diffusion technique (Goudsmit *et al.*, 1967), the values are estimated as between 0.5 and 2.0 milli immunochemical units per milliliter of plasma; with the hemagglutination inhibition assay (Lange, 1971) as between 6 and 50 milli immunochemical units per milliliter of serum, and with the radioimmune assay (Garcia, 1972) as between 4.5 and 11.0 milli radioimmune units per milliliter of plasma. Practical use of the radioimmune assay would appear to depend on the continued availability of a pure labeled Ep and the development of a species-specific anti-Ep antibody (Garcia, 1972).

The ability of the immunochemical methods to assay quantities of Ep

TABLE I

COMPARISON OF SENSITIVITY OF *in Vivo* AND *in Vitro* ASSAYS FOR Ep[a]

Assay method	Minimal detectable dose (IU Ep)	Index of precision
1. Hypertransfused polycythemic mouse (Rosse et al., 1962)	0.03	0.364
2. Exhypoxic polycythemic mouse (Cotes, 1968)	0.05	0.31–0.52
3. Starved rat (Gordon and Weintraub, 1962)	0.50	0.128–0.467
4. Rat marrow *in vitro* (R. H. Painter, unpublished observations)	0.02	0.053–0.14
5. Fetal liver *in vitro* (Stephenson and Axelrad, 1971a)	0.01	0.036–0.060

Immunological assays	Minimal detectable dose (immunochemical units)
1. Hemagglutination inhibition (Lange et al., 1972)	0.87×10^{-4}
2. Radioimmune assay (Fisher et al., 1972)	0.010×10^{-3}

[a] Taken in part from Stephenson and Axelrad (1971a).

as low as 0.01 milliunit of the IRP of Ep (Fisher *et al.*, 1972) should permit ready detection of Ep not only in the body fluids of normal subjects but also in conditions associated with lowered production of Ep (e.g., chronic renal disease and possibly polycythemia vera). Despite objections that immunochemical methods may also be measuring chemically related contaminants in relatively impure preparations, the present evidence suggests that these procedures provide a useful tool for screening large numbers of human plasma samples and in the detection of subnormal quantities of Ep in these materials. Table I provides a summary of the sensitivity of *in vivo* and *in vitro* assays for Ep.

III. CHEMISTRY AND PURIFICATION

Past difficulty in achieving purification and characterization of Ep arose from the unavailability of large supplies of the hormone. The most lucrative present sources are plasma from sheep rendered severely anemic by phenylhydrazine (White *et al.*, 1960; Goldwasser *et al.*, 1962; Goldwasser and Kung, 1968, 1971, 1972a) and urine from anemic human subjects (Espada and Gutnisky, 1970a,b).

A. PLASMA EP

The observation that plasma Ep is inactivated by trypsin and sialidase suggested that Ep is a sialic-acid containing protein (Winkert and Gordon, 1960). Goldwasser and Kung (1971, 1972a) have reported on preparations of Ep, extracted from anemic sheep plasma, with activities in the range of 8000 to 9000 IU per milligram of protein. A summary of the procedure utilized follows (Goldwasser and Kung, 1972). Plasma from sheep made intensely anemic with phenylhydrazine was dialyzed at pH 4.5 against 5 volumes of water, and batch adsorption on DEAE-cellulose was followed by elution at high salt concentration (step I). This material was subjected to dialysis and then passed through IRC-50 at pH 6. The pH of the effluent (step II) was lowered to 5.0 before adsorption on IRC-50; elution was carried out at pH 6 and the material was dialyzed and lyophilized (step III). Step III was placed into solution and precipitated with ammonium sulfate between 0.53 saturated at pH 6.3 and 0.67 saturated at pH 3.3. Dialysis and lyophilization followed, yielding step IV. This fraction was dissolved in $3 M$ LiCl, precipitated with alcohol, desalted, and chromatographed on sulfoethyl Sephadex. Elution was carried out with acetate buffers; the eluates were adsorbed on hydroxyapatite at low ionic strength and eluted with phosphate buffer at pH 7.4. This material was chromatographed on methylated-albumin kieselguhr and eluted with phosphate buffer at pH 7.2. This preparation (MAK-7) was almost completely pure, with a specific activity of approximately 8300 IU per milligram of protein as determined by *in vivo* assay procedures. Of interest is that the major contaminant in this fraction was desialated Ep. Since the desialated Ep was not active *in vivo*, the true potency of the pure Ep was calculated to be 8900 IU per milligram of protein. Preliminary and tentative analysis of the MAK-7 fraction showed it to contain 74% protein and 26% carbohydrate. The carbohydrate moiety consisted of 10% sialic acid, 6% galactose, 4% mannose, 4% glucosamine, and 2% glucose. Microanalysis of the amino acid content indicated the presence of small amounts of arginine, tyrosine, and valine; methionine and cysteine were absent. Studies by Lowy (1970) showed that some residues of tryptophan, lysine, and/or arginine and possibly tyrosine are essential components of its polypeptide structure while free sulfhydryl and hydroxyl groups do not appear to be required for activity. Using an ^{125}I-labeled MAK-7 preparation of sheep plasma desialated Ep subjected to electrophoresis in gels containing sodium dodecyl sulfate, the molecular weight of "native" Ep was calculated to be 46,000 with a sedimentation coefficient of 4.65 (Gold-wasser and Kung, 1972b). The presence of only a single peak of label on the gel suggested that Ep is composed of a single chain or chains attached by covalent bonds that are not disulfide in nature (Goldwasser and Kung, 1972a). Of interest is the observation that desialated Ep is inactive when assayed in the mouse but retains its ability to stimulate heme synthesis by isolated bone marrow cells (Goldwasser and Kung, 1968). It may be that sialic acid serves as an attachment site of Ep to a carrier substance and may aid in preventing destruction of Ep within the organism. Of relevance here also is the observation by Goldwasser and Kung (1972a) that the clearance of desialated Ep from the blood occurs more rapidly than normal Ep. This may arise from the fact that the galactose moiety situated next to the sialic acid component is recognized by the liver. Administration of desialated ceruloplasmin appears to block the clear-ance of desialated Ep by binding to receptor sites in the liver. By pre-injecting desialated orosomucoid, subsequent administration of desialated Ep now proved to be effective; however, full activity was not seen.

B. URINARY EP

As with plasma Ep, considerable purification of urinary Ep has been recently achieved (Espada and Gutnisky, 1970a,b). The source material is urine obtained from human subjects with anemia arising from hook-worm infestation. The procedure used involves precipitation of the active protein with benzoic acid and ethanol. The precipitate is fractionated successively on DEAE-cellulose, hydroxyapatite, Sephadex G-25, again on DEAE-cellulose, then on a Sephadex G-100 column with refractiona-tion on Sephadex G-100 at least 3 times to produce specific activities of approximately 8300 IU per milligram of protein. All the biological ac-tivity was localized in a single band upon subjecting the purified Ep to polyacrylamide gel electrophoresis (Espada et al., 1972). This highly purified Ep contained 65.5% protein, 13.0% total hexoses, 8.9% hex-osamine, and 7.5% sialic acid. Amino acids in the purified fraction in-cluded aspartic acid, threonine, serine, glutamic acid, proline, glycine, alanine, valine, methionine, isoleucine, leucine, tyrosine, phenylalanine, histidine, lysine, and arginine (Espada et al., 1972). The relative insta-bility of human urinary Ep during fractionation may be the result of the presence in the extracts of protease and/or sialidase. This can be circumvented by extraction of the hormone into phenol (Lowy and Keighley, 1961; Chiba et al., 1972) followed by precipitation with alcohol (Chiba et al., 1972).

The purification of plasma and urinary Ep constitutes a distinct ad-vance in the field of Ep physiology and chemistry. It is hoped that the availability of this purified material will increase and that more efficient methods for its extraction will be developed.

IV. SITE(S) AND MECHANISMS OF ACTION

There is little convincing evidence that Ep influences tissues other than those concerned with erythropoiesis. Thus, continuous injections of Ep into mice for as long as 240 days, while resulting in continued augmented erythropoiesis, exerted no influence on the numbers of platelets or on the differential leukocyte values; actually, leukocyte counts underwent a decrease at the midpoint of the experiment (Keighley et al., 1964). A recent article (Sugiyama, 1971) indicating that Ep is required for bone marrow cells to become susceptible to chromosome damage by dimethylbenzanthracene requires confirmation. The same holds for the claim that Ep stimulates growth of cultures of human synovial membrane cells and human monocytic leukemia cells (Leaders et al., 1964) and that it increases the incidence of leukemia and mammary tumors in female conventional CFW_w mice (Leaders et al., 1967). These experiments require repetition with more highly purified preparations of Ep than used since it is possible that the effects observed are due to contaminants rather than the active Ep in the materials administered.

It will become evident in the descriptions made below that Ep is a unique agent. It specifically causes differentiation of a hematopoietic precursor cell, the Ep-responsive cell (ERC), into the earliest recognizable members of the nucleated erythroid cell line (Stohlman et al., 1968; McCulloch, 1970). Thus it constitutes an excellent tool for investigating molecular events associated with and resulting in formation of a unique product—hemoglobin. The suggestion was made originally (Rambach et al., 1957) that Ep results in a shortening of the generation time and an increase in the frequency of mitoses in the erythrogenic tissues. However, Alpen and Cranmore (1959) reported no change in generation time, no alteration in the number of nucleated erythroid cell divisions or mitotic rates, and no earlier entry of reticulocytes into the circulation after subjecting dogs to hemorrhage. This research, along with other experimental evidence (Erslev, 1959), lent support to the view that the effect of Ep is exerted primarily on undifferentiated precursor cells. Additional cogent evidence for an action of Ep on the precursor cell population derives from studies performed on plethoric mice (Filmanowicz and Gurney, 1961) and on exhypoxic polycythemic mice (Orlic et al., 1965, 1968). In these animals, nucleated erythroid cells are considerably reduced in numbers or may be almost completely absent. A single injection of Ep in these mice induces a sequential succession of cohorts of proerythroblasts, and basophilic, polychromatophilic, and orthochromatic erythroblasts, terminating at approximately 72 hours with a peripheral reticulocytosis. This corresponds to a time sequence of effects consonant with an initial differentiative action exerted on the precursor stem cell (ERC) population. A recent scheme depicting the site of action of Ep and its relation to the generative cycle of erythroid cells is shown in Fig. 1. The mechanism by which Ep causes this differentiative action has been studied in two main types of *in vitro* systems: (A) bone marrow cells (Krantz *et al.*, 1963) and (B) fetal liver cells (Cole and Paul, 1966).

A. Bone Marrow Cells

In this system, Krantz *et al.* (1963) utilize bone marrow cells from the femora and tibiae of 6- to 7-week-old rats. The technique employed by Gross and Goldwasser (1969) employs a medium composed of 60% NCTC-109, 35% newborn calf serum, and 5% rat serum. Ferric nitrate in a concentration of $7.3 \times 10^{-5}\ M$ is added to the suspensions which are incubated at an atmosphere of 5% CO_2 and 95% air. Ep is added directly to the cultures, and at various intervals the cells are washed from the plates and dispersed for biochemical determinations. For estimating the ability of these cells to form heme, ^{59}Fe attached to transferrin is added and, after several hours of incubation with the radioiron, the cells are lysed, heme is extracted, and the heme radioactivity is determined. It was

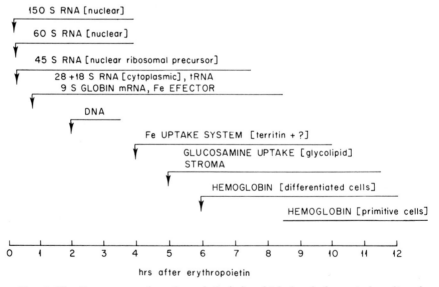

Fig. 1. The time course of erythropoietin-induced biochemical events in cultured rat marrow cells. From Goldwasser (1972). Reprinted with publisher's (Il Ponte, Milan) permission.

found here that 93% of the radioactivity in heme was associated with hemoglobin, thus indicating that measurement of heme implies synthesis of hemoglobin (Gallien-Lartigue and Goldwasser, 1964).

In both the control and Ep-containing systems, a fall in the rate of heme synthesis occurred from hour 4 to hour 10 of the incubation period (Krantz et al., 1963). However, starting with hour 10, although the control values continued to decline, the marrow cells exposed to Ep showed a rapid rise in heme synthesis. At 29 hours the Ep-containing cultures produced heme at approximately 3 times the rate of the control cultures and about twice their own original rate. Even at 49 hours, although the rate of heme synthesis had diminished in the cultures containing Ep, it was still approximately 6 times that measured in the controls. Thus the capacity of bone marrow cells to produce heme in culture could be maintained at normal or higher levels by Ep. Preparations of high purity Ep (950 IU/mg protein) produced the same effects on heme synthesis as cruder material such as plasma from anemic rats (Krantz et al., 1963).

Additional work indicated that Ep induced highly significant effects on nucleic acid and protein metabolism, actions that preceded and were essential for the production of heme and hemoglobin. The finding that the stimulatory action of Ep on heme synthesis could be abolished by actinomycin D (Gallien-Lartigue and Goldwasser, 1965) suggested that the primary action of the hormone was exerted on DNA-dependent RNA synthesis. Furthermore, it seemed possible that the differentiative action exerted by Ep on the ERC might depend on prior DNA-directed RNA formation and the production of neoproteins programmed by the newly synthesized messenger RNA. Actually a small quantity of an RNA not found in control marrow cells was formed within 5 minutes after the addition of Ep (Gross and Goldwasser, 1969; Goldwasser, 1972). This RNA, unique to Ep stimulation, is large and possesses a sedimentation coefficient of 150 S and a minimum molecular weight of approximately 30 million. It appears to be confined to the nuclei of the marrow cells and exhibits a half-life of about 6 minutes (Goldwasser, 1972). A short time later, another large nuclear RNA with a sedimentation coefficient of about 60 S is formed. Since the base composition of the 150 S and 60 S is different, it would appear that these two RNAs do not represent precursor and product. New ribosomal RNA is synthesized beginning at about 15 minutes after Ep addition. This RNA probably augurs the early events leading to the formation of hemoglobin. At approximately 45 minutes "processed" ribosomal tRNA appears, a substance that permits iron to influence cell function (Fe effector, Gross and Goldwasser, 1970a) and a 9 S RNA is produced which may represent the globin messenger or a histone messenger. Since some 9 S RNA is formed even when erythropoiesis is completely suppressed, it has been conjectured that this RNA codes for a protein with a molecular weight of approximately 16,000 which is not implicated in erythropoiesis (Gross and Goldwasser, 1971). The addition of Ep to marrow cells from erythropoietically depressed (polycythemic) animals results in the synthesis of 9 S RNA about 9–10 hours before the initiation of hemoglobin synthesis. This possibly represents some regulatory mechanism in the control of hemoglobin formation.

An increase in DNA synthesis is not apparent until about 2 hours after addition of Ep (Gross and Goldwasser, 1970b). This would indicate that molecular events are triggered by Ep before increased cell division occurs, a point supported by findings that although DNA synthesis induced by Ep is inhibited by actinomycin D and by puromycin, RNA synthesis is not affected by fluorodeoxyuridine (a DNA inhibitor) (Goldwasser, 1972). The increased DNA synthesis may relate to erythroid maturational divisions or to replicatory activity of the ERC that replace those undergoing differentiation into the earliest nucleated erythroid cell compartment (Goldwasser, 1972). The synthesis of new protein, concerned with the uptake of Fe from the medium, occurs about 4 hours after addition of Ep to marrow cells (Hrinda and Goldwasser, 1969). Ferritin and an unidentified protein known as "fraction I" may constitute a part of this protein complex.

Ep also stimulates the uptake of glucosamine involved in the formation of glycolipid and stroma of marrow cells, but this is not apparent until approximately 5 hours after addition of the hormone (Dukes, 1968). At about 6 hours the normal marrow cells exposed to Ep exhibit increased hemoglobin synthesis. A scheme summarizing the molecular effects of Ep upon rat marrow cells is depicted in Fig. 2.

Of interest are the findings of Bottomley and Smithee (1969) indicating that Ep is capable of enhancing δ-aminolevulinic acid (ALA) synthetase activity in rabbit bone marrow cells cultured *in vitro*. The increase in δ-ALA synthetase activity evoked by Ep in marrow cells appears to be dependent on prior protein synthesis since the rise in enzyme activity is prevented by puromycin. The apparent requirement for DNA-dependent production of RNA is noted from the ability of actinomycin D to block the increase in marrow δ-ALA synthetase activity induced by Ep. These experiments, coupled with those performed on the spleens of plethorized mice treated with Ep (Nakao *et al.*, 1968) suggest that Ep increases the production of δ-ALA-synthetase in mammalian erythroid tissues. It is known that δ-ALA-synthetase is the rate-limiting enzyme for both heme and globin synthesis in erythroid progenitor cells (Levere and Granick, 1965). The finding that Ep stimulates both heme and globin synthesis (Hodgson, 1970; Mizoguchi and Levere, 1971) lends further support to the concept that a principal action of Ep is the induction of δ-ALA

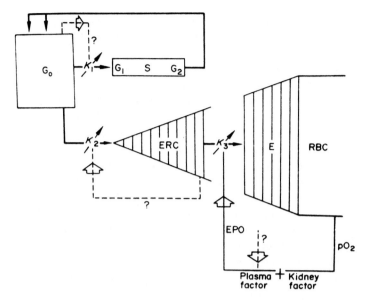

FIG. 2. Interrelation of colony-forming cells (CFU: pluripotential stem cell), erythropoietin-responsive cells (ERC), and erythron. CFU in steady state, primarily in G_0 state. The population control triggers cells into cycle at rate K_1. In steady state, cells are differentiating at rate K_2 into ERC (and K_1 would equal K_2 if there were no other lines of differentiation). The rate K_2 is controlled by some feedback from (? late) ERC. Erythropoietin (EPO) regulated by pO_2 in the kidney causes differentiation of ERC into erythron at rate K_3. From Lajtha et al. (1971). Reprinted with publisher's (Blackwell Scientific Publications, Oxford) permission.

synthetase. These effects of Ep are associated with a comparable degree of stimulation of both alpha and beta polypeptide synthesis in human bone marrow cell cultures (Mizoguchi and Levere, 1972).

It is still unclear as to which subcellular structure constitutes the initial target site of Ep in the ERC. The possibility exists that this locus is membrane in nature (with a possible derepression of adenyl cyclase that triggers 3′,5′-cyclic AMP production) or that the primary receptor is in the nuclear genome. The answer to this fundamental question must await development of techniques that will permit isotopic labeling of "pure" Ep of high specific activity and then determining its location in the ERC by a combination of electron microscopy and autoradiography.

B. FETAL YOLK SAC AND LIVER CELLS

Mammalian erythropoiesis begins in the yolk sac during early embryogenesis and then shifts progressively to the liver and spleen and finally the bone marrow (Paul et al., 1972). In the mouse, erythropoiesis is first

seen in the yolk sac blood islands at about day 8 post fertilization. Cells
originating in the yolk sac are noted in the fetal circulation on day 9 and
through about day 14. These cells are large, nucleated, undergo mitosis,
and continue to synthesize hemoglobins that differ from those produced
later in development. In the liver, erythropoiesis begins at about the time
this organ is seen, namely at about 10.5 days after fertilization. The
hemoglobins produced by fetal liver cells are similar to those formed in
the adult. Splenic erythropoiesis commences on about day 15 of gestation
and continues throughout life.

With regard to responsivity to Ep, although yolk-sac erythropoiesis
was originally considered to be refractory to Ep (Cole and Paul, 1966),
Bateman and Cole (1971) have recently demonstrated that Ep stimulates
heme synthesis in cultures of disaggregated cells from whole 8-day
embryos and also yolk-sac tissues suggesting that the differentiation
of primary embryonic cells may be regulated by Ep within the early
embryo.

The first stages of hepatic erythropoiesis involve a high proportion of
primitive erythroblasts (Paul et al., 1969; Rifkind et al., 1969). Maturation of these cells follows and, beginning with day 15 of gestation,
orthochromatic erythroblasts are prominent. It has been shown that liver
cells from 10.75- to 14.5 day mouse fetuses synthesize hemoglobin at a low
rate in tissue culture (Cole and Paul, 1966; Cole et al., 1968; Paul and
Hunter, 1969). Addition of Ep during this period induces a markedly
increased rate of hemoglobin synthesis. After this time of Ep sensitivity
(beyond day 15), the rate of hemoglobin synthesis in cultured liver cells
remains high but cannot be further enhanced by Ep. Cole and Paul (1966)
and Cole et al. (1968) had speculated that no Ep was elaborated in the
embryo before day 15 of gestation and that, as a result, liver cells in
culture from younger fetuses (e.g., 13.5-day-old) are highly sensitive
to Ep. They further suggested that Ep was produced in appreciable
amounts from day 15 onward and thus, because erythropoiesis was already maximally stimulated, the hepatic cells had become refractory to
exogenous Ep added to the cultures. It is conceivable that the assumption
of function and susceptibility of the extrarenal source of Ep to changes
in fetal oxygen tension constitute the major factors determining the
time(s) and duration of appearance of Ep during fetal development.

The macromolecular events occurring after addition of Ep to liver
cells from 13.5-day-old mouse fetuses have been documented (Paul and
Hunter, 1969). An increase in the rate of DNA synthesis occurs within
20 minutes after addition of Ep. RNA and hemoglobin levels are elevated
at approximately 2 hours. The accelerated production of hemoglobin,
which continues for 24 hours provided Ep is present in the medium, may

be prevented by actinomycin D and by 5-fluorodeoxyuridine (FdUrd). Interruption of hemoglobin synthesis may also be achieved with puromycin. In addition, the increase in DNA synthesis can be blocked, under certain conditions, by both puromycin and by actinomycin D. On the basis of these results Paul and Hunter (1969) and Paul et al. (1972) have delineated the biochemical events associated with the induction of erythropoiesis in mouse fetal liver cells. It is proposed that directly after Ep is made available to the earliest responsive cells (precursor stem cells and early erythroblasts), a small quantity of RNA is produced. The formation of some protein follows, an event which appears to be necessary for the production of DNA. A period of approximately 20 minutes then ensues during which DNA synthesis is elevated within fetal liver cells responsive to Ep. An increase in the synthesis of RNA and protein follows approximately 90 minutes later. The secondary phase of RNA synthesis, which appears essential for hemoglobin synthesis, depends on the preceding DNA synthesis. This latter result stands in contrast to the situation for cultured rat marrow cells in which the early stimulatory effects of Ep on heme synthesis (Gross and Goldwasser, 1970b) and on glucosamine incorporation (Ortega and Dukes, 1970) are not dependent on prior DNA synthesis. However, Paul et al. (1972) have confirmed their earlier results in the fetal liver cell culture system, namely, that early DNA synthesis is a prerequisite for the secondary RNA appearance and/or hemoglobin production. This view has been fortified by their recent experiments (Paul et al., 1972) involving inhibitors which indicate that effective suppression of DNA synthesis by cytosine arabinoside or hydroxyurea results in a reduction in the secondary RNA and hemoglobin synthesis responses of fetal liver cells to Ep. The dependence of RNA and hemoglobin synthesis on prior DNA formation may be characteristic of the liver cells of 13.5-day mouse embryos, not a feature of rat bone marrow cells. Nicol et al. (1972) have recently shown that 5-FdUrd inhibited the stimulation of Hb synthesis but only partially blocked the enhancement of DNA synthesis induced by Ep. (The reason for the inability of FdUrd to depress DNA synthesis more effectively in these experiments is not clear.) In addition, employing autoradiography, it was demonstrated that Ep stimulated RNA synthesis in proerythroblasts, basophilic and polychromatophilic erythroblasts and that the inhibition of this enhancing action by FdUrd took place only in basophilic and polychromatophilic erythroblasts. Thus the types of nucleated erythroid elements present in the culture system may determine the nature of the effects produced not only by Ep but by metabolic inhibitors as well.

The work of the Marks and Rifkind group is most relevant and significant in the area pertaining to the basic mechanism of Ep action on fetal erythropoiesis. They have examined cultures of fetal mouse liver cells (12–13 days of gestation) for total and differential cell counts, DNA and RNA synthesis, and hemoglobin formation (Rifkind *et al.*, 1969; Chui *et al.*, 1971). In this system addition of Ep results in increased RNA synthesis, confined primarily to the proerythroblasts, within 1 hour. The production of the RNA moiety is not dependent upon prior DNA synthesis (Marks and Rifkind, 1972), a point in seeming conflict with results reported by Paul *et al.* (1972). A 3-fold rise in globin chain and hemoglobin synthesis as well as a 100% increase in the total number of nucleated erythroid elements was observed after 24 hours of culturing in the presence of Ep. This hormone evidently achieves this effect by maintaining the capacity of precursor cells to synthesize DNA, to replicate and to produce differentiated erythroid cells for a more prolonged time than in cultures lacking Ep. These studies suggest that a primary action of Ep in the fetal mouse liver system may be to stimulate RNA synthesis in a population of immature precursor cells that is morphologically indistinguishable from the proerythroblasts (Djaldetti *et al.*, 1970). The increase in hemoglobin production in each culture is ascribed to a rise in the number of hemoglobin synthesizing elements developing from precursor cells, not to increased synthesis by individual erythroblasts.

It is becoming apparent that the action of Ep is not confined to a stimulation of differentiation of the hematopoietic stem cells (i.e., the ERC). Thus evidence has been presented to suggest that Ep induces a recruitment of ERC's (Schooley, 1965) and an increased rate of ERC division (Reissmann and Samorapoompichit, 1969, 1970). In fact there is a growing feeling (Lamerton, 1970) that the primary action of Ep may be to cause precursor cell proliferation initially before its differentiative action on the ERC becomes apparent. This concept would be in accord with the behavior of other cell systems in which a close relation between cell division and cell differentiation occurs at the molecular level (Konrad, 1963). Other actions of Ep include direct effects *in vitro* on erythroblast morphology (Borsook *et al.*, 1968) and on DNA and heme synthesis (Powsner and Berman, 1967) as well as on erythroblast division (Necheles *et al.*, 1968). Of considerable interest are recent findings suggesting that Ep may be responsible for the increase in production of a soluble cell fraction that directs a cell-free system toward hemoglobin production (Izak and Karsai, 1972). Additional actions concern an early release of reticulocytes (Gordon *et al.*, 1962; Fisher *et al.*, 1965b) and a switching of hemoglobin A to C in nonanemic A/A sheep (Thurmon *et al.*, 1970). This latter result suggests the possibility that Ep may derepress the β^c globin gene, thus permitting synthesis of an RNA for $\beta^{\hat{c}}$ globin chains.

Ep may also play a significant role in the gradual switch from fetal to adult hemoglobin production (Gabuzda *et al.*, 1970). In addition, recent experiments indicate that a distinct vaso-proliferative activity in transplanted splenic tissue follows treatment of donor mice with Ep (Feleppa *et al.*, 1971).

Along the same lines, it has been demonstrated that Ep increases blood flow and stimulates the opening of sinusoids in the splenic microcirculation of mice (McClugage *et al.*, 1971). Although foci of early proliferative cells in the bone marrow and spleen were coated with sulfated acid mucopolysaccharides, this envelope was replaced in later stages of erythropoiesis by a coating of neutral mucopolysaccharide (McCuskey *et al.*, 1972a). These important studies suggest that stem cell transformation into the erythroid cell line *in vivo* can occur only in a microenvironment that is highly vascularized, displays high rates of blood flow, and contains neutral mucopolysaccharide and that these phenomena are under Ep control. The McCuskey group speculates that these conditions may comprise a part of the hematopoietic inductive microenvironment (Trentin, 1970) that furnish a site conducive to erythropoiesis. The microvascular response to Ep is apparently specific for erythroid tissue (spleen and bone marrow) since it is not seen in nonerythropoietic organs like the pancreas. It has been further suggested that the microvascular effects exerted by Ep may be mediated through the release of a vasoactive metabolite from the erythrogenic tissues surrounding the sinusoids, possibly from the ERC (McCuskey *et al.*, 1972b). Further support for this hypothesis is derived from observations made upon the splenic microvascular system and stroma of mice with genetically derived anemias (McCuskey and Meineke, 1973). The defect in Sl/Sl^d mice appears to stem from persistently elevated concentrations of sulfated acid mucopolysaccharide in the splenic stroma while the abnormality in W/W^v mice is related not only to a deficiency in the number of undifferentiated hemopoietic cells, but also to a lowered number of such cells with a coating of sulfated acid mucopolysaccharide. These findings lend additional credence to the concept (McCuskey and Meineke, 1973) that precursor cell coating with sulfated acid mucopolysaccharide is essential for differentiation of the stem cell into early erythroid elements (under the influence of Ep) whereas a microenvironment containing excessive quantities of this type of mucopolysaccharide does not permit later erythroid development.

It is of interest that cell suspensions derived from mouse spleen, bone marrow, and fetal liver as well as from bone marrow of rat and human origin grown in semisolid agar give rise only to granulocyte and macrophage colonies (Pluznik and Sachs, 1965; Bradley and Metcalf, 1966), not to erythroid colonies even with addition of Ep to the system (Paran and Sachs, 1968). More recently, it has been possible, through modification of the medium (use of bovine serum albumin and medium conditioned with mouse kidney tubules instead of the conventional semisolid agar), to induce the *in vitro* formation of colonies of fetal mouse liver cells capable of synthesizing hemoglobin (Stephenson *et al.*, 1971). The development of these colonies is dependent on the presence of Ep. It would be of considerable interest to determine the specific microenvironmental ("inducer") factors that favor erythroid cell development in such cultures. Obviously the conditions of increased vascularity and blood flow that appear to be required for or accompany erythroid cell development *in vivo* (McCuskey *et al.*, 1972a) are not operative in the culture system.

The possibility exists that the various effects exerted by Ep are due to the actions of different forms of Ep. This finds support in the observation that some Ep preparations may contain a number of biological entities with differing *in vivo* and *in vitro* actions (Dukes *et al.*, 1970). Evidence that could be construed as favoring the existence of a family of Eps is derived from studies (Dorado *et al.*, 1972) indicating that human urinary Ep, upon being subjected to polyacrylamide gel electrophoresis, is distributed over a wide area between the pre- and postalbumin regions, and separates into a number of components with different molecular charge, all endowed with erythropoietic activity.

It becomes evident from the above discussions that the specific cells upon which Ep exerts its effects must be identified and separated for morphological and biochemical studies before a complete comprehension of the fundamental actions of the hormone can be disclosed. Attempts at separation of hematopoietic precursor cells have been made. The techniques employed include density gradient methods utilizing polyvinyl pyrrolidone (Takaku *et al.*, 1964), dextran (Morrison and Toepfer, 1967), sucrose (Peterson and Evans, 1967), Ficoll (Niewisch *et al.*, 1967; Murphy *et al.*, 1971), or bovine serum albumin (Turner *et al.*, 1967). Fractionation of mouse spleen cells has also been carried out with countercurrent distribution procedures (Brunette *et al.*, 1968), and unit gravity sedimentation has been employed to separate ERC from spleen colony-forming cells (CFC) of fetal mouse liver (Stephenson and Axelrad, 1971b). Enriched fractions of cell precursors for erythroblasts have been obtained after bone marrow filtration through glass wool (Bennett and Cudkowicz, 1968), and a high degree of purification of ERC from fetal mouse liver has been recently achieved with immune hemolysis techniques (Cantor *et al.*, 1972).

In the studies by Murphy *et al.* (1971), cells obtained from post-hypoxic "rebound" mice that appeared most competent in repopulating the spleens of irradiated hosts were in the density range of 1.0200 to 1.0440 in a linear Ficoll gradient. The predominant cell type in this fraction avidly incorporated ^{3}H-labeled thymidine, showed a high incidence of mitotic figures and contained a leptochromatic nucleus with well defined nucleoli and an undifferentiated cytoplasm. This morphology conforms to that of the "transitional" cell described by Yoffey's group (Yoffey, 1966; Moffatt et al., 1967). Similar appearing mononuclear cells with precursor characteristics have been described by others (Niewisch et al., 1967; DeGowin et al., 1971, 1972). A good deal of the literature thus favors a cell or cells of "lymphoid" morphology as possessing hematopoietic precursor properties. On the other hand, there is evidence not in accord with this hypothesis. Thus the monocytoid cell has been implicated in some experiments (Caffrey Tyler and Everett, 1966; Barnes and Loutit, 1967). Moreover, it is now well recognized that not all forms of lymphocytes assume a stem cell role. "Conditioning" factors, the proper hematopoietic inductive microenvironment as well as long-range (humoral) and short-range (cell contact) feedback mechanisms undoubtedly determine whether a given cell can assume stem cell function. It is obvious that the resolution of the problem as to which cell type possesses a precursor role must await the development of cell separation techniques that will yield functionally pure populations of cells. In this regard, methods that hold promise involve separation of cells according to their electronically determined volume or by continuous particle electrophoresis (cited in Krantz and Jacobson, 1970). The not-as-yet achieved experiment involving isolation of a single, morphologically identifiable precursor cell, observed in the proper microenvironment and made to undergo development into a differentiated cell type (e.g., hemoglobiniferous) with a specific hormonal factor (e.g., Ep) would represent the ultimate proof of the identity of the stem cells for the various blood element lines.

V. Site(s) of Production

A. Biogenesis of Ep and the Kidney

A renal relation to erythropoiesis is suggested from both clinical and experimental studies. Thus, anemia often accompanies renal-deficient states in man (Brown and Roth, 1922; Loge et al., 1950), and erythrocytosis is noted on occasion in humans with hypernephroma (Forssell, 1954) or hydronephrosis (Cooper and Tuttle, 1957). Experimental investigations demonstrated that bilateral nephrectomy inhibited the erythropoietic response of rats to different forms of hypoxia (Jacobson *et al.*, 1957). Thus, nephrectomized rats displayed a markedly reduced ability to produce Ep when subjected to acute hemorrhage, lowered oxygen tensions or cobalt treatment (Jacobson *et al.*, 1959a,b). The depression in erythropoiesis following renal ablation could not be attributed to unexcreted wastes that are present in the renoprival state since bilateral ureteral ligation in the rat (Jacobson *et al.*, 1959a,b) or implantation of the ureter into the iliac vein of the dog (Naets, 1963) does not result in an appreciable lowering of the erythropoietic response or in the ability to produce Ep following exposure to similar types and degrees of hypoxia. The appearance of Ep in fluids circulated through isolated and *in situ* perfused kidneys subjected to oxygen deficiency (Kuratowska *et al.*, 1961; Pavlovic-Kentera *et al.*, 1965) and to cobalt treatment (Fisher and Birdwell, 1961) has provided direct support for a renal origin of Ep, and there has been satisfying confirmation of this concept (Gordon and Zanjani, 1970a; Krantz and Jacobson, 1970; Fisher, 1972).

Despite the persuasive evidence that has been offered to support a renal origin of Ep, past attempts to extract this principle from the kidney have not been altogether successful (Gordon *et al.*, 1967b; Gordon and Zanjani, 1970a). It seemed possible that this lack of ability to detect really significant quantities of Ep even in the kidneys of hypoxic animals, at least in amounts equivalent to those present in plasma, was the result of (1) a tenacious binding of Ep to subcellular particles rendering it nonextractable with the usual isotonic procedures (Contrera *et al.*, 1965); (2) the presence of an inhibitor to Ep in renal extracts (Erslev and Kazal, 1968; Fisher *et al.*, 1968a; Kuratowska, 1968); or (3) the existence of an activator or precursor of Ep, but not the Ep itself, in renal tissue. In the latter regard, Kuratowska and Kopeć (1969) and Kuratowska (1970) demonstrated a renal erythropoietic factor (REF) associated with the nuclei of kidneys from cobalt-treated or anemic rabbits. This REF has been localized in the acidic nuclear protein fraction of kidneys and is destroyed by proteolytic enzymes and neuraminidase (Kuratowska and Kopeć, 1969). Preliminary studies on the characterization of this renal nuclear factor indicate that it contains 85% protein, 3–5% RNA and 0.05–0.10% of protein bound N-acetylneuraminic acid (Kuratowska and Kopeć, 1969). The nuclear fractions injected alone into assay mice are erythropoietically inactive. Prior incubation with plasma results in the formation of Ep. Kuratowska's studies suggest that the nuclear REF is a precursor of Ep which requires interaction with a plasma component, an α-globulin, for the production of Ep.

In 1966, our laboratory reported on the extraction of a factor from the kidneys of hypoxic rats which, when administered alone intraperitoneally to exhypoxic polycythemic mice, was not erythropoietically active but that, when incubated with normal serum, production of Ep occurred (reviewed by Gordon et al., 1967b). This principle was also named the renal erythropoietic factor (REF), but more recently erythrogenin (Gordon et al., 1971). Fractionation procedures have been employed to determine the subcellular location of erythrogenin in kidneys from rats exposed to hypobaric hypoxia (Gordon and Zanjani, 1970b). Four fractions were examined: the nuclear, heavy-mitochondrial, light-mitochondrial, and microsomal (La Bella et al., 1963). No erythropoietic activity was detected in hypotonic extracts of the nuclear and heavy-mitochondrial fractions either before or after incubation with normal serum. However, extracts of the light-mitochondrial and microsomal fractions, although erythropoietically inactive when administered alone, were capable of generating significant quantities of Ep when incubated with dialyzed normal serum from rats and other mammalian species (Zanjani et al., 1969a). The inability of these extracts to stimulate erythropoiesis when given alone may be the result of failure of sufficient amounts of the intraperitoneally injected erythrogenin to pass from the abdominal cavity into the blood. In fact, direct intravenous administration of large amounts of erythrogenin does result in the generation of some Ep by 2 hours after its injection (Zanjani et al., 1971). The relation of renal erythrogenin to the Ep-generating factor (EGF) extracted from urine (Lewis et al., 1969) remains to be determined.

Studies on the kinetics of the erythrogenin–serum system have suggested that erythrogenin may function as an enzyme that converts a serum substrate into the active circulating form of Ep (Zanjani et al., 1967a). It is of interest that erythrogenin possesses no component that corresponds to circulating Ep in mobility on DEAE columns. Similarly erythrogenin does not display the acid and heat stability of Ep in hypoxic rat plasma (Contrera and Gordon, 1966; Contrera et al., 1966). Moreover, although the renal erythrogenin–serum–Ep system appears analogous to the renin–serum–angiotensin mechanism, the two are functionally dissimilar. Thus neither erythrogenin nor Ep exerts vasopressor effects and neither renin nor angiotensin stimulates erythropoiesis when administered intraperitoneally to assay mice (Zanjani et al., 1967b).

That it is actually Ep which is generated in the erythrogenin–serum incubation system was seen from the finding that the generated erythropoiesis-stimulating activity was completely abolished by the addition of anti-Ep serum to the incubation mixture (Zanjani et al., 1968a). In addition, anti-Ep did not inhibit the biological activity of erythrogenin and failed to antagonize the ability of serum or plasma to function as a substrate for erythrogenin (Schooley et al., 1970). On the other hand, an antierythrogenin serum, developed in rabbits against human erythrogenin and which inhibited the action of erythrogenin *in vitro*, did not inhibit the erythropoietic activity of Ep (McDonald *et al.*, 1971b). These experiments support our concept that erythrogenin, the serum substrate, and the product of their interaction, namely Ep, are three immunochemically dissimilar substances. The finding that anti-Ep did not abolish the activity of erythrogenin or the serum substrate is in support of this concept and suggests that antigenic sites on the serum substrate combine with anti-Ep only after the substrate has reacted with erythrogenin. It may be that a pro-Ep, erythropoietically inactive, circulates normally in plasma and that its conversion into active Ep is dependent not only on the presence of this precursor substance (erythropoietinogen), but also on erythrogenin, the release of which is triggered by hypoxia. In this connection, it is of interest that erythropoietically inactive preparations of plasma (Campbell *et al.*, 1961) and urine (Lowy and Keighley, 1968), having chemical properties closely similar to those with high erythropoietic activity, have been obtained during the extraction procedures. These observations lend additional support to the proposal that a protein in normal plasma functions as a precursor substance that is converted to the circulating Ep by erythrogenin. Cleavage of a part of the serum substrate in a manner similar to that seen in the renin–angiotensin system may occur in this reaction. The identity of the serum factor remains obscure although recent work would suggest that the α-globulins, of which kininogen is a member, may serve as the substrate for the production of Ep (Smith and Contrera, 1972).

Another concept regarding the role of the kidney in Ep physiology relates to the existence in renal tissue of inhibitors of Ep (Erslev and Kazal, 1968; Fisher *et al.*, 1968a; Kuratowska, 1968). One of these is lipid in nature (Erslev and Kazal, 1968). When fresh serum is added to a human urinary Ep–lipid complex, some of the bound Ep is released. It has been proposed (Erslev *et al.*, 1972) that Ep may exist in an inactive lipid-bound form in kidneys and that a serum factor may control the release of bound Ep into the blood. However, this mechanism appears to operate only for urinary Ep. Ep in plasma or mixed with plasma is not inhibited by the lipid. Moreover, the lipid inhibitor of Ep is found not only in kidney, but in liver, spleen, lung, muscle, stomach, and intestine as well. It is absent in bone marrow, subcutaneous fat, and brain (Erslev *et al.*, 1972). Despite its seeming nonspecific distribution, this inhibitor mechanism of Ep action is worthy of further investigation, and its relation to the erythrogenin-serum-Ep system remains to be explored.

B. Feedback Relations in the Erythrogenin– Erythropoietinogen–Ep System

An inhibitory influence of Ep on its own production has been reported (Zanjani et al., 1968b; Gordon and Zanjani, 1970b). The evidence for this is derived from experiments in which normal adult rats were injected with Ep just prior to exposure to hypoxia. This resulted in a highly significant depression in the expected rise in plasma Ep levels in response to the hypoxia. This inhibitory effect of Ep on the Ep response to hypoxia was unaccompanied by alterations in the quantity of erythrogenin extractable from the kidneys. However, a significant decrease in the concentration of plasma substrate for erythrogenin did occur (Zanjani et al., 1968b). These results would suggest that Ep exerts a negative feedback action on its own production and that this inhibitory effect is mediated through a depression in the production and/or availability of the plasma substrate (erythropoietinogen). Of interest in this connection is a clinical case of hepatocellular carcinoma associated with erythrocytosis and increased quantities of Ep in the plasma (Gordon et al., 1970b). Homogenates of the tumorous portions of the liver contained highly significant quantities of plasma substrate which were not detectable in the normal segments of the liver. It is speculated here that production of excess substrate by the hepatoma forms the basis of the erythrocytosis in this patient and that this abnormality is not subject to the negative feedback action of Ep.

C. Specific Renal Site(s) of Ep Production

There is still question as to the specific renal site of origin or activation of Ep. On a priori grounds, it might be expected that the kidney possesses a chemoreceptor mechanism capable of detecting a lowered O_2 content of the blood relative to O_2 demand which would trigger the formation of erythrogenin and then Ep. A specialization of the renal microcirculation may enable the kidney to serve as a sensitive O_2 receptor. This involves a shunting of a considerable proportion of RBC in the efferent arteriole directly to the renal vein so that the tubules become exposed to blood of lower hematocrit (Pappenheimer and Kinter, 1956; Chinard et al., 1964). It has been shown that renal oxygen tensions are highest in the outer and probably middle regions of the cortex and decrease progressively as blood flows from the midcortex to the deeper areas of the medulla (Leonhardt and Landes, 1963). In this regard, several studies have implicated the renal tubules as loci of Ep production. Thus a highly significant reduction in the erythropoietic response of rats occurred following injection of $HgCl_2$ 3 days before a phenylhydrazine-induced anemia (Reissmann et al., 1960). Similarly, Fisher et al. (1963) have shown that diuretic drugs, such as meralluride, mercaptomerin, benzhydroflumethiazide, and triamterene, lowered Ep production induced in rats by cobalt, presumably by decreasing renal tubular function.

Other studies have implicated the renal cortex as a site of Ep formation. Thus, considerably higher levels of erythropoiesis-stimulating activity have been detected in extracts of cortical than in medullary extracts of kidneys from anemic dogs (Muirhead et al., 1968). Osnes (1958) demonstrated that bleeding resulted in a decrease in the size and numbers of granules in the juxtaglomerular (JG) apparatus and, on this basis, implicated this structure in the control of Ep production. On the other hand, hyperplasia or increased granularity of the JG cells has been described following unilateral renal artery constriction (Takaku et al., 1962; Hansen, 1964) or after hemorrhage or phenylhydrazine treatment (Hirashima and Takaku, 1962; Kaley and Demopoulos, 1963). The JG apparatus is probably the chief site of renin secretion (Edelman and Hartroft, 1961) and the JG granular cells located in the media of the afferent renal arterioles have been suggested to be stretch receptors sensitive to changes in the volume of the renal vascular bed (Skinner et al., 1963). Since the experimentally induced anemias result in alterations in renal vascular volume (Goldfarb and Tobian, 1962), it is conceivable that the concurrent secretion of renin by the JG apparatus and Ep (or erythrogenin) by other renal elements could have occurred. In this connection, there are experimental conditions which indicate a dichotomy of the renin-angiotensin and the erythrogenin-Ep generating systems. Thus, differences in the time of appearance of renin and Ep in the renal venous blood of dogs are associated with the development of renal infarcts following injection of plastic microspheres into one renal artery of dogs (Abbrecht et al., 1966). A similar dissociation of the renin and Ep systems is suggested by the work of Donati et al. (1968), who reported that restriction of salt resulted in an increase and deoxycorticosterone led to a decrease in renin secretion without influencing the plasma levels of Ep. On the other hand, an increase in Ep production occurred following salt loading, acute hypoxia or cobalt injections without an influence on renin secretion. It would appear from these and other results that a correlation between JG cellular granularity and Ep production has not as yet been unequivocally established. The difficulty may relate to the fact that unless the animals subjected to various forms of hypoxia are maintained normovolemic during the experiment, changes in JG granularity may be reflecting alterations in renin secretion rather than in Ep (or erythrogenin) production. It should also be evident that an elevated JG granularity need not necessarily represent an increased production, but rather increased storage, and similarly, a decrease in granularity could stem from an increased rate of discharge of the factor instead of a decreased production.

Of interest in the field relating to the intrarenal site of Ep production are experiments utilizing indirect fluorescent antibody techniques which have demonstrated that Ep can be localized in the peripheral portion of the renal glomerulus (Fisher et al., 1965a; Frenkel et al., 1968). No fluorescence was observable in the peritubular capillary beds, the JG cells or the capillaries of the lung, liver, or spleen (Fisher et al., 1965a). Localization of the fluorescent antibody to Ep has recently been noted in the glomerular tufts of kidneys from anemic humans and hypoxic dogs (Busuttil et al., 1971, 1972). The epithelial cells of the tuft appeared to be the site of localization. Blockage of the fluorescence reaction in the glomerular tuft occurred when the anti-Ep was incubated with purified Ep. Moreover, intravenous injection of Ep in normal dogs (Busuttil et al., 1972) did not increase the fluorescence in the glomerular tuft, a finding which does not support the criticism that a nonspecific trapping of Ep by the glomerulus had occurred. The possibility cannot be precluded that erythrogenin is the substance formed in the glomerular tuft and that Ep is produced at this site as a result of interaction of erythrogenin with plasma. Resolution of this problem should be gained through the use of fluorosceinated antibody to erythrogenin and such experiments are presently underway in our laboratory.

D. *In Vitro* PRODUCTION OF EP

A significant number of experiments have been performed indicating that isolated kidneys of rabbits and dogs, perfused with hypoxemic blood, produce and release Ep into the perfusates (Kuratowska et al., 1961, 1964; Fisher and Birdwell, 1961; Fisher and Langston, 1967). However, all these perfusions have been of short duration and have yielded relatively small amounts of Ep. On a *priori* grounds, it would seem probable that long-term culture experiments utilizing renal tissue or separated cells might yield greater quantities of the hormone. In this regard, cultured renal cells have been found to produce renin. Thus, human juxtaglomerular cells (Robertson et al., 1966) and cells obtained from renal cortices of fetal, neonatal, and adult animals (Szalay and Gyevac, 1967), cultured under hypoxic conditions, released renin into the medium. That actual production of renin had occurred was indicated from the finding that the appearance of renin in the culture medium was inhibited by puromycin and actinomycin D (Robertson et al., 1966). Earlier attempts to produce Ep *in vitro* by incubating kidney, liver, and spleen slices in normal plasma were unsuccessful (Erslev, 1962). However, Ozawa (1967) studied the incorporation of ^{59}Fe into heme in rabbit bone marrow cells cultured with and without kidney cells from a newborn rabbit. Increased heme synthesis by the marrow cells was observed only in those cultures in which kidney cells were present and which were subjected to a hypoxic environment. Another requirement for this action was the presence of rabbit serum in the medium. Since, as pointed out by McDonald *et al.* (1969), the incorporation of ^{59}Fe into heme in such cultures is affected by pH, specific ions, and heme concentrations, it is not clear whether the increased incorporation of radioiron into heme was due to Ep produced by the renal cells or by other factors. However, that Ep is actually produced by cultures of kidney cells is indicated in recent experiments (McDonald *et al.*, 1969). Here monolayers of bovine renal cells were cultured in fluid containing Hank's MEMS essential medium with 10% calf serum under hypoxic conditions for several days. Erythropoiesis-stimulating activity, as tested in polycythemic mice, appeared in the medium. Evidence that this activity was attributable to Ep was shown by the ability of anti-Ep to completely antagonize the erythropoiesis-stimulating effects of the medium (McDonald *et al.*, 1969). More recently, organ cultures of kidneys obtained from hypoxic rats have been found to produce erythrogenin (Sherwood *et al.*, 1972). Production of this factor was similar in four different anatomic regions of the kidneys (i.e., outer and inner cortex, outer and inner medulla) suggesting that erythrogenin may be produced diffusely throughout the kidney in support of previous extraction studies (Zanjani *et al.*, 1967c). It is of interest that production of erythrogenin was generally insignificant during the first 3.5 days of culture (a period of autolysis), but became apparent during the second 3.5 days. The latter period was characterized by the appearance in electron micrographs of epithelial elements with ultrastructural indications of active protein synthesis (i.e., hypertrophic Golgi apparatus, rough-surfaced endoplasmic reticulum, and numerous polyribosomes). These features typify regenerating epithelial cells in experimental tubular nephrons (Cuppage and Tate, 1967). Along the same lines, goat kidney glomeruli have been shown to produce Ep in long-term culture systems (Burlington *et al.*, 1972). Although it has been stated that Ep, not erythrogenin or the serum substrate, appears in the medium bathing these glomerular structures (Burlington *et al.*, 1972), the possibility cannot be precluded that continuous secretion of small, nonassayable, quantities of erythrogenin and continuous utilization of substrate in the medium have occurred. Moreover, the erythrogenin produced may interact with substrate within the glomerular cells to produce Ep which is subsequently discharged into the medium. This would be analogous to the demonstration (Itskovitz and Odya, 1971) that angiotensin I, resulting from the interaction of renin and a protein substrate, may actually be produced within the kidney and then released.

Regardless of the mechanisms concerned, these culture techniques hold considerable promise and may provide eventually sources of large quantities of Ep for purification and characterization studies.

E. Extrarenal Sources of Ep

Extrarenal sources of Ep appear to function in some species of mammals. Thus the rise in plasma Ep in response to various forms of hypoxia is not completely inhibited by bilateral nephrectomy in rats (Piliero et al., 1960; Mirand et al., 1959; Jacobson et al., 1959a,b; Baciu et al., 1963), rabbits (Erslev, 1958; Mirand and Murphy, 1970), and tamarins (Mirand, 1965). In dogs, however, the kidney may represent the sole site of Ep production. Thus, a striking inhibition of erythropoiesis with an almost complete disappearance of nucleated erythroid cells occurs rapidly in the bone marrows of anephric dogs maintained by peritoneal dialysis (Naets, 1960a).

Quantitation of the extrarenal production of Ep in response to reduced oxygen tensions and/or bleeding has been achieved by Fried et al. (1969). Anti-Ep serum abolished the activity of this extrarenal Ep (Fried et al., 1969), thus indicating a chemical similarity between renal and extrarenal Ep. Fried et al. (1971b) have also shown that greater concentrations of Ep appear in the plasma of both nephrectomized and intact male rats subjected to oxygen deficiency than in similarly treated females, suggesting that Ep production by the kidney and by extrarenal sites is stimulated by chronic exposure to androgenic hormone. It is of interest that the extrarenal differences in Ep production of male and female rats are first observed at a later age (8–10 weeks) than the sex differences noted for renal production of Ep (2–8 weeks). Castration of males resulted in an abolition of the sex difference for both renal and extrarenal Ep production. On the other hand, spaying of rats led to an increase in the amount of Ep in the plasma of hypoxic rats possessing kidneys, but not in hypoxic nephrectomized animals (Wang and Fried, 1972). It would seem possible that the extrarenal sites of Ep production are less sensitive to the actions of the sex steroids than are those of the kidney.

The findings that Ep may appear in the plasma of the anephric human (Erslev et al., 1968) and that the amount detected increases following hemorrhage or androgen treatment (Mirand et al., 1968; Mirand and Murphy, 1970) attest to an extrarenal source of Ep in man that responds to the same stimuli that affect renal production of Ep in the normal subject. Likewise, Naets and Wittek (1968a) have reported heightened plasma Ep levels in one anephric human following severe blood loss. The fact emerges from these studies that relatively intense hypoxic stimuli are required to trigger extrarenal Ep production in man (Fisher *et al.*, 1971b). The finding that renal allografts made to nephrectomized patients lead to no greater increases in the already heightened levels of plasma Ep (Mirand *et al.*, 1968) may mean that (1) the transplant rather than the extrarenal site now constitutes the source of Ep; (2) the extrarenal site remains the sole source (the transplant is nonfunctional in this regard); or (3) both are contributing Ep.

The precise location of the extrarenal site(s) of Ep production remains to be determined. The possibility that the liver functions in the production of Ep is suggested from perfusion experiments (Reissmann and Nomura, 1962) and from liver extirpation studies (Katz *et al.*, 1968). In the latter experiments, hepatectomized rats displayed significantly lower levels of plasma Ep than sham-hepatectomized rats during an 8-hour exposure to hypoxia. Similarly, Fried (1972) found that although nephrectomized rats subjected to intense hypoxia produced some Ep, this extrarenal Ep was not detectable if an 80% hepatectomy was performed before exposure to hypoxia. On the other hand, removal of 80% of the liver exerted no effect on the plasma Ep response to hypoxia in rats with intact kidneys (Fried, 1972). The discrepancy between these latter results and those of Katz *et al.* (1968) may relate to the fact that in Katz's experiments total hepatectomy was performed whereas in Fried's only 80% of the liver was extirpated. Kaplan *et al.* (1973) have recently demonstrated the presence of high levels of erythrogenin in the livers and spleens of young nephrectomized male rats exposed to severe hypoxia (0.35 atmosphere of air). The quantities detected were equivalent to those extracted from the kidneys of intact young rats subjected to the same intensity of hypoxia. The possibility is presently being tested that the reticuloendothelial system, common to both liver and spleen, functions as an extrarenal source of erythrogenin. It should be mentioned that erythrogenin has been demonstrated in the livers and spleens of both hypoxic and nonhypoxic nephrectomized baboons (Mirand and Murphy, 1971a). Similarly, the spleen had been previously reported as containing an erythropoiesis-stimulating factor (de Franciscis *et al.*, 1965), and more recently that this organ serves as a storage site for an erythropoietic factor exhibiting properties similar to erythrogenin (Liotti *et al.*, 1972).

It is of interest that in rodents, the time elapsing between nephrectomy and exposure to hypoxia must be relatively short in order for Ep to appear in plasma (Peschle *et al.*, 1971b, 1972b). Thus a progressive decline in plasma Ep levels was noted in adult male rats subjected to hypoxia (0.45 atmosphere of air) at 1, 6, or 12 hours after nephrectomy and no activity was discernible when the hypoxia was initiated 18 or 24 hours after surgery. Confirmatory results have been reported independently by others (Schooley and Mahlmann, 1972b; Erslev *et al.*, 1972). Uremia does not appear to be responsible for the decrease in the Ep response to hypoxia following nephrectomy. Thus, male rats nephrectomized 18 hours after ureteral ligations and subsequently exposed to 6 hours of hypoxia exhibited plasma Ep levels no different from those noted in rats subjected to sham ureter-ligation procedures (Peschle *et al.*, 1972b,c). Neither could the decline in Ep production observed during the first 6–8 hours after nephrectomy be attributed to alterations in pH or pCO_2 of the blood (Peschle *et al.*, unpublished observations). Of considerable significance is the finding that intravenous administration of erythrogenin to male rats at 18 hours after renal ablation led to an elevation of their Ep response to hypoxia to the level of animals subjected to the same hypoxic stimulus shortly after nephrectomy. It would thus appear that the reason for the temporal decline in the ability of nephrectomized rats to respond to hypoxia with increased Ep may be a decrease in the production and/or availability of erythrogenin. However, administration of erythrogenin to nephrectomized rats *not* exposed to hypoxia was not followed by generation of clearly demonstrable amounts of Ep in plasma. This suggests that an additional factor evoked by hypoxia is essential for maximum production of Ep by erythrogenin (Peschle *et al.*, 1972b,c). More recent experiments by Schooley and Mahlmann (1972c) implicate a protein(s) formed *de novo* in the biosynthesis of Ep. Evidence for this contention is derived from experiments which show that injection of actinomycin D before but not after subjection to hypoxia, and puromycin or cycloheximide given after the hypoxic exposure inhibited the increase in serum Ep that would have normally occurred. The precise nature and site of origin of this protein component(s) remain to be determined.

VI. FACTORS INFLUENCING EP PRODUCTION

It is known that a variety of agents, physiological and nonphysiological, influence the production of Ep within the organism. As pointed out in previous sections of this review, the fundamental stimulus for erythropoiesis is considered to be oxygen deficiency. Thus hypobaric hypoxia, bleeding, cardiorespiratory disturbances, and agents that are stated to decrease the capacity of tissues to utilize oxygen (e.g., cobalt) (Fisher and Langston, 1967; Thorling and Erslev, 1972) tend to stimulate RBC production. Possession of hemoglobins that show greater affinity for oxygen than normal hemoglobin as well as RBC that contain decreased amounts of 2,3-DPG would also create a state of relative oxygen deficiency, thus leading to an enhancement of erythropoiesis. The bulk of evidence presently available favors the view that many diverse agents or states which stimulate RBC formation in the animal operate, at least in part, through the evocation of Ep. It is the purpose of this section to review the evidence that supports this concept.

A. VASOACTIVE AGENTS

This group includes norepinephrine, vasopressin, and angiotensin, which, when administered in certain doses and via specific routes, cause a decrease in renal blood flow and, through a resulting renal hypoxia, in increased Ep production (Fisher, 1972).

1. Angiotensin

Although, at first, no significant effects of angiotensin upon erythropoiesis in polycythemic animals were observed (Bilsel et al., 1963; Mann et al., 1966), subsequent reports indicated that it stimulated erythropoiesis provided it was administered by slow intravenous infusion (Fisher et al., 1967b; Nakao et al., 1962). Under these conditions it would appear that a sufficient decline in kidney blood flow occurs to produce renal hypoxia, which, in turn, triggers Ep production. Moreover, the finding that the erythropoietic action of angiotensin can be blocked in mildly plethoric mice by anti-Ep (Fisher et al., 1967b) suggests that this effect is mediated through Ep production.

2. Norepinephrine

Infusions of this catecholamine in dogs resulted in a decrease in renal blood flow associated with a rise in the levels of Ep in the plasma (Fisher et al., 1968b). However, this rise in plasma levels of Ep was not as great as that induced by equivalent quantities of angiotensin probably because of a slower rate of decline in renal blood flow with norepinephrine than with angiotensin.

3. Vasopressin

Since vasopressin also reduces renal blood flow, it might likewise be expected to possess erythropoiesis stimulating activity. Indeed, this agent caused an increase in RBC-^{59}Fe incorporation values in polycythemic mice and evoked a significant rise in the amounts of Ep found in the urine of a hypopituitary subject (Jepson et al., 1968).

4. Serotonin

Serotonin (5-hydroxytryptamine, 5-HT) is also capable of elevating the incorporation of radioiron into the RBC of polycythemic mice (Lowy *et al.*, 1970; Noveck and Fisher, 1971). That this action of 5-HT is Ep dependent was shown from the ability of anti-Ep to block this effect (Noveck and Fisher, 1971). Similarly, the dependence of the erythropoietic action of 5-HT on the kidney was noted from the observation that this agent increases plasma Ep levels in normal, but not in nephrectomized, mice (Lowy *et al.*, 1970). This capacity to augment Ep production was seen also in the dog given infusions of 5-HT into the renal arteries (Noveck and Fisher, 1971). Although the reduction in renal blood flow induced by 5-HT was not marked (Noveck and Fisher, 1971), Lowy *et al.* (1970) demonstrated that India ink penetration into the renal blood vessels was greatly inhibited by 5-HT, suggesting once again that renal hypoxia may constitute the mechanism for increased Ep production following 5-HT as with other renal vasoconstrictor agents.

5. *Prostaglandins*

Erythropoietic effects have recently been demonstrated for the prostaglandins, compounds which exert a potent vasoactive influence on a variety of vascular beds. Thus, it has been shown that prostaglandins of the E series (PGE) increased the incorporation of radioiron into the RBC of the hypertransfused mouse (Schooley and Mahlmann, 1971b) and in the exhypoxic polycythemic mouse (Paulo *et al.*, 1973). Moreover, the stimulation of erythropoiesis in the plethoric mouse by PGE_1 could be completely prevented by treatment of the mice with anti-Ep (Schooley and Mahlmann, 1971b). In addition, PGE_1 stimulated Ep production in the isolated perfused dog kidney (Paulo *et al.*, 1973). Whether the accompanying increase in the cyclic AMP levels in renal tissue induced by PGE_1 (Paulo *et al.*, 1973) constitutes the cause of the increased Ep production is not presently known. It may be that the dosages of PGE administered produce renal hypoxia through a vasoconstrictor action. Along these lines, it has been demonstrated that, as with 5-HT, PGE_1 markedly decreased the ability of India ink to penetrate the renal vasculature (Cohen and Keighley, unpublished observations). PGE not only increases Ep production, but also appears to potentiate the effects of low doses of exogenous Ep on glucosamine incorporation by marrow cells *in vitro* (Dukes, 1971) and on RBC-^{59}Fe incorporation into heme in polycythemic mice (Dukes *et al.*, 1972).

B. Nucleotides

The role of 3′,5′-adenosine monophosphate (cyclic AMP) as an intracellular messenger mediating the effects of hormones on their target organs has been well established (Sutherland, 1972). The dibutyryl derivative of cyclic AMP (db-cyclic AMP) was found to stimulate the incorporation of radioiron into the RBC of exhypoxic polycythemic mice (Winkert and Birchette, 1969; Winkert et al., 1971). This observation utilizing either cyclic AMP or its db derivative has been confirmed by others (Gidari et al., 1971; Rodgers et al., 1971; Schooley and Mahlmann, 1971a). The ability of cyclic AMP to stimulate erythropoiesis has been reported to be either partially abolished in vivo by anti-Ep (Gidari et al., 1971; Rodgers et al., 1971; Cohen and Keighley, unpublished observations) or completely by it (Schooley and Mahlmann, 1971a). These results indicate, therefore, that the enhancing action of cyclic AMP on erythropoiesis is mediated, at least in part, by increased production of Ep. The erythropoiesis-stimulating influence of cyclic AMP may be a phenomenon attributable to nucleotides in general. Thus, administration of 5′-AMP,5′-ATP (Gidari et al., 1971) and of the pyridine nucleotides NAD⁺, NADP⁺ and their reduced derivatives (Gidari et al., 1972) evoked increases in the incorporation of radioiron into the circulating RBC of polycythemic mice. It is of interest that the erythropoiesis-stimulating effects of NAD⁺ and NADP⁺ were completely antagonized by anti-Ep (Gidari et al., 1972). Attention should be given to the possibility that the erythropoietic nucleotides may also act in part by altering renal blood flow in a way to reduce the oxygen supply to the sites in the kidney concerned with erythrogenin production.

Since in the hands of some, the in vivo erythropoietic effects of cyclic AMP are not entirely eliminated by anti-Ep, it would be anticipated that this nucleotide should also stimulate phases of erythropoiesis in vitro. Indeed, direct stimulatory effects of db-cyclic AMP on heme synthesis by human marrow explants have been reported (Gorshein and Gardner, 1970a). The uptake of radioiron by these human marrow cells was increased by theophylline, an effect attributed to inactivation of phosphodiesterase, which allowed the nucleotide to operate for a longer time. On the other hand, cyclic AMP and db-cyclic AMP have been reported not to stimulate heme synthesis in cultures of marrow cells obtained from rabbits (Bottomley et al., 1971) or starved rats (Graber et al., 1972). The reasons for this discrepancy require elucidation. However, Bottomley et al. (1971) did observe that cyclic AMP enhances δ-ALA synthetase activity in cultures of rabbit marrow and that cyclic AMP and Ep acted synergistically in this system. Similarly, a synergism occurred between cyclic AMP and Ep on ¹⁴C-labeled glucosamine incorporation and on ⁵⁹Fe incorporation into heme of rat marrow cells in culture (Dukes, 1971). Dukes has suggested that cyclic AMP plays a role in the regulation of erythroid cell differentiation by potentiating the action of Ep. Confirmation of this hypothesis would be derived if, after eliminating all Ep present in the system (both in vivo and in vitro), cyclic AMP would be found to have lost its erythropoiesis-stimulating effect. Of considerable interest are findings by Rodgers et al. (1972), indicating that treatment of rats with cobalt, an erythropoietic agent, induces sequentially a rise in renal cyclic AMP, an increase in renal erythrogenin followed by the appearance of increased levels of Ep in the plasma. These authors propose that cobalt activates renal adenyl cyclase thus inciting the formation of cyclic AMP, which in turn evokes a protein kinase enzyme system involved in the activation of erythrogenin. This hypothesis, if further verified, would assign cyclic AMP a pivotal position in the biogenesis of Ep.

That cyclic AMP may play a role in the regulation of the hemopoietic stem cell cycle is indicated from the observation that since db-cyclic AMP enhances the sensitivity of the colony-forming unit (CFU) to the destructive action of ^{3}H-labeled thymidine, it may act by permitting the CFU to enter the cell cycle (Byron, 1971). How these observations can be reconciled to those of Morley et al. (1971) that cyclic AMP inhibits the proliferation of mouse marrow cells cultured on soft agar is not clear.

C. PRODUCTS OF RED CELL DESTRUCTION

One of the oldest concepts proposed regarding feedback influences on erythropoiesis relates to a stimulatory action exerted by the products of RBC destruction. Thus, Itami (1908) reported that RBC destroyed by intravascular lysis were regenerated more rapidly than RBC lost by hemorrhage. There has been recent confirmation and extension of these earlier findings. Thus, administration of hemolyzed RBC to rats and dogs stimulated erythropoiesis (Sanchez-Medal et al., 1963; Labardini et al., 1968). In these studies the increase in reticulocyte numbers and in the RBC-^{59}Fe incorporation values were accompanied by more than a doubling in the numbers of erythroblasts in the bone marrows and spleens, observations in accord with a true increase in erythropoiesis induced by the hemolysates. This erythropoietic effect was apparently caused by the heme moiety in the hemolysates and was not due to an increased supply of iron from the catabolized hemoglobin (Sanchez-Medal et al., 1970). In seeking an explanation for the increased rate of erythropoiesis caused by hemolysates, Okamura et al. (1971) showed that injections of anti-Ep serum abolished the increased RBC-radioiron incorporation and reticulocyte levels noted in gerbils treated with crude hemoglobin solutions prepared from rat or mouse blood. Similarly, the stimulation of erythropoiesis induced in hypertransfused rats by crude hemolysates was inhibited by injections of anti-Ep (Erslev, 1971). These experiments suggest that the ability of hemolysates to stimulate erythropoiesis in the rat and gerbil is mediated through the production of endogenous Ep. As Erslev (1971) has stated, it seems possible that the large amounts of hemolysate employed may deplete the available haptoglobin, thereby exposing the kidneys to toxic concentrations of free hemoglobin which, through the production of renal ischemia, results in the formation of Ep. However, since injections of these hemolysates did not produce any alteration in the oxygen tension within subcutaneous air pockets in hyper-transfused rats, it has been proposed that such substances act directly on the renal parenchyma to evoke Ep production (Thorling and Erslev, 1972). Studies with more refined materials including heme and heme-related compounds, and examination of the action of these substances on kidney function, are required before physiological significance can be ascribed to hemoglobin and its products in RBC production.

Of interest is the finding that hemoglobin injections did not stimulate erythropoiesis in polycythemic mice (Okamura et al., 1971; Erslev, 1971). Further it is known that, with similar magnitudes of the hemato-crit, practically complete suppression of erythropoiesis occurs in poly-cythemic mice whereas incomplete inhibition is noted in polycythemic rats. It is conceivable that the latter difference may be attributable to the ability of products of RBC destruction to enhance erythropoiesis in the rat but not in the mouse (Okamura et al., 1971).

D. Hormones of the Adenohypophyseal–Target Organ Axis

The recognition of Ep as a hormonal factor of prime significance has refocused attention on the mechanisms by which endocrine organs exert their influence on RBC production.

1. Androgens

It now seems clear that androgens like testosterone stimulate erythro-poiesis in laboratory animals (Mirand et al., 1965a; Fried and Gurney, 1965) and in man (Alexanian et al., 1968; Alexanian, 1969), at least in part, by increasing production of Ep. In this regard, anti-Ep completely blocks the ability of testosterone to stimulate erythropoiesis in mice (Schooley, 1966; Fried et al., 1966). In rodents, the stimulatory effect of testosterone on Ep production appears to be mediated through increased production of renal erythrogenin (Gordon et al., 1966). Androgens may achieve this effect by virtue of their anabolic action exerted on the kid-ney (Kochakian and Harrison, 1962), thus possibly decreasing the ratio of kidney oxygen supply to demand with a consequent renal hypoxia which triggers the production of erythrogenin and then Ep. Other possi-ble mechanisms include an inhibition of renal enzymes concerned with the utilization of oxygen or an impairment of the ability of hemoglobin to deliver adequate quantities of oxygen to the tissues.

Of importance are observations that increased quantities of Ep have been detected in the urine of normal, hypogonadal, and anemic humans treated with the androgen fluoxymesterone (Alexanian, 1969). In these subjects the greatest increases in urinary Ep levels that followed androgen therapy were noted in anemic subjects in whom the levels of Ep were already elevated prior to initiation of treatment. At least one third of the androgen-treated anemic patients with some degree of marrow failure (e.g., myelofibrosis, multiple myeloma, lymphosarcoma) exhibited an erythropoietic response associated with the appearance of increased quantities of Ep in their urines (Alexanian, 1969). It seems possible that the markedly elevated levels in Ep evoked by androgen may be partly responsible for the increased erythropoiesis noted in these patients, at least in those who initially exhibited at least some degree of bone marrow function.

There is evidence that androgens may also induce erythropoietic actions in $vitro$. Thus Erslev (1964) observed a stimulatory effect of testosterone on ^{59}Fe uptake by rabbit bone marrow cells in culture, an action most pronounced at 21 hours of incubation. Utilizing human bone marrow cells cultured for 8 days, a stimulatory influence of testosterone on erythropoiesis was noted (Reisner, 1966); here the number of hemoglobin-containing cells was used as the criterion. On the other hand, testosterone was not found to exert a stimulatory effect on ^{59}Fe incorporation by cultures of rabbit bone marrow cells, and the action of Ep was not significantly enhanced in this system by testosterone (McDonald et $al.$, 1971a). Thus whether a stimulatory action of testosterone on erythropoiesis can be demonstrated in marrow culture systems remains equivocal.

Of interest are the in $vitro$ effects of 5β-H C_{19} and C_{21} steroid metabolites, which stimulate heme synthesis in chick embryo liver cells and in the erythroid cell precursors of the chick blastoderm (Levere et $al.$, 1967; Kappas et $al.$, 1968). The suggested mechanism for this action of the steroid metabolites is the induction of δ-ALA synthetase, the rate-limiting enzyme in the heme biosynthetic pathway. An enhancing effect of 5β-H steroids on heme and globin formation in cultures of human bone marrow cells has also been reported (Necheles and Rai, 1969; Gorshein and Gardner, 1970a; Mizoguchi and Levere, 1971). These 5β-H steroids have been demonstrated to stimulate erythropoiesis in normal and hypertransfused mice (Gordon et $al.$, 1970a) and in exhypoxic polycythemic mice (Gorshein and Gardner, 1970b; Gordon et $al.$, 1970a) as well as in polycythemic mice provided the latter are treated with such steroids shortly after discontinuation of the hypoxic stimulus (Goldwasser and Gross, personal communication). It has been suggested that these steroid metabolites operate by stimulating stem cell differentiation (Gordon *et al.*, 1970a) by triggering hemopoietic stem cells into cell cycle or shortening their cell cycle (Byron, 1970), or by enhancing heme synthesis in nucleated erythroid cells (Goldwasser and Gross, personal communication).

The inability of other workers (Schooley and Mahlmann, 1971a; Fisher *et al.*, 1971a) to confirm a stimulatory action of 5β-H steroid metabolites on erythropoiesis *in vivo* may relate to slight structural differences in the steroids employed (e.g., a 3-β-ol vs a 3-α-ol configuration or use of the acetate ester forms of the steroids). Whatever the discrepancies may be due to, there is still the hope that when these have been reconciled, this group of steroids, devoid of masculinizing side effects, may find use in the treatment of a variety of anemias in man.

2. Adrenal Cortical Steroids and ACTH

Adrenal cortical steroids have been shown to exert either stimulatory (Gordon *et al.*, 1951; Fisher, 1958; Cohen and Gardner, 1965; Bozzini and Alippi, 1971; Peschle *et al.*, 1972d) or inhibitory (Gordon *et al.*, 1967a; Glader *et al.*, 1968; Bozzini *et al.*, 1968; Peschle *et al.*, 1972d) actions on erythropoiesis. This difference in effect, as is the case for other hormones, may be largely attributable to the duration of treatment and to the dose employed with smaller more physiological quantities stimulating, and larger amounts inhibiting, erythropoiesis. The erythropoiesis-stimulating action of ACTH (Fisher *et al.*, 1967a) and of cortisol and 6-methylprednisolone (Peschle *et al.*, 1971a, 1972d) in polycythemic mice can be inhibited by anti-Ep serum suggesting that these hormones operate through the mediation of Ep. Others have reported (Bozzini *et al.*, 1972) that the erythropoietic effect of another cortical steroid, dexamethasone, is not completely abolished by anti-Ep. It is of interest that prednisolone did not potentiate the wave of erythropoiesis initiated by Ep but produced a synergistic enhancement of both the erythropoietic response and Ep plasma levels induced by hypoxia (Peschle *et al.*, 1972d).

The effects of adrenal cortical steroids, including aldosterone (Cooper *et al.*, 1968; Zivny *et al.*, 1972a) on Ep production may be the result of an alteration in the ratio of oxygen supply to demand in the kidney (Fisher and Crook, 1962), with a consequent influence on erythrogenin production. Depressive actions of large doses of prednisolone on Ep production in response to hypoxia may stem from an inhibition of production of the plasma factor (erythropoietinogen) which interacts with erythrogenin to produce Ep (Gordon *et al.*, 1967a).

Teruel *et al.* (1971) have reported that the spleen and bone marrow respond in opposite manner to adrenal cortical steroids. Thus normal or anemic mice injected with β-methasone exhibited depressed ^{59}Fe uptake in the spleen associated with an increased radioiron uptake by the bone marrow. Whether the latter apparent increase in marrow erythropoiesis is due to accumulation of erythroid cell progenitors in the marrow as a result of maturation arrest remains to be determined (Teruel and Scaro, 1971).

3. *TSH and Thyroid Hormones*

TSH and thyroid hormones have been reported to exert a stimulatory influence on erythropoiesis in rats (Gordon *et al.*, 1946; Crafts and Meineke, 1959; Fisher and Crook, 1962). Earlier studies (Evans *et al.*, 1961; Donati *et al.*, 1964) had indicated that no Ep was detectable in the plasmas of animals treated with triiodothyronine (T_3) or thyroxine (T_4). However, the finding that bilateral nephrectomy abolished the erythropoiesis-stimulating action of thyroid hormone (Lucarelli *et al.*, 1966; Shalet *et al.*, 1966) suggested that Ep might be involved in this response. Indeed, T_4 in doses of 5 μg daily for 4–6 days has recently been found to stimulate erythropoiesis in normal mice (Peschle *et al.*, 1971c). This increase was found to occur approximately 24 hours after the appearance of elevated levels of Ep in the plasma, suggesting that the augmentation of erythropoiesis evoked by T_4 was due to Ep production. This, in turn, may have been the result of increased production of renal erythrogenin (Peschle *et al.*, 1971c). T_4 also potentiated the action of hypoxia on both erythropoiesis and the production of Ep. Whether or not the erythropoiesis-stimulating action of T_4 is dependent upon its calorigenic effect requires further elucidation (Donati *et al.*, 1964; Bozzini *et al.*, 1971). It seems possible that the inability of previous workers to evoke Ep production with thyroid hormone may have been attributable to differences in dosage and the time over which the hormone was administered as well as a relatively low sensitivity of the Ep assay system employed.

4. *Adenohypophyseal Growth Hormone (GH)*

Reports have appeared attesting to a stimulatory effect of GH on erythropoiesis in normal and hypophysectomized rodents (Fruhman *et al.*, 1954; Gordon, 1954). The observation by Meineke and Crafts (1968) that the erythropoietic effect of GH in hypophysectomized rats was partially blocked by bilateral nephrectomy suggested that either GH operates through increased production of Ep or that Ep is required for the stimulation of erythropoiesis induced by GH. Evidence for the mediation of Ep in the response to GH is provided by observations that daily administration of GH to hypophysectomized rats resulted in elevated quantities of Ep in the plasma and that this effect could be antagonized by simultaneous administration of anti-Ep serum (Peschle et al., 1972a). As with the thyroid hormones, the stimulatory influence of GH on Ep production is associated with elevated quantities of erythrogenin (Peschle et al., 1972a) in the kidneys, suggesting once again that this renal factor is responsible for the rise in plasma Ep levels noted with GH treatment.

5. Prolactin and Parathyroid Hormone

Stimulatory effects of prolactin on erythropoiesis have been reported (Vollmer et al., 1942; Jepson and Lowenstein, 1967). Thus, injections of a purified preparation of human placental lactogen (HPL) led to an increase in RBC-^{59}Fe incorporation in polycythemic mice (Jepson and Friesen, 1968). In these studies, the capacity of HPL to stimulate erythropoiesis was abolished after its incubation with anti-HPL serum but not with anti-Ep. However, prior treatment of polycythemic test mice with anti-Ep inhibited the ability of subsequently administered HPL to enhance erythropoiesis (Jepson and Friesen, 1968), suggesting that HPL may operate by augmenting the action of Ep. Of relevance here are data indicating that the increased plasma erythropoiesis-stimulating activity during pregnancy in the mouse was not completely abolished by hyperoxia, suggesting the existence in such plasma of erythropoietic factors, the production of which is not influenced by oxygen feedback mechanisms (Jepson and Lowenstein, 1968a). This is supported by the additional observation that the remaining erythropoietic activity of plasma from pregnant mice subjected to hyperoxia was not antagonized after incubation with anti-Ep serum (Jepson and Lowenstein, 1968a).

A possible role of the parathyroid hormone (PTH) in erythropoiesis has been suggested. An increase in mitotic activity of the bone marrow followed by a rise in reticulocyte numbers in bone marrow and peripheral blood as well as an increase in RBC-^{59}Fe incorporation occurred after the administration of PTH to rats (Perris et al., 1971). Thyroparathyroidectomy was followed by a decrease in bone marrow mitosis and erythropoiesis; these effects could be reversed by injections of either parathyroid hormone or calcium. It would appear that these actions are independent of Ep production since the same response could be induced by PTH in nephrectomized rats. However, the possibility that PTH had evoked Ep production by extrarenal sources was not tested.

6. Estrogen

Early work demonstrated that spaying of rats led to increased numbers of circulating red cells and hemoglobin content and that administration of estrogen was accompanied by a decline in these parameters to levels seen in normal females (Vollmer and Gordon, 1941). Administration of moderate quantities of estradiol-17β (2–10 μg) to male rats led to a depression of erythropoiesis by 72 hours after its administration (Dukes and Goldwasser, 1961). Since estrogens also blunted the response to Ep, it was suggested that the estrogenic hormone acted upon the blood-forming tissue to inhibit the action of Ep (Dukes and Goldwasser, 1961). Confirmatory results were reported by Jepson and Lowenstein (1966), who utilized plethoric female mice and employed hypoxia instead of exogenous Ep as the erythropoietic stimulus. When very large doses of estrogen were given to male rats, mice, or tamarins, production of Ep in response to hypoxia was inhibited (Mirand and Gordon, 1966). Recent experiments have dealt with the effects of moderate quantities of estradiol on erythropoiesis in rats (Peschle et al., 1973). Thus daily administration of estradiol benzoate in the range of 2.5–10.0 μg/day inhibited the production of Ep in female rats subjected to different intensities of hypoxia (Peschle et al., 1973). This effect could not be ascribed to the presence of either residual estradiol or an inhibitor to Ep in the plasma samples. Of significance was the observation that ovariectomy increased the levels of plasma Ep in response to hypoxia almost to the values found in normal males, in agreement with results recently reported by Wang and Fried (1972). On the other hand, treatment with estradiol depressed the Ep response of ovariectomized rats to the level seen in normal females (Peschle et al., 1973). In confirmation of previous results obtained by Mirand and Gordon (1966), large doses of estradiol inhibited Ep production in hypoxic male rats (Peschle et al., 1973). In seeking an explanation of the inhibitory effects manifested by estrogen on erythropoiesis and Ep formation, this hormone could conceivably operate by causing a shift to the right in the oxygen-hemoglobin dissociation curve thereby augmenting the oxygen supply to the Ep-generating sites. Whatever the mechanism may be, the present evidence points to a physiological role of estrogens, along with the androgens, in initiating and maintaining the well known sex difference in erythropoiesis and Ep production.

The action of the endocrine system on erythropoiesis may be summarized by stating that hormones like the androgens, thyroxine, adrenal cortical steroids, and GH, administered in certain doses, stimulate RBC production, at least in part, through the mediation of Ep. There is increasing evidence that this action is preceded or accompanied by increased production of renal erythrogenin. Inhibitory influences on erythropoiesis may be induced by large quantities of adrenal cortical steroids and by moderate doses of estrogen. In high doses, these effects may stem from inhibition of production of the plasma substrate for erythrogenin. The possibility exists that hormones also directly activate or depress the erythrogenic tissue, modify its response to Ep or alter the metabolism of Ep and therefore its effectiveness on erythropoiesis.

VII. Fetal Ep

Evidence is available to indicate that Ep can be produced by the mammalian fetus. In the human, the presence of greater erythropoiesis-stimulating activity has been demonstrated in samples of cord blood from anemic than from normal newborn infants (Halvorsen, 1963; Finne, 1966). Similar activity was noted in amniotic fluid of women who subsequently gave birth to erythroblastotic infants (Halvorsen and Finne, 1963). More recently, Ep was detected in high concentrations in the plasmas of fetal lambs rendered anemic by intravenous injections of phenylhydrazine (Zanjani et al., 1969b). That this fetal Ep resembled adult Ep was shown from the ability of adult anti-Ep to completely neutralize the erythropoietic effects of plasma from anemic fetal lambs (Zanjani and Gordon, 1971). Subjection of fetal goats (108–115 days of gestation) at 6 hours after nephrectomy to bleeding did not prevent their ability to produce and/or release Ep (Gordon et al., 1972). These findings are in accord with those of Lucarelli et al. (1968), who reported that, unlike the situation in the adult, bilateral nephrectomy does not result in a decrease in erythropoiesis in neonatal rats. Similarly it has been demonstrated (Carmena et al., 1968) that, in the neonatal rat, bilateral nephrectomy, performed prior to exposure to hypoxia, inhibited but did not eliminate completely the production of Ep. These observations suggest that extrarenal sites of Ep production operate in the fetus and newborn animal.

Transfusion of fetal goats with packed maternal red cells markedly suppressed their erythropoiesis. Injections of adult Ep into these transfused fetuses resulted in strong stimulation of erythropoiesis. This suggests that red cell production in the fetus, as in the adult, is subject to the negative feedback influence of elevated numbers of circulating RBC and is stimulated by Ep (Gordon et al., 1972).

Bleeding of pregnant goats did not result in elevation of their plasma Ep levels until approximately 15 hours after the hemorrhage. However, increases in fetal plasma Ep levels were evident as early as 2–3 hours after the maternal bleeding (Fig. 3). The same rise in fetal Ep plasma values was also observed after bleeding mothers that had been previously nephrectomized (Zanjani *et al.*, 1973). These bled nephrectomized mothers failed to produce Ep up to 24 hours after they had been bled. Thus, these results make it clear that anemia induced in either the fetus or the mother stimulates the production of fetal Ep. In this regard, the fetus appears to be more sensitive to reductions in maternal RBC levels than the mother. The fact that the oxygen dissociation curve for fetal blood is normally shifted to the left of that for the adult (Behrman, 1968) suggests that the fetus is normally on the brink of hypoxia and superimposition of maternal hypoxia, by exacerbating the oxygen deficiency in the fetus, results in rapid production of larger quantities of Ep by the fetus.

It is known that in the fetal goat, hematopoiesis in the bone marrow is initiated shortly before day 70 of intrauterine life (Buckman, 1959). In the fetuses examined in the studies reported above (average age: 110 days; gestation period in the goat is 150 days), erythropoiesis is occurring actively in the bone marrow, although there is evidence of continuation of hepatic and splenic erythropoiesis even at birth. Procedures are presently being developed for studying Ep production in fetuses of

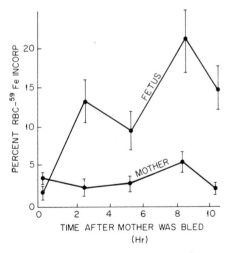

FIG. 3. Ep activity of plasmas (judged as % RBC-^{59}Fe incorporation values in exhypoxic polycythemic mice) from maternal and fetal goats at zero hour and at varying times after the mother was bled. Vertical lines through the means indicate ±1 SEM. From Zanjani and Gordon (1971). Reprinted with permission of the *Isr. J. Med. Sci.*

younger age. The possibility exists that erythropoiesis occurring at earlier stages of development is autonomous and not dependent on Ep.

VIII. Sites of Inactivation and Elimination of Ep

Mechanisms proposed for the inactivation or metabolism of Ep include the role of the liver and the state of activity of the blood-forming elements upon which Ep exerts its influence.

A. The Liver

In rabbits with severe anemia induced by phenylhydrazine, highest quantities of Ep in the plasma were noted in those animals displaying severely damaged livers (Jacobsen et al., 1956). The concept was proposed that hepatic injury diminished an Ep inactivating function of the liver, thus resulting in higher levels of Ep in the blood. This hypothesis received support from studies by Mirand et al. (1959), indicating less ability of Ep-containing plasma to stimulate erythropoiesis when administered directly into the hepatic portal circulation than when given by way of the jugular vein. Similarly, Burke and Morse (1962) showed that higher levels of Ep occurred in blood circulated through isolated rat livers that had been treated with carbon tetrachloride than in perfusates circulating through normal livers. On the other hand, no evidence was found for inactivation of Ep by perfused rat liver (Fischer and Roheim, 1963). This disparity may relate to the use by Burke and Morse of blood perfusates obtained from rats injected with cobalt to raise the endogenous levels of Ep whereas Fischer and Roheim employed exogenous sheep plasma Ep. It has been shown recently (Roh et al., 1972a) that a rapid decrease occurred in the amount of Ep in hypoxic dog plasma perfused through isolated dog livers. However, when the dogs supplying the livers were pretreated with SKF 525-A (2-diethylamino-ethyl-2,2-diphenylvalerate hydrochloride), a drug that inhibits hepatic microsomal enzymes, the rate of disappearance of the Ep in the perfusate was significantly reduced. These results suggest that SKF 525-A may have inhibited microsomal enzymes concerned with the destruction of Ep. Further evidence for this contention is derived from experiments which indicated an ability of hepatic microsomal fractions from normal, but not from SKF 525-A injected dogs, to inhibit Ep in vitro (Fisher and Roh, 1970). The observation that the rate of disappearance of exogenous Ep in the plasma of germfree mice was less than in conventional mice (Mirand et al., 1972) may relate to findings that the liver is less developed, both functionally and morphologically, in the former than in the latter animals (Thorbecke and Benacerraf, 1959; Miyakawa et al., 1965).

Clinical findings would also appear to implicate the liver in the disappearance of Ep. Thus, heightened levels of plasma and urinary Ep have been reported in patients with hepatic dysfunction occurring, for example, in viral hepatitis, hepatic necrosis, toxic conditions resulting from alcohol or carbon tetrachloride as well as in patients with infiltration of the liver secondary to other systemic illness, states not consistently associated with anemia (Mirand and Murphy, 1971b). Such observations may be interpreted to mean that these forms of hepatic dysfunction in man are associated with a decreased ability of the liver to metabolize Ep. Of direct relevance here are findings indicating that whereas homogenates of normal human liver rapidly inactivated human Ep *in vitro*, similarly prepared homogenates of the affected liver lobes from a patient with hepatocellular carcinoma failed to metabolize Ep (Gordon *et al.*, 1970b).

Not favoring a hepatic role in the inactivation of Ep are reports that some rabbits treated with phenylhydrazine, exhibiting little or no liver damage, showed higher levels of Ep in their plasmas than some of those sustaining hepatic damage (Lowy *et al.*, 1959). In addition, Keighley (1962) observed that, in his hands, injections of hepatotoxic quantities of carbon tetrachloride in rats did not alter the rate of clearance of exogenous Ep from their plasma.

Thus, although a good deal of evidence supports a role of the liver in the inactivation of Ep, further experimentation is essential to strengthen this contention. In this regard, as Krantz and Jacobson (1970) have asserted, the effects attributed to the liver may stem from its nonspecific proteolytic activity and do not necessarily indicate a physiological role for this organ.

B. THE BLOOD-FORMING TISSUES

There are indications that the blood-forming tissues (locus of action of Ep) may serve as a site of metabolism of Ep. Of relevance are observations (Stohlman, 1959; Finne, 1965; Faura *et al.*, 1969) that rodents and man subjected to oxygen deficiency display rises in plasma Ep for only a relatively short time (e.g., 18–24 hours), after which the Ep levels decline despite prolongation of the hypoxia. This was explained in terms of an augmented utilization of Ep by the increased numbers of erythropoietic elements in the blood-forming tissues. It would now seem more likely that the decreased level of Ep observed after 72 hours of hypoxia is better interpreted as a lowered production of Ep rather than increased utilization (Fried *et al.*, 1970). Thus, after an 8-hour period at room pressure at the termination of the 72-hour hypoxic exposure, the capacity of these rats to produce Ep again in response to hypoxia was

noted. Experiments which appear to shed further light on this phenomenon involved subjection of humans to high altitudes (4000 meters)
(Miller *et al.*, 1972). In the initial period, the blood pO_2 50 shifted to the
left, the arterial pH rose from 7.40 to 7.46 and the plasma Ep levels
increased significantly at 18 and 24 hours of exposure. The rise in arterial
blood pH could be prevented by administration of acetazolamide, an
agent that counteracted the initial respiratory alkalosis. No increase in
plasma Ep was seen under these conditions. It would thus appear that
the decrease in plasma levels of Ep noted with durations of hypoxia
greater than 24 hours may reflect changes in the arterial pO_2 50, due to
observed increases in RBC 2,3-DPG rather than to augmented utilization
of Ep (Miller *et al.*, 1973).

Requiring explanation are observations that the plasma Ep levels are
higher in animals with defective bone marrows than in those with normal
or highly erythroid marrows. In this connection, a slower rate of disappearance of endogenously produced Ep from the plasma has been
reported in irradiated than in control rats (Stohlman, 1959). Similar
results have been observed for exogenous Ep in both irradiated conventional and germfree mice (Mirand *et al.*, 1972). In addition, Mc-
Donald *et al.* (1970) have indicated that transplants of bone marrow
lowered the increased levels of Ep present in the plasma of mice 10 days
after the exposure to X-radiation. These observations may be construed
as supporting the view that plasma Ep values are influenced by the
functional state of the marrow. Similarly, it was reported earlier by
Stohlman (1959) that the plasma levels of Ep in anemic subjects were
related not only to the intensity of hypoxia, but also to the functional
condition of the erythroid marrow. Thus greater amounts of Ep are
usually detected in the plasma of subjects with refractory anemia when
compared to those with hemolytic anemia. In conformance with these
results are observations (Hammond and Ishikawa, 1962) showing that,
after transfusion, a more rapid disappearance of Ep occurred in the
plasma of patients with erythroid hyperplasia (hemolytic anemia) than
in those with erythroid hypoplasia (congenital hypoplastic anemia). On
the other hand, significant evidence not favoring the concept of utilization
of Ep by marrow is seen from experiments performed by Naets and
Wittek (1968b, 1969). They demonstrated that a similar rate of disappearance of endogenous Ep occurred in plasmas of dogs subjected to
experimentally induced marrow hyperplasia and in normal dogs (Naets
and Wittek, 1968b). Similarly, no difference in the rate of disappearance
of endogenous Ep was seen in plasmas from rats with marrow hyperplasia, hypoplasia or aplasia (Naets and Wittek, 1969). These results
would suggest that Ep utilization is not related to erythroid marrow

activity. Essentially similar results had been obtained by Bozzini (1966) using exogenous Ep in dogs.

It becomes apparent that the problem whether the blood-forming tissues play a significant role in the inactivation or metabolism of Ep requires considerably more clarification. Additional studies are needed to control a number of variables in the above-cited experiments. These include determinations as to whether Ep production and excretion as well as the volumes and compartments of distribution remain unvarying during the course of measuring the diminishing titers of plasma Ep. It might be expected that those blood-forming cells which are responsive to Ep would consume at least a part of the Ep with which it interacts. Controlled *in vitro* studies which involve incubation of Ep with blood-forming tissue in the spleen and bone marrow, in various stages of erythroid activity, may help in the resolution of this vexing problem although, as yet, no reliable methods have been recommended for ascertaining the metabolism of Ep by the blood-forming elements.

Experiments which may shed new light on the problem of factors influencing plasma levels of Ep concern studies on WWv mice. These mutants normally have higher levels of plasma Ep and require larger quantities of Ep for stimulation of erythropoiesis than do normal (+ +) nonmutants (Keighley *et al.*, 1962). The increased amounts of Ep present normally in the plasma of these mutant mice were no longer apparent at 7 days after transplantation of normal (+ +) marrow cells (Fried *et al.*, 1971a). It was proposed by these workers that the rate of production of Ep at any level of anemia is related to the capacity of the hemato-poietic tissue to respond to Ep. These experiments may help to interpret the studies describing the rate of disappearance of endogenous Ep in animals and man exhibiting different degrees of marrow activity.

C. RENAL EXCRETION

The amount of Ep excreted normally into the urine of humans varies between 0.9 and 4.0 units per day (Adamson *et al.*, 1966; Alexanian, 1966). The Ep appearing in urine is most likely derived from plasma since anemic patients, following blood transfusion, showed proportional decreases of Ep in their plasmas and urines (Medici *et al.*, 1957; Rosse and Waldmann, 1964b). Calculations indicated that the renal clearance of endogenously produced Ep was 0.60 to 0.67 ml/min, and the total excretion into urine amounted to only 10% of the daily loss (Rosse and Waldmann, 1964b). For exogenous Ep, Weintraub *et al.* (1964) reported that a 70% decrease in the plasma levels of the hormone occurred during the first 3.5 hours after intravenous administration of sheep Ep. A biphasic curve was found in these experiments. The first component, probably attributable to a rapid passage of the exogenous Ep into the extravascular space (Reissmann *et al.*, 1965) exhibited a half-time disappearance of 20–45 minutes whereas the value for the slower component was 9–10.5 hours. The slow phase probably represents metabolism and excretion of the Ep. Somewhat similar results have been observed in experiments also performed in dogs (Bozzini, 1966; Naets and Wittek, 1968b). Apparently, disappearance rates with highly purified fractions of exogenous Ep show little deviation from those reported with relatively impure preparations. Thus Roh *et al.* (1972b) utilizing ^{125}I-labeled human urinary Ep (8300 units per milligram of protein), reported the mean half-time disappearances for the rapid and slow phases to be approximately 35.9 minutes and 10.3 hours in rabbits. Similar values were obtained for unlabeled Ep. These estimations are almost identical to those reported by Weintraub *et al.* (1964) in dogs. The rapid phase of disappearance was absent for endogenously produced Ep (Rosse and Waldmann, 1964b) probably because, under these circumstances, there is time for the Ep to saturate the entire distribution space before production is curtailed and the disappearance rate of the hormone is determined (Reissmann *et al.*, 1965). It is possible that the variations noted for half-time Ep disappearances in different species may relate to differences in the rates of consumption and distribution of Ep among the various intracellular and extracellular compartments as well as differences in the rates of excretion. In the latter case, however, calculations indicate that only 2–5% of exogenous sheep Ep administered to dogs was recoverable in the urine, and this was associated with a renal clearance of 0.1 to 0.6 ml/min (Weintraub *et al.*, 1964). Problems relating to the role of the kidney in the excretion of Ep that need to be clarified concern the possible reabsorption of Ep by the kidney and inactivation by renal inhibitory factors (Erslev and Kazal, 1968; Fisher *et al.*, 1968a; Naets and Wittek, 1971).

IX. Neural Relations to Ep Production

Although renal hypoxia continues to be considered as the direct trigger mechanism for the production of Ep, the fact that the blood supply to the kidney is very extensive and the arteriovenous oxygen difference is so small have led some to question whether this organ is able to perform as a sensitive oxygen sensor device. For this reason consideration has been given to the possibility that the primary oxygen sensor mechanism resides in extrarenal sites, as, for example, in the nervous system.

Attempts to demonstrate a relation between the central nervous system and erythropoiesis date back to the experiments by Schulhof and Mathies

(1927), who reported that injections of infusorial earth into the diencephalon of rabbits induced polycythemia. More convincing experiments have recently lent support to a hypothalamic relation to erythropoiesis. Thus reticulocytosis and an increase in circulating RBC mass were reported after 14 days of discontinuous electrical stimulation of the hypothalamus and ventral thalamus in 8 of 28 rabbits examined (Seip et al., 1961). These effects were accompanied by elevated erythropoiesis stimulating activity of the plasma. Likewise, it has been demonstrated that chronic stimulation of the region of the supraoptic nucleus, preoptic nucleus, and posterior median eminence in the rhesus monkey resulted in the appearance of significant amounts of Ep in the plasma (Mirand et al., 1967; Mirand, 1968). Stimulation of certain areas including the mammillary body and the anterior commissure did not evoke a similar response. Other reports (Feldman et al., 1966; Medado et al., 1967; Segal et al., 1971) indicated that electrical stimulation of the posterior hypothalamus and midbrain of rats resulted in significant reticulocytosis, an increase in radioiron incorporation into newly formed RBC and an augmented circulating red cell mass. These effects were not associated with the presence of elevated quantities of Ep in the serum, attributable perhaps to differences in intensity and duration of the electrical stimulation employed when compared to those utilized by the Mirand group. The mechanisms responsible for the influences exerted by the hypothalamus on erythropoiesis have not been completely elucidated. Although mediation through the hypothalamico-adenohypophyseal axis represents an obvious pathway, some of the evidence is not in accord with this concept. Thus the increase in plasma Ep observed following chronic hypothalamic stimulation in rabbits is not affected by hypophysectomy (Halvorsen et al., 1972). A similar result has been reported in the monkey (Mirand, 1968).

Another possible mode of hypothalamic influence on erythropoiesis and Ep production involves the autonomic nervous system. Thus, destruction or stimulation of hypothalamic areas, by modifying autonomic nerve function, might alter cardiopulmonary activity with ensuing changes in arterial blood pO_2 and saturation values or alterations in vascular bore and a resultant change in blood flow through the kidney. That an action through the kidney does not provide a complete explanation is derived from experiments showing that the elevation in plasma Ep values resulting from hypothalamic stimulation is seen in nephrectomized as well as in intact rabbits (Halvorsen, 1968). Since the renoprival rabbit continues to show some erythropoiesis, it would seem possible that this animal has extrarenal sources of Ep that become activated after nephrectomy. Should this prove to be true, it could be assumed that hypothalamic stimulation in the anephric rabbit stimulates the production of Ep by these extrarenal sites. A logical experiment would be a repetition of these studies in the dog, a species in which extrarenal production of Ep does not appear to exist (Naets, 1960a,b).

Requiring exploration is the possibility that hypothalamic effects are relayed directly to the bone marrow by way of the autonomic nerve supply present in this organ. Studies by Calvo (1968) indicate that myelinated nerve fibers actually traverse the marrow parenchyma and that nonmyelinated fibers end in sphincters at the origin of the arterial tree. Of additional interest is the finding (Calvo and Forteza-Vila, 1969) that the time of maturation of nerve elements within the rat bone marrow, at approximately 15 days after birth, coincides with the initial period of Ep responsiveness in the rat (Garcia and Van Dyke, 1961). These facts may provide a structural basis for a direct neural action on bone marrow function.

The operation of the autonomic nervous system as a mediator in the augmented erythropoiesis induced by hypothalamic stimulation is seen from the ability of atropine to abolish this effect (Medado et al., 1967). Atropine has also been reported to block the reticulocyte response to hypothalamic stimulation and to inhibit the rise in plasma Ep observed in rabbits subjected to hypoxia (Paulo et al., 1972a). Such studies appear to implicate a cholinergic mechanism underlying the stimulatory influence of hypothalamic activation as well as oxygen deficiency on erythropoiesis.

It would seem possible that, despite some evidence to the contrary, the hypothalamus may function as an accessory mechanism in the regulation of erythropoiesis in the normal animal. This might be accomplished through already established neural-humoral pathways, such as through the discharge of adenohypophyseal tropins controlled by appropriate releasing factors originating in the hypothalamus (Schally et al., 1973). Alterations in hypothalamic activity might also induce changes in respiratory and vascular dynamics as a result of variations in autonomic outflow transmitted through the brainstem and cord. A consequent influence on the rate of blood flow and oxygen delivered to the kidney, liver, and bone marrow could then affect the rate of erythropoiesis.

The question as to whether a neural center functions in the regulation of erythropoiesis has gained impetus with the recent report that bilateral carotid body resection in cats prevents the rise in peripheral reticulocyte numbers evoked by bleeding (Tramezzani et al., 1971). These workers also observed increased erythropoiesis-stimulating activity in the blood draining the carotid bodies after subjecting cats to hemorrhage. In addition, extracts of the carotid body were found to stimulate erythropoiesis as judged by increased RBC-radioiron incorporation in transfused plethorized rats or by peripheral reticulocytosis in normal cats. On the basis of these results, it was suggested by Tramezzani et al. (1971) that the carotid body is a neuroendocrine gland controlling the production of 2 factors: one concerned with rapid reticulocyte release and the second with increased erythropoiesis. Although the ascribing of an endocrine function in erythropoiesis to the carotid bodies is an attractive hypothesis, especially since these structures play a major part in the sensing of arterial hypoxemia (Wade et al., 1970), results at variance with those obtained by Tramezzani et al. (1971) have appeared. Thus, it has been demonstrated that denervation of the carotid bodies in rabbits resulted in a greater rise in hematocrit, red cell counts and peripheral reticulocyte numbers following chronic exposure to hypoxia than in similarly exposed normal rabbits (Grant, 1951). Similarly, plasma levels of Ep in rabbits (Paulo et al., 1972a) and cats (Paulo et al., 1972b) subjected to hypoxia for 18 hours were higher following carotid body ablation than in sham-operated controls. In the human, removal of the carotid bodies failed to influence the reticulocyte and hematocrit response following acute phlebotomy (Lugliani et al., 1971). It should be pointed out, however, that 6 of their patients developed a secondary polycythemia following carotid body ablation which required phlebotomy. Further work is required to determine whether the carotid body-hypothalamic axis can be implicated as a normal extrarenal oxygen sensor in the physiological regulation of erythropoiesis.

X. Clinical Implications and Applications

A. The Polycythemias

Clinical states exist in which the quantities of Ep in the plasma and urine are considerably elevated (Krantz and Jacobson, 1970; Fisher, 1972). These include the erythrocytoses (secondary polycythemias), such as those arising from respiratory (Shaw and Simpson, 1961) or cardiac abnormalities (Stroebel and Fowler, 1956) which lead to renal hypoxia and appropriate compensatory hyperproduction of Ep.

The erythrocyte itself is able to regulate the ability of hemoglobin to combine with oxygen. This stems in part from its content of 2,3-DPG which exists in the same molar quantities as hemoglobin. In states of cardiac failure or pulmonary disease, the 2,3-DPG content of the RBC may increase with a resulting shift of the blood oxygen dissociation curve to the right thus making more oxygen available to the tissues. Similarly, the decrease in plasma Ep levels which occurs in the plasma of human subjects exposed for more than 24 hours to high altitudes is associated with increased 2,3-DPG generation and a shift in the oxygen dissociation curve to the right (Miller *et al.*, 1973).

Oxygen affinity in the RBC is also altered in states associated with structural changes in the hemoglobin molecule. A considerable number of variants of human hemoglobin display abnormal oxygen-binding features. Subjects who are heterozygous for an abnormal hemoglobin with a greater affinity for oxygen may exhibit familial erythrocytosis, a condition which appears to have as its underlying cause an increased production of Ep (Kontras and Romshe, 1967; Alperin *et al.*, 1968). In this connection, increased quantities of urinary Ep have been reported in human subjects with hemoglobin Yakima or Rainier, both characterized by a shift in the oxygen dissociation curve to the left (Adamson, 1970).

An enigmatic category of erythrocytosis, termed paraneoplastic (Thorling, 1972), relates to those associated with certain tumors and cysts in man. These include renal adenocarcinomas and cysts, cerebellar hemangioblastomas, hepatomas, pheochromocytomas, adrenal cortical adenomas, and uterine leiomyomas. In these states, elevated quantities of Ep are detected, on occasion, not only in the tumor extract and/or cyst fluid but in the plasma as well (for reviews of this subject, see Krantz and Jacobson, 1970; Fisher, 1972; Thorling, 1972). Although it is possible that these tumors are extracting Ep from the plasma and are merely storing this hormone, it would seem more likely that they are producing it, especially since removal of the neoplasm or cystic mass is often followed by regression of the polycythemia and the disappearance of Ep from the plasma. That it is actually Ep which is being produced by the tumors receives credence from the finding that the erythropoiesis stimulating activity is completely neutralized by anti-Ep serum (Rosse and Waldmann, 1964a; Nakao *et al.*, 1971). The mechanism by which these neoplasms engage in inappropriate Ep production remains undetermined. A unitarian origin lies in the possibility that they all may represent manifestations of the von Hippel-Lindau syndrome (Melman and Rosen, 1964). This state is characterized classically by tumors or cysts of the kidneys and pancreas as well as angiomatous cysts of the cerebellum and retina. It is conceivable in these conditions that a common vascular lesion resulting in marked hypoxia induces some component of the altered blood vessel itself to elaborate Ep inappropriately. Another possibility is that, in the process of neoplastic transformation, the tumor cells, by derepression of a genome, commence the production of a glycoprotein or some active biological core which resembles Ep chemically and possesses erythropoiesis stimulating activity (Thorling, 1972). Worthy of mention here is that a marked drop in hematocrit (from 64% to 39%) in a patient with erythrocytosis associated with a cerebellar hemangioblastoma did not result in any alteration in the amount of Ep produced, as judged by the urinary output, suggesting that autonomous production of Ep occurs in these neoplastic states (Adamson, 1968). Of interest are recent observations (Zanjani et al., 1972a) that plasma from patients with tumor-associated erythrocytosis is considerably more active in releasing exogenous Ep bound to a lipid inhibitor than are plasmas obtained from normal or PV subjects. This finding raises the question whether the heightened plasma Ep levels noted in these paraneoplastic states not only arise from hyperproduction but also from release of Ep from storage sites.

In contrast to the secondary polycythemias, primary polycythemia or polycythemia rubra vera (PV), a panmyelopathy, is not associated with increased production of Ep. Actually, little or no Ep is detectable in the urine of PV patients in contrast to a basal excretion of 0.9 to 4.2 units per day in normal human subjects (Adamson, 1968). These observations, coupled with the finding that phlebotomy performed in PV patients does not evoke as great an Ep response as seen in normal subjects (Adamson, 1968) suggests that PV is not under Ep regulation. In this connection, the observations of Krantz (1968) indicate a lower capacity of Ep to stimulate in vitro heme synthesis in marrow cells from PV patients than from normal subjects. However, following a busulfan-induced remission, the ability of this PV patient's marrow to synthesize heme was restored to normal. These findings give support to the view that PV is the result of proliferation of an autonomous blood cell line that competes with normal cells in development. In relapse, the cell line which does not respond to Ep predominates while in remission, normal reactive cells appear in larger numbers resulting in a greater response to Ep and the attainment of relatively normal marrow morphology. Zanjani et al. (1972b) have reported the existence of a substance (not Ep) in the serum of a significant number of PV patients (16 of 43) which enhances the activity of Ep. This action may be achieved through an increase in the numbers of ERC and/or the ability of these cells to respond to Ep. Information is needed on the precise chemical nature, site of origin and the possible role of this factor in the PV subject. A possible animal counterpart of PV is that induced in mice by certain viral filtrates (Mirand, 1970). As in PV, this murine viral-induced polycythemia is also characterized by elevated leukocyte and platelet counts with no increase in Ep levels in the plasma (Mirand, 1970). It may be speculated that the virus, like Ep, acts directly on the stem cells to induce differentiation into the erythroid cell line.

B. The Anemias

The anemias stemming from either blood loss or hemolysis in animals including man are usually associated with elevated levels of Ep in the body fluids and with a bone marrow and/or spleen displaying erythroid hyperplasia (Gordon, 1959; Krantz and Jacobson, 1970). Increases in the plasma and urinary levels of Ep are also characteristic of the anemias resulting from defective RBC production, such as those of aplastic origin as well as in red cell aplasia (Krantz and Jacobson, 1970). In these latter states, at any particular hemoglobin or hematocrit level, the plasma content of Ep is usually greater than in those anemias associated with blood loss or destruction (Stohlman and Brecher, 1959). Possible explanations for this phenomenon are given in Section VIII, "Sites of Inactivation and Elimination of Ep." With increasing severities of anemia, greater quantities of Ep appear in the urine (Winkert *et al.*, 1958) and a direct relation between the serum and urinary levels of Ep was found to exist with the concentration in the serum amounting to approximately 2 to 3 times that in the urine (Hammond *et al.*, 1962).

Anemias also exist that may have as their underlying cause an underproduction of Ep. These include anemias arising from chronic renal disease (Gallagher *et al.*, 1959), from protein deficiency (Reissmann, 1964), cirrhosis of the liver (Naets and Heuse, 1962), rheumatoid arthritis (Ward *et al.*, 1969), and chronic inflammation associated with infections (Gutnisky *et al.*, 1971). Relevant here are findings indicating that the anemia induced by the Rauscher leukemia virus in mice displaying hematocrit values as low as 10–20% is not usually accompanied by the appearance of significant levels of Ep in the plasma (Ebert *et al.*, 1972; Camiscoli *et al.*, 1972). The mechanism responsible for this inappropriate underproduction of Ep in the Rauscher virus-infected mouse requires elucidation.

Of considerable significance are the observations that in addition to the large quantities of Ep found in red cell aplasia, factors that inhibit heme synthesis *in vitro* and antibodies directed against erythroblast nuclei are also detectable in the plasmas of some of these patients (Krantz and Kao, 1967, 1969). These substances are recoverable in the gamma G fraction of plasma. Treatment with 6-mercaptopurine (Krantz and Kao, 1967) or cyclophosphamide (Krantz and Kao, 1969) resulted in the disappearance of the plasma inhibitory activity and a resumption of normal erythropoiesis in these subjects. Similarly, a case of red cell aplasia which developed 2 years after removal of a thymoma was treated successfully with immunosuppressive therapy, but only after the patient had been splenectomized (Safdar *et al.*, 1970). The spleen may have acted by blunting the effectiveness of the immunosuppressive agents used. In a fourth patient, a combination of cyclophosphamide and horse antihuman thymocyte γ-globulin was employed as the therapeutic regimen (Krantz, 1972). A definite increase in RBC production ensued, but the development of a severe febrile reaction precluded further treatment with the anti-γ-globulin. These important observations make it likely that in some cases of red cell aplasia a plasma immunological complex functioning as an antibody to marrow erythroblasts, and in some instances as an inhibitor of heme synthesis, prevents further erythroblast maturation or lyses erythroblasts as they form. These studies, at the same time, demonstrate the validity of judicious therapeutic use of immunosuppressive agents in this disease state.

A plasma factor which inhibits erythropoiesis has also been reported in a patient displaying red cell aplasia associated with a thymoma (Al-Mondhiry et al., 1971). The inhibitor is extractable in the IgG fraction. Hematologic remission with disappearance of the inhibitor from the plasma was seen following thymectomy. It was further shown that the inhibitor operates against the erythroid cells and not against Ep (Al-Mondhiry et al., 1971). In a case of panhypoplasia of the marrow, the Ep levels of the plasma were not increased despite the presence of severe anemia (Jepson and Lowenstein, 1968b). In this patient, an inhibitor directed against Ep appeared to be present in the plasma. It would thus seem possible that some forms of anemia have as their origin inhibitors against erythroblast nuclei or Ep itself.

C. Possible Therapeutic Use

There appears now to be adequate basis for use of Ep, when it has been sufficiently purified and made available in large enough quantities, for clinical trials. Perhaps the most clearly indicated application is chronic renal disease in which the levels of Ep in the body fluids are most often considerably depressed despite severe degrees of anemia. The fact that uremic animals respond with increased erythropoiesis to Ep (Naets, 1958) in the face of an often accompanying toxic depression of the marrow cells, hemolysis, or hemorrhage (Erslev, 1970) suggests that Ep may prove to be beneficial in the treatment of the anemia. The report that the anemia seen in patients with renal disease responds favorably to cobalt (Gardner, 1953), a metal that stimulates erythropoiesis as a result of its ability to enhance Ep production (Goldwasser et al., 1958), favors this point of view. Although previous trials with Ep in patients with chronic renal disease have not as yet been successful, the amounts utilized [e.g., 54 units/kg daily for 3 days (Van Dyke et al., 1967)] may not have been sufficient. In fact, it has been estimated that a dosage of 200 units/kg per day would be required to evoke a favorable response in severely uremic patients. In this connection, dialysis of the patient prior to administration of Ep would probably lower the quantity of hormone required for a beneficial effect (Eschbach et al., 1967). Another point worthy of consideration is that repeated blood transfusions of renally insufficient patients may lead to sensitization to a subsequently grafted kidney should such a transplant be warranted. For this reason, it would seem more desirable to maintain erythropoiesis in dialyzed subjects with Ep rather than to administer transfusions.

Additional possible indications for the clinical use of Ep relate to anemias that are not consistently characterized by heightened levels of Ep such as those accompanying protein deficiency, chronic inflammatory states, hepatic disease and neoplasia. Still of interest are the early observations of Gurney et al. (1957b) that an increase in erythropoiesis occurred in patients with congenital hypoplastic anemia following treatment with plasma from anemic human donors. It may be that in such patients, already exhibiting high levels of circulating Ep, the requirements for this hormone to maintain erythropoiesis are greater than those already present in these subjects. This same explanation may also apply to the ability of androgenic steroids, which are known to stimulate Ep production (Mirand et al., 1965a; Fried and Gurney, 1965), to alleviate some types of refractory anemias in patients initially displaying increased quantities of plasma Ep (Alexanian, 1969). Alternatively, there is the possibility that the Ep appearing in greatly increased amounts in severe hypoplastic anemia is a defective one that undergoes activation in the normal assay animal but which is noneffective in the patient. In this regard, it has been reported (Hasegawa et al., 1968) that although plasma from some patients with aplastic anemia stimulated erythropoiesis in starved rats, it was ineffective in vitro in increasing the mitotic index of bone marrow erythroblasts or the synthesis of heme by bone marrow cells. Administration to these subjects with aplastic anemia of Ep-rich plasma from patients with secondary anemias in doses ranging from 2800 to 6600 ml over a period of 22 to 80 days succeeded in stimulating erythropoiesis to a degree not attained by conventional treatments previously applied. Normal human plasma, given in similar quantities was ineffective. Whether the beneficial effects seen with the plasma from anemic subjects were the result of factors other than Ep, inhibition of an inhibitor to erythropoiesis or a combination of such factors remains to be resolved. At any event, these findings, as well as those originally reported by Gurney et al. (1957b) suggest consideration of clinical trials with purified human Ep, preferably from secondary anemia sources, in hypoplastic anemias.

Other possible applications include the administration of Ep to patients receiving bone marrow grafts where the hormone should result in a more rapid recovery of erythropoiesis. It may also find use as a radioprotective agent (Vittorio and Amey, 1970), and in patients receiving blood transfusions, thus helping to override the inhibition of erythropoiesis induced by the transfused RBC. As stated earlier (Gordon, 1971), in view of these possible applications, it is the opinion of this reviewer that Ep is no longer a hormone "looking for a disease." It is anticipated that when highly purified human urinary Ep is cleared of pyrogen, thromboplastic, and possibly viral contamination, clinical trials will be initiated. The ultimate hope is that the structure of Ep houses a small-sized biologically active core or subunit and that this will ultimately be isolated, characterized, and synthesized.

XI. Summary

Erythropoietin (Ep), a glycoprotein hormone, is now acknowledged to be the prime regulator of red cell production. Both *in vivo* and *in vitro* assays have been utilized for its detection in body fluids and in organ extracts. The further development of the radioimmune assay should make it possible to assess Ep quantitatively in those experimental and disease states in which it seems likely that Ep is present in subnormal quantities. A high degree of purity (8000–9000 IU/mg) has been achieved for both plasma and urinary Ep. The principal target site of action of the hormone is the primitive Ep-responsive cell (ERC), which it causes to differentiate into the earliest members of the nucleated erythroid cell series. This effect is achieved through the induction of a sequence of RNAs concerned with the formation of hemoglobin and other organic substances in the reactive blood cells. Evidence is accumulating to indicate that Ep also exerts a variety of influences on already differentiated nucleated erythroid elements. The possibility that these diverse actions are evoked by different forms of Ep remains to be tested.

It is now clear that hypoxia constitutes the fundamental erythrocytogenic stimulus. This action is mediated, in part, through production by the kidney of a principle, erythrogenin, which upon incubation with normal plasma or serum yields functional Ep. Erythrogenin can be extracted from the light-mitochondrial and microsomal fractions of hypoxic kidneys. The erythrogenin–plasma interaction conforms to first-order kinetics, and it is suggested that erythrogenin may function as an enzyme converting a plasma protein substrate (erythropoietinogen) into Ep. Studies with anti-Ep serum demonstrate different immunological properties for erythrogenin, the plasma substrate and Ep. Erythrogenin is found in approximately equal quantities in renal cortical and medullary tissues. Kidney tissue, cultured *in vitro*, produces erythrogenin. Extra-renal sources of Ep probably exist (e.g., liver and spleen). However, the full operation of these sites in the adult may require prior removal of the kidneys and application of severe degrees of hypoxia.

Production of Ep is increased by a multiplicity of factors including vasoactive agents (e.g., norepinephrine, vasopressin, serotonin, prosta-glandin), adenine nucleotides, products of red cell destruction and a variety of hormones of adenohypophyseal–target organ origin. It would seem likely that these actions are mediated, in part, through renal and perhaps extrarenal production of Ep. Direct *in vitro* effects of androgens and some of their derivatives as well as *in vivo* actions of thyroid hor-mones, adrenal cortical steroids, and adenohypophyseal growth hormone upon erythropoiesis and Ep production have also been reported.

Ep is demonstrable in the amniotic fluid and cord blood of human subjects, especially in cases of Rh incompatibility. It is also found in high concentrations in the plasmas of fetal lambs and goats subjected to severe anemia. Fetal Ep is antagonized by adult anti-Ep serum, which suggests a chemical similarity between Ep of adult and fetal origin. It is of interest that Ep production by the fetus may be stimulated either by inducing anemia in the fetus or by rendering the mother anemic.

Although considerable evidence has implicated the liver and blood-forming organs as sites of metabolism of Ep, complete agreement in this area of investigation has not yet been achieved. Excretion through the kidney represents only a minor pathway of Ep elimination. See Fig. 4.

A relation appears to exist between the central nervous system and erythropoiesis. Electrical stimulation of certain areas of the hypothala-mus results, in some instances, in increased levels of plasma Ep. Recent work has demonstrated that removal of the carotid bodies enhances Ep production in response to oxygen deficiency. However, additional work is required before the carotid body and hypothalamus can be considered normal components of an extrarenal oxygen sensor system governing Ep production and erythropoiesis.

Ep is present in high concentrations in the plasma and urine of human subjects with secondary polycythemias and in certain tumorous (para-neoplastic) states. It is low in concentration or absent in the body fluids of patients with polycythemia rubra vera (PV). There is evidence to suggest that PV may arise from development of hemopoietic cell clones not under Ep regulation. The plasma and urine of humans with primary and secondary anemias usually contain elevated levels of Ep. A factor(s) is present in the plasma of some patients with red cell aplasia that in-hibits heme synthesis *in vitro* and functions as an antibody directed against erythroblast nuclei. Purified Ep, when available in sufficient

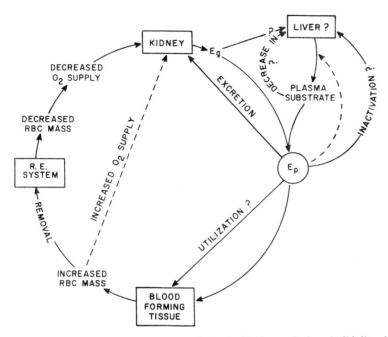

Fig. 4. Scheme of biogenesis of Ep and its feedback regulation (solid line indicates stimulation and dashed line, inhibition). Removal and/or destruction of red blood cells (RBC), by decreasing blood oxygen content, stimulates production of renal erythrogenin. This renal factor interacts with a substrate in plasma to yield the functional circulating Ep. This interaction may occur in the kidney, in the plasma, or both. There is some preliminary evidence to suggest that Eg may stimulate substrate production. Utilization of substrate may also constitute a stimulus to production and/or release of substrate. The liver probably represents the chief source of the plasma substrate for erythrogenin. Elevation in the quantity of circulating Ep of either exogenous or endogenous origin, serves to inhibit production of Ep; this appears to be accomplished through a reduction in the available levels of substrate. The increased RBC mass (increased oxygen supply) induced by Ep, through a negative feedback action on the kidney, reduces erythrogenin production. Excess as well as old and effete RBC are removed by the reticuloendothelial system. Elimination through the kidney constitutes only a minor pathway for elimination of Ep. Other organs, possibly concerned with elimination or inactivation of Ep include the liver and the blood-forming tissues. From Gordon et al. (1973). Reprinted with permission of Academic Press, New York.

amounts, may find application in the treatment of anemic states in man, particularly those associated with reduced production of Ep, notably the anemia of chronic renal disease.

There is need for additional information on the mechanisms underlying the actions of Ep on erythropoiesis, its biogenesis, particularly in extrarenal sites and its relation to hematological dyscrasias. Further efforts should be made in the development of more lucrative sources of Ep and toward its possible use in the treatment of indicated blood diseases in man.

REFERENCES

Abbrecht, P. H., Malvin, R. L., and Vander, A. J. (1966). *Nature (London)* **211**, 1318.

Adamson, J. W. (1968). *Blood* **32**, 597.

Adamson, J. W. (1970). *In* "Hemopoietic Cellular Proliferation" (F. Stohlman, Jr., ed.), pp. 112–121. Grune & Stratton, New York.

Adamson, J. W., Alexanian, R., Martinez, C., and Finch, C. A. (1966). *Blood* **28**, 354.

Alexanian, R. (1966). *Blood* **28**, 344.

Alexanian, R. (1969). *Blood* **33**, 564.

Alexanian, R., Vaughn, W. K., and Ruchelman, M. W. (1968). *J. Lab. Clin. Med.* **70**, 777.

Al-Mondhiry, H., Zanjani, E. D., Spivack, M., Zalusky, R., and Gordon, A. S. (1971). *Blood* **38**, 576.

Alpen, E. L., and Cranmore, D. (1959). *In* "The Kinetics of Cellular Proliferation" (F. Stohlman, Jr., ed.), pp. 290–300. Grune & Stratton, New York.

Alperin, J. B., Levin, W. C., Alexanian, R., and Houston, E. W. (1968). *Clin. Res.* **16**, 40. (Abstr.)

Annable, L., Cotes, P. M., and Mussett, M. V. (1972). *Bull. W. H. O.* **47**, 99.

Baciu, I., Oprisiu, C., Dorofteiu, M., Rosenfeld, E., Rusin, M., and Cherebetin, C. (1963). *J. Physiol. (Paris)* **55**, 551.

Barnes, D. W. H., and Loutit, J. F. (1967). *Lancet* **ii**, 1138.

Bateman, A. E., and Cole, R. J. (1971). *J. Embryol. Exp. Morphol.* **26**, 475.

Bayliss, W. M., and Starling, E. H. (1904). *Proc. Roy. Soc. (London), Croonian Lect.* **73**, 310.

Behrman, R. D. (1968). *J. Appl. Physiol.* **25**, 224.

Bennett, M., and Cudkowicz, G. (1968). *J. Cell. Physiol.* **72**, 129.

Bilsel, Y. C., Wood, J. E., and Lange, R. D. (1963). *Proc. Soc. Exp. Biol. Med.* **114**, 475.

Borsook, H., Graybiel, A., Keighley, G., and Windsor, E. (1954). *Blood* **9**, 734.

Borsook, H., Ratner, K., Tattrie, B., and Teigler, D. (1968). *Nature (London)* **217**, 1024.

Bottomley, S. S., and Smithee, G. A. (1969). *J. Lab. Clin. Med.* **134**, 501.

Bottomley, S. S., Whitcomb, W. H., Smithee, G. A., and Moore, M. Z. (1971). *J. Lab. Clin. Med.* **77**, 793.

Bozzini, C. E. (1966). *Nature (London)* **209**, 1140.

Bozzini, C. E., and Alippi, R. M. (1971). *Acta Physiol. Lat. Amer.* **21**, 21.

Bozzini, C. E., Barrio Rendo, M. E., Kofoed, J. A., and Frey, G. O. (1968). *Experientia* **24**, 800.

Bozzini, C. E., Alippi, R. M., and Perec, C. J. (1971). *Acta Physiol. Lat. Amer.* **21**, 25.

Bozzini, C. E., Alippi, R. M., and Martinez, M. A. (1972). *Acta Physiol. Lat. Amer.* **22**, 6.

Bradley, T. R., and Metcalf, D. (1966). *Aust. J. Exp. Biol. Med. Sci.* **44**, 287.

Brown, G. E., and Roth, G. M. (1922). *Arch. Intern. Med.* **30**, 817.

Brunette, D. M., McCulloch, E. A., and Till, J. E. (1968). *Cell Tissue Kinet.* **1**, 319.

Buckman, M. J. (1959). Ph.D. Thesis, Univ. of Minnesota, Minneapolis.

Burke, W. T., and Morse, B. S. (1962). *In* "Erythropoiesis" (L. O. Jacobson and M. Doyle, eds.), pp. 111–119. Grune & Stratton, New York.

Burlington, H., Cronkite, E. P., Riencke, U., and Zanjani, E. D. (1972). *Proc. Nat. Acad. Sci. U. S.* **69**, 3547.

Busuttil, R. W., Roh, B. L., and Fisher, J. W. (1971). *Proc. Soc. Exp. Biol. Med.* **137**, 327.

Busuttil, R., Roh, B., and Fisher, J. W. (1972). *Acta Haematol.* **47**, 238.

Byron, J. W. (1970). *Nature (London)* **228**, 1204.

Byron, J. W. (1971). *Nature (London)* **234**, 39.

Caffrey Tyler, R. W., and Everett, N. B. (1966). *Blood* **28**, 873.

Calvo, W. (1968). *Amer. J. Anat.* **123**, 315.

Calvo, W., and Forteza-Vila, J. (1969). *Amer. J. Anat.* **126**, 355.

Camiscoli, J. F., and Gordon, A. S. (1970). *In* "Regulation of Hematopoiesis" (A. S. Gordon, ed.), pp. 369–393. Appleton, New York.

Camiscoli, J. F., Weintraub, A. H., and Gordon, A. S. (1968). *Ann. N. Y. Acad. Sci.* **149**, 40.

Camiscoli, J. F., LoBue, J., Gordon, A. S., Alexander, P., Schultz, E. F., and Weitz-Hamburger, A. (1972). *Cancer Res.* **32**, 2843.

Campbell, B. J., Schlueter, R. J., Weber, G. F., and White, W. F. (1961). *Biochim. Biophys. Acta* **46**, 279.

Cantor, L., Morris, A., Marks, P., and Rifkind, R. (1972). *Proc. Nat. Acad. Sci. U. S.* **69**, 1337.

Carmena, A., Howard, D., and Stohlman, F., Jr. (1968). *Blood* **32**, 376.

Chiba, S., Kung, C. K.-H., and Goldwasser, E. (1972). *Biochem. Biophys. Res. Commun.* **47**, 1372.

Chinard, F. P., Enns, T., and Nolan, M. F. (1964). *Amer. J. Physiol.* **207**, 128.

Chui, D. H. K., Djaldetti, M., Marks, P. A., and Rifkind, R. A. (1971). *J. Cell Biol.* **51**, 585.

Cohen, P., and Gardner, F. H. (1965). *J. Lab. Clin. Med.* **65**, 88.

Cole, R. J., and Paul, J. (1966). *J. Embryol. Exp. Morphol.* **15**, 245.

Cole, R. J., Hunter, J., and Paul, J. (1968). *Brit. J. Haematol.* **14**, 477.

Contrera, J. F., and Gordon, A. S. (1966). *Science* **152**, 653.

Contrera, J. F., Camiscoli, J. F., Weintraub, A. H., and Gordon, A. S. (1965). *Blood* **25**, 809.

Contrera, J. F., Gordon, A. S., and Weintraub, A. H. (1966). *Blood* **28**, 330.

Cooper, G. W., Zanjani, E. D., and Gordon, A. S. (1968). *Fed. Proc., Fed. Amer. Soc. Exp. Biol.* **27**, 383. (Abstr.)

Cooper, W. M., and Tuttle, W. B. (1957). *Ann. Intern. Med.* **47**, 1008.

Cotes, P. M. (1968). *Ann. N. Y. Acad. Sci.* **149**, 12.

Cotes, P. M. (1970). *In* "Kidney Hormones" (J. W. Fisher, ed.), pp. 243–267. Academic Press, New York.

Crafts, R. C., and Meineke, H. A. (1959). *Ann. N. Y. Acad. Sci.* **77**, 501.

Cuppage, F. E., and Tate, A. (1967). *Amer. J. Pathol.* **51**, 405.

de Franciscis, P., de Bella, G., and Cifaldi, S. (1965). *Science* **150**, 1831.

DeGowin, R. L., Hoak, J. C., and Miller, S. H. (1971). *Radiat. Res.* **48**, 495.

DeGowin, R. L., Hoak, J. C., and Miller, S. H. (1972). *Blood* **40**, 881.

Djaldetti, M., Chui, D., Marks, P. A., and Rifkind, R. A. (1970). *J. Mol. Biol.* **50**, 345.

Donati, R. M., Warnecke, M. A., and Gallagher, N. I. (1964). *Proc. Soc. Exp. Biol. Med.* **115**, 405.

Donati, R. M., Burgoignie, J. J., Kuhn, C., Gallagher, N. I., and Perry, H. M., Jr. (1968). *Circ. Res.* **22**, 91.

Dorado, M., Langton, A. A., Brandan, N. C., and Espada, J. (1972). *Biochem. Med.* **6**, 238.

Dukes, P. P. (1968). *Biochem. Biophys. Res. Commun.* **31**, 345.

Dukes, P. P. (1971). *Blood* **38**, 822. (Abstr.)

Dukes, P. P., and Goldwasser, E. (1961). *Endocrinology* **69**, 21.

Dukes, P. P., Hammond, D., Shore, N. A., and Ortega, J. A. (1970). *J. Lab. Clin. Med.* **76**, 439.

Dukes, P. P., Datta, M. C., Hammond, D., Ortega, J. A., and Shore, N. A. (1972). *15th Annu. Meet. Amer. Soc. Hematol.*, p. 100.

Ebert, P. S., Maestri, N. E., and Chirigos, M. (1972). *Cancer Res.* **32**, 41.

Edelman, R., and Hartroft, P. M. (1961). *Circ. Res.* **9**, 1069.

Erslev, A. J. (1958). *Arch. Intern. Med.* **101**, 407.

Erslev, A. J. (1959). *In* "The Kinetics of Cellular Proliferation" (F. Stohlman, Jr., ed.), pp. 312–317. Grune & Stratton, New York.

Erslev, A. J. (1962). *In* "Erythropoiesis" (L. O. Jacobson and M. Doyle, eds.), pp. 275–285. Grune & Stratton, New York.

Erslev, A. J. (1964). *Proc. Congr. Int. Soc. Hematol., 9th, Mexico City, 1962* **3**, 143.

Erslev, A. J. (1970). *Arch. Intern. Med.* **126**, 774.

Erslev, A. J. (1971). *J. Lab. Clin. Med.* **78**, 1.

Erslev, A. J., and Kazal, L. A. (1968). *Proc. Soc. Exp. Biol. Med.* **128**, 845.

Erslev, A. J., McKenna, P. J., Capelli, J. P., Hamburger, R. J., Cohn, H. E., and Clark, J. E. (1968). *Arch. Intern. Med.* **122**, 230.

Erslev, A. J., Kazal, L. A., Miller, O. P., and Abaidoo, K.-J. R. (1972). *In* "First International Conference on Hematopoiesis. Regulation of Erythropoiesis" (A. S. Gordon, M. Condorelli, and C. Peschle, eds.), pp. 217–224. Il Ponte, Milan.

Eschbach, J. W., Funk, D., Adamson, J., Kuhn, I., Scribner, B. H., and Finch, C. A. (1967). *New Engl. J. Med.* **276**, 653.

Espada, J., and Gutnisky, A. (1970a). *Acta Physiol. Lat. Amer.* **20**, 122.

Espada, J., and Gutnisky, A. (1970b). *Biochem. Med.* **3**, 475.

Espada, J., Langton, A. A., and Dorado, M. (1972). *Biochim. Biophys. Acta* **285**, 427.

Evans, E. S., Rosenberg, L. L., and Simpson, M. E. (1961). *Endocrinology* **68**, 517.

Faura, J., Ramos, J., Reynafarje, C., English, E., Finne, P., and Finch, C. A. (1969). *Blood* **33**, 668.

Feldman, S., Rachmilewitz, E. A., and Izak, G. (1966). *J. Lab. Clin. Med.* **67**, 713.

Feleppa, A. E., Jr., Meineke, H. A., and McCuskey, R. S. (1971). *Scand. J. Haematol.* **8**, 86.

Filmanowicz, E., and Gurney, C. W. (1961). *J. Lab. Clin. Med.* **57**, 65.

Finne, P. H. (1965). *Scand. J. Clin. Lab. Invest.* **17**, 135.

Finne, P. H. (1966). *Acta Paediat. Scand.* **55**, 478.

Fischer, S., and Roheim, P. S. (1963). *Nature (London)* **200**, 899.

Fisher, J. W. (1958). *Proc. Soc. Exp. Biol. Med.* **97**, 502.

Fisher, J. W. (1972). *Pharmacol. Rev.* **24**, 459.

Fisher, J. W., and Birdwell, B. J. (1961). *Acta Haematol.* **26**, 224.

Fisher, J. W., and Crook, J. J. (1962). *Blood* **19**, 557.

Fisher, J. W., and Langston, J. W. (1967). *Blood* **29**, 114.

Fisher, J. W., and Roh, B. L. (1970). *Blood* **36**, 847. (Abstr.)

Fisher, J. W., and Roh, B. L. (1971). *In* "Renal Pharmacology" (J. W. Fisher, ed.), pp. 167–196. Appleton, New York.

Fisher, J. W., Knight, D. B., and Couch, C. (1963). *J. Pharmacol. Exp. Ther.* **141**, 113.

Fisher, J. W., Taylor, G., and Porteous, D. D. (1965a). *Nature (London)* **205**, 611.

Fisher, J. W., Lajtha, L. G., Buttoo, A. S., and Porteous, D. D. (1965b). *Brit. J. Haematol.* **11**, 342.

Fisher, J. W., Roh, B. L., and Halvorsen, S. (1967a). *Proc. Soc. Exp. Biol. Med.* **126**, 97.

Fisher, J. W., Samuels, A. I., and Langston, J. W. (1967b). *J. Pharmacol. Exp. Ther.* **157**, 618.

Fisher, J. W., Hatch, F. E., Roh, B. L., Allen, R. C., and Kelley, B. J. (1968a). *Blood* **31**, 440.

Fisher, J. W., Samuels, A. I., and Langston, J. (1968b). *Ann. N. Y. Acad. Sci.* **149**, 308.

Fisher, J. W., Samuels, A. I., and Malgor, L. A. (1971a). *Isr. J. Med. Sci.* **7**, 892.

Fisher, J. W., Stuckey, W. J., Lindholm, D. D., and Abshire, S. (1971b). *Isr. J. Med. Sci.* **7**, 991.

Fisher, J. W., Thompson, J. F., and Espada, J. (1971c). *Isr. J. Med. Sci.* **7**, 873.

Fisher, J. W., Espada, J., Taylor, P., Lertora, J. J. L., and Roh, B. L. (1972). *In* "First International Conference on Hematopoiesis. Regulation of Erythropoiesis" (A. S. Gordon, M. Condorelli, and C. Peschle, eds.), pp. 122–131. Il Ponte, Milan.

Fogh, J. (1966). *Scand. J. Clin. Lab. Invest.* **18**, 33.

Forssell, J. (1954). *Acta Med. Scand.* **150**, 155.

Frenkel, E. P., Suki, W., and Baum, J. (1968). *Ann. N. Y. Acad. Sci.* **149**, 292.

Fried, W. (1972). *Blood* **40**, 671.

Fried, W., and Gurney, C. W. (1965). *Nature (London)* **206**, 1160.

Fried, W., Plzak, L., Jacobson, L. O., and Goldwasser, E. (1956). *Proc. Soc. Exp. Biol. Med.* **92**, 203.

Fried, W., Marver, D., Lange, R. D., and Gurney, C. W. (1966). *J. Lab. Clin. Med.* **68**, 947.

Fried, W., Kilbridge, T., Krantz, S., McDonald, T. P., and Lange, R. D. (1969). *J. Lab. Clin. Med.* **73**, 244.

Fried, W., Johnson, C., and Heller, P. (1970). *Blood* **36**, 607.

Fried, W., Gregory, S. A., Knospe, W. H., and Trobaugh, F. E., Jr. (1971a). *J. Lab. Clin. Med.* **78**, 449.

Fried, W., Knospe, W. H., and Trobaugh, F. E. (1971b). *Proc. Soc. Exp. Biol. Med.* **137**, 255.

Fruhman, G. J., Gerstner, R., and Gordon, A. S. (1954). *Proc. Soc. Exp. Biol. Med.* **85**, 93.

Gabuzda, T. G., Silver, R. K., Chenry Chui, L., and Lewis, H. B. (1970). *Brit. J. Haematol.* **19**, 621.

Gallagher, N. I., McCarthy, J. M., Hart, K. T., and Lange, R. D. (1959). *Blood* **14**, 662.

Gallien-Lartigue, O., and Goldwasser, E. (1964). *Science* **145**, 277.

Gallien-Lartigue, O., and Goldwasser, E. (1965). *Biochim. Biophys. Acta* **103**, 319.

Garcia, J. F. (1972). *In* "First International Conference on Hematopoiesis. Regulation of Erythropoiesis" (A. S. Gordon, M. Condorelli, and C. Peschle, eds.), pp. 132–155. Il Ponte, Milan.

Garcia, J. F., and Van Dyke, D. C. (1959). *J. Appl. Physiol.* **14**, 233.

Garcia, J. F., and Van Dyke, D. C. (1961). *Proc. Soc. Exp. Biol. Med.* **106**, 585.

Gardner, F. H. (1953). *J. Lab. Clin. Med.* **41**, 56.

Gidari, A. S., Zanjani, E. D., and Gordon, A. S. (1971). *Life Sci.* **10**, 895.

Gidari, A. S., Zanjani, E. D., Gordon, A. S., Carmichael, R. D., Stux, S. V., and Rappaport, I. A. (1972). *Proc. Soc. Exp. Biol. Med.* **141**, 59.

Glader, B. E., Rambach, W. A., and Alt, H. L. (1968). *Ann. N. Y. Acad. Sci.* **149**, 383.

Goldfarb, B., and Tobian, L. (1962). *Proc. Soc. Exp. Biol. Med.* **113**, 35.

Goldwasser, E. (1972). *In* "First International Conference on Hematopoiesis. Regulation of Erythropoiesis" (A. S. Gordon, M. Condorelli, and C. Peschle, eds.), pp. 227–235. Il Ponte, Milan.

Goldwasser, E., and Kung, C. K.-H. (1968). *Ann. N. Y. Acad. Sci.* **149**, 49.

Goldwasser, E., and Kung, C. K.-H. (1971). *Proc. Nat. Acad. Sci. U. S.* **68**, 697.

Goldwasser, E., and Kung, C. K.-H. (1972a). *In* "First International Conference on Hematopoiesis. Regulation of Erythropoiesis" (A. S. Gordon, M. Condorelli, and C. Peschle, eds.), pp. 159–166. Il Ponte, Milan.

Goldwasser, E., and Kung, C. K.-H. (1972b). *J. Biol. Chem.* **247**, 5159.

Goldwasser, E., Jacobson, L. O., Fried, W., and Plzak, L. (1958). *Blood* **13**, 55.

Goldwasser, E., White, W. F., and Taylor, K. B. (1962). *In* "Erythropoiesis" (L. O. Jacobson and M. Doyle, eds.), pp. 43–49. Grune & Stratton, New York.

Gordon, A. S. (1954). *Recent Progr. Horm. Res.* **10**, 339.

Gordon, A. S. (1959). *Physiol. Rev.* **39**, 1.

Gordon, A. S. (1968). *Proc. Congr. Int. Soc. Hematol., 12th, Plenary Sess. Sci. Contrib.*, pp. 288–303.

Gordon, A. S. (1971). *Brit. J. Haematol.* **21**, 611.

Gordon, A. S., and Weintraub, A. H. (1962). *In* "Erythropoiesis" (L. O. Jacobson and M. Doyle, eds.), pp. 1–16. Grune & Stratton, New York.

Gordon, A. S., and Zanjani, E. D. (1970a). *In* "Regulation of Hematopoiesis" (A. S. Gordon, ed.), pp. 413–457. Appleton, New York.

Gordon, A. S., and Zanjani, E. D. (1970b). *In* "Formation and Destruction of Blood Cells" (T. J. Greenwalt and G. A. Jamieson, eds.), pp. 34–64. Lippincott, Philadelphia, Pennsylvania.

Gordon, A. S., and Zanjani, E. D. (1970c). *In* "Hemopoietic Cellular Proliferation" (F. Stohlman, Jr., ed.), pp. 97–111. Grune & Stratton, New York.

Gordon, A. S., Kadow, P. C., Finkelstein, G., and Charipper, H. A. (1946). *Amer. J. Med. Sci.* **212**, 385.

Gordon, A. S., Piliero, S. J., and Landau, D. (1951). *Endocrinology* **49**, 497.

Gordon, A. S., Piliero, S. J., Freedman, H. H., and Kleinberg, W. (1954). *Proc. Soc. Exp. Biol. Med.* **86**, 255.

Gordon, A. S., Piliero, S. J., Tannenbaum, M., and Siegel, C. D. (1955). *Proc. Soc. Exp. Biol. Med.* **89**, 246.

Gordon, A. S., LoBue, J., Dornfest, B. S., and Cooper, G. W. (1962). *In* "Erythropoiesis" (L. O. Jacobson and M. Doyle, eds.), pp. 321–327. Grune & Stratton, New York.

Gordon, A. S., Katz, R., Zanjani, E. D., and Mirand, E. A. (1966). *Proc. Soc. Exp. Biol. Med.* **123**, 475.

Gordon, A. S., Mirand, E. A., and Zanjani, E. D. (1967a). *Endocrinology* **81**, 363.

Gordon, A. S., Zanjani, E. D., and Cooper, G. W. (1967b). *Semin. Hematol.* **4**, 337.

Gordon, A. S., Zanjani, E. D., Levere, R. D., and Kappas, A. (1970a). *Proc. Nat. Acad. Sci. U. S.* **65**, 919.

Gordon, A. S., Zanjani, E. D., and Zalusky, R. (1970b). *Blood* **35**, 151.

Gordon, A. S., Zanjani, E. D., and McLaurin, W. D. (1971). *In* "Renal Pharmacology" (J. W. Fisher, ed.), pp. 141–165. Appleton, New York.

Gordon, A. S., Zanjani, E. D., Peterson, E. N., Gidari, A. S., LoBue, J., and Camiscoli, J. (1972). *In* "First International Conference on Hematopoiesis. Regulation of Erythropoiesis" (A. S. Gordon, M. Condorelli, and C. Peschle, eds.), pp. 188–200. Il Ponte, Milan.

Gordon, A. S., Zanjani, E. D., Gidari, A. S., and Kuna, R. A. (1973). *In* "Humoral Control of Growth and Differentiation" (J. LoBue and A. S. Gordon, eds.). Academic Press, New York. In press.

Gorshein, D., and Gardner, F. H. (1970a). *Blood* **36**, 847. (Abstr.)

Gorshein, D., and Gardner, F. H. (1970b). *Proc. Nat. Acad. Sci. U. S.* **65**, 564.

Goudsmit, R., Kruger Dagneaux, P. G. L. C., and Krijnen, H. W. (1967). *Folia Med. Neer.* **10**, 39.

Graber, S. E., Carrillo, M., and Krantz, S. B. (1972). *Proc. Soc. Exp. Biol. Med.* **141**, 206.

Grant, W. C. (1951). *Amer. J. Physiol.* **164**, 226.

Gross, M., and Goldwasser, E. (1969). *Biochemistry* **8**, 1795.

Gross, M., and Goldwasser, E. (1970a). *Biochim. Biophys. Acta* **217**, 461.

Gross, M., and Goldwasser, E. (1970b). *J. Biol. Chem.* **245**, 1632.

Gross, M., and Goldwasser, E. (1971). *J. Biol. Chem.* **246**, 2480.

Gurney, C. W., Goldwasser, E., and Pan, C. (1957a). *J. Lab. Clin. Med.* **50**, 534.

Gurney, C. W., Pierce, M. I., Schrier, S. E., Carson, P. E., and Jacobson, L. O. (1957b). *J. Lab. Clin. Med.* **50**, 821.

Gutnisky, A., Barrios, L., and Malgor, L. A. (1971). *Acta Physiol. Lat. Amer.* **21**, 51.

Halvorsen, S. (1963). *Acta Paediat. Scand.* **52**, 425.

Halvorsen, S. (1968). *Ann. N. Y. Acad. Sci.* **149**, 84.

Halvorsen, S., and Finne, P. H. (1963). *Brit. Med. J.* **1**, 1132.

Halvorsen, S., White, R. P., Roh, B. L., and Fisher, J. W. (1972). *In* "First International Conference on Hematopoiesis. Regulation of Erythropoiesis" (A. S. Gordon, M. Condorelli, and C. Peschle, eds.), pp. 247–257. Il Ponte, Milan.

Hammond, D., and Ishikawa, A. (1962). *In* "Erythropoiesis" (L. O. Jacobson and M. Doyle, eds.), pp. 128–133. Grune & Stratton, New York.

Hammond, D., Ishikawa, A., and Keighley, G. (1962). *In* "Erythropoiesis" (L. Jacobson and M. Doyle, eds.), pp. 351–358. Grune & Stratton, New York.

Hansen, P. (1964). *Acta Pathol. Microbiol. Scand.* **60**, 465.

Hasegawa, M., Matsuki, Y., Ozawa, S., and Ando, Y. (1968). *Keio J. Med.* **17**, 109.

Hirashima, K., and Takaku, F. (1962). *Blood* **20**, 1.

Hodgson, G. (1970). *In* "Regulation of Hematopoiesis" (A. S. Gordon, ed.), pp. 459–469. Appleton, New York.

Hrinda, M. E., and Goldwasser, E. (1969). *Biochim. Biophys. Acta* **195**, 165.

Huff, R. L., Hennessy, T. G., Austin, R. C., Garcia, J. F., Roberts, B. M., and Lawrence, J. H. (1950). *J. Clin. Invest.* **29**, 1041.

Hurst, J. M., Turner, M. S., Yoffey, J. M., and Lajtha, L. G. (1969). *Blood* **23**, 859.

Itami, S. (1908). *Arch. Exp. Pathol. Pharmakol.* **62**, 93, 104.

Itskovitz, H. D., and Odya, C. (1971). *Science* **174**, 58.

Izak, G., and Karsai, A. (1972). *Blood* **39**, 814.

Jacobsen, E. M., Davis, A. K., and Alpen, E. L. (1956). *Blood* **11**, 937.

Jacobson, L. O., Goldwasser, E., Fried, W., and Plzak, L. (1957). *Nature (London)* **179**, 633.

Jacobson, L. O., Goldwasser, E., Gurney, C. W., Fried, W., and Plzak, L. (1959a). *Ann. N. Y. Acad. Sci.* **77**, 551.

Jacobson, L. O., Marks, E. K., Gaston, E. D., and Goldwasser, E. (1959b). *Blood* **14**, 635.

Jepson, J. H., and Friesen, H. G. (1968). *Brit. J. Haematol.* **15**, 465.

Jepson, J. H., and Lowenstein, L. (1966). *Proc. Soc. Exp. Biol. Med.* **123**, 457.

Jepson, J. H., and Lowenstein, L. (1967). *Acta Haematol.* **38**, 292.

Jepson, J., and Lowenstein, L. (1968a). *Brit. J. Haematol.* **14**, 555.

Jepson, J. H., and Lowenstein, L. (1968b). *Can. Med. Ass. J.* **99**, 99.

Jepson, J. H., McGarry, E. E., and Lowenstein, L. (1968). *Arch. Intern. Med.* **122**, 265.

Kaley, G., and Demopoulos, H. B. (1963). *Fed. Proc., Fed. Amer. Soc. Exp. Biol.* **22**, 664. (Abstr.)

Kaplan, S., Rothmann, S. A., Gordon, A. S., Rappaport, I. A., Camiscoli, J. F., and Peschle, C. (1973). *Proc. Soc. Exp. Biol. Med.* **143**, 310.

Kappas, A., Song, C. S., Levere, R. D., Sachson, R. A., and Granick, S. (1968). *Proc. Nat. Acad. Sci. U. S.* **61**, 509.

Katz, R., Cooper, G. W., Gordon, A. S., and Zanjani, E. D. (1968). *Ann. N. Y. Acad. Sci.* **149**, 120.

Keighley, G. (1962). *In* "Erythropoiesis" (L. O. Jacobson and M. Doyle, eds.), pp. 106–110. Grune & Stratton, New York.

Keighley, G. H., Russell, E. S., and Lowy, P. (1962). *Brit. J. Haematol.* **8**, 429.

Keighley, G., Hammond, D., and Lowy, P. H. (1964). *Blood* **23**, 99.

Kochakian, C. D., and Harrison, D. G. (1962). *Endocrinology* **70**, 99.

Konrad, C. G. (1963). *J. Cell Biol.* **19**, 267.

Kontras, S. B., and Romshe, C. (1967). *Amer. J. Dis. Child.,* **113**, 473.

Krantz, S. B. (1968). *J. Lab. Clin. Med.* **71**, 999.

Krantz, S. B. (1972). *Blood* **39**, 347.

Krantz, S. B., and Jacobson, L. O. (1970). "Erythropoietin and the Regulation of Erythropoiesis," 330 pp. Univ. of Chicago Press, Chicago, Illinois.

Krantz, S. B., and Kao, V. (1967). *Proc. Nat. Acad. Sci. U. S.* **58**, 493.

Krantz, S. B., and Kao, V. (1969). *Blood* **34**, 1.

Krantz, S. B., Gallien-Lartigue, O., and Goldwasser, E. (1963). *J. Biol. Chem.* **238**, 4085.

Kretchmar, A. L. (1966). *Science* **152**, 367.

Kuratowska, Z. (1968). *Ann. N. Y. Acad. Sci.* **149**, 128.

Kuratowska, Z. (1970). *Pol. Acad. Sci., Ann. Med. Sect.* **15**, 189.

Kuratowska, S., and Kopeć, M. (1969). *Brit. J. Haematol.* **16**, 465.

Kuratowska, Z., Lewartowski, B., and Michalak, E. (1961). *Blood* **18**, 527.

Kuratowska, Z., Lewartowski, B., and Lipinski, B. (1964). *J. Lab. Clin. Med.* **64**, 226.

Labardini, J., Sanchez-Medal, L., Arriaga, L., Lopez, D., and Smythe, J. F. (1968). *J. Lab. Clin. Med.* **72**, 419.

La Bella, F. S., Reiffenstein, R. J., and Beaulieu, G. (1963). *Arch. Biochem. Biophys.* **100**, 399.

Lajtha, L. G., Gilbert, C. W., and Guzman, E. (1971). *Brit. J. Haematol.* **20**, 343.

Lamerton, L. F. (1970). *Proc. Int. Congr. Hematol., 13th, Plenary Sess. Sci. Contrib.,* pp. 132–137.

Lange, R. D. (1971). *In* "Kidney Hormones" (J. W. Fisher, ed.), pp. 373–396. Academic Press, New York.

Lange, R. D., Simmons, M. L., and Dibelius, N. R. (1966). *Proc. Soc. Exp. Biol. Med.* **122,** 761.

Lange, R. D., McDonald, T. P., and Jordan, T. (1969). *J. Lab. Clin. Med.* **73,** 78.

Lange, R. D., Jordan, T. A., Ichiki, A. T., and Chernoff, A. I. (1972). *In* "First International Conference on Hematopoiesis. Regulation of Erythropoiesis" (A. S. Gordon, M. Condorelli, and C. Peschle, eds.), pp. 107–121. Il Ponte, Milan.

Leaders, F. E., Werder, A. A., and Schmidt, C. (1964). *Proc. Soc. Exp. Biol. Med.* **115,** 658.

Leaders, F. E., Chapman, A. L., Kornhaus, B., Nielsen, A. H., and Werder, A. A. (1967). *Int. J. Cancer* **2,** 365.

Leonhardt, K. O., and Landes, R. R. (1963). *New Engl. J. Med.* **269,** 115.

Levere, R. D., and Granick, S. (1965). *Proc. Nat. Acad. Sci. U. S.* **54,** 134.

Levere, R. D., Kappas, A., and Granick, S. (1967). *Proc. Nat. Acad. Sci. U. S.* **58,** 985.

Lewis, J. P., Alford, D. A., Moores, R. R., Gardner, E., Jr., Wright, C.-S., Smith, L. L., Scharnitzky, W. A., and Neal, W. A. (1969). *J. Lab. Clin. Med.* **73,** 154.

Linman, J. W., and Pierre, R. V. (1968). *Ann. N. Y. Acad. Sci.* **149,** 25.

Liotti, F. S., Giovanni, E., and Bruschelli, G. M. (1972). *Riv. Biol.* **65,** 33.

Loge, J. P., Lange, R. D., and Moore, C. V. (1950). *J. Clin. Invest.* **29,** 830.

Lowy, P. H. (1970). *In* "Regulation of Hematopoiesis" (A. S. Gordon, ed.), pp. 395–412. Appleton, New York.

Lowy, P. H., and Keighley, G. (1961). *Nature (London)* **192,** 75.

Lowy, P. H., and Keighley, G. (1968). *Ann. N. Y. Acad. Sci.* **149,** 54.

Lowy, P. H., Keighley, G., Borsook, H., and Graybiel, A. (1959). *Blood* **14,** 262.

Lowy, P. H., Keighley, G., and Cohen, N. S. (1970). *Brit. J. Haematol.* **19,** 711.

Lucarelli, G., Ferrari, L., Rizzoli, V., Porcellini, A., Carnevali, C., Monica, C., Tanzi, B., and Butturini, V. (1966). *Biochim. Biol. Sper.* **5** 475.

Lucarelli, G., Porcellini, A., Carnevali, C., Carmena, A., and Stohlman, F., Jr. (1968). *Ann. N. Y. Acad. Sci.* **149,** 544.

Lugliani, R., Whipp, B. J., Winter, B., Tanaka, K. R., and Wasserman, K. (1971). *New Engl. J. Med.* **285,** 1112.

McClugage, S. G., McCuskey, R. S., and Meineke, H. A. (1971). *Blood* **38,** 96.

McCulloch, E. A. (1970). *In* "Regulation of Hematopoiesis" (A. S. Gordon, ed.), pp. 132–158. Appleton, New York.

McCuskey, R. S., and Meineke, H. A. (1973). *Amer. J. Anat.* **137,** 187.

McCuskey, R. S., Meineke, H. A., and Townsend, S. F. (1972a). *Blood* **39,** 697.

McCuskey, R. S., Meineke, H. A., and Kaplan, S. M. (1972b). *Blood* **39,** 809.

McDonald, T. P., Martin, D. H., Simmons, M. L., and Lange, R. D. (1969). *Life Sci.* **8,** 949.

McDonald, T. P., Lange, R. D., Congdon, C. C., and Toya, R. E. (1970). *Radiat. Res.* **42,** 151.

McDonald, T. P., Mitchell, T. J., and Lange, R. D. (1971a). *Isr. J. Med. Sci.* **7,** 885.

McDonald, T. P., Zanjani, E. D., Lange, R. D., and Gordon, A. S. (1971b). *Brit. J. Haematol.* **20,** 113.

Mann, D. L., Donati, R. M., and Gallagher, N. I. (1966). *Proc. Soc. Exp. Biol. Med.* **121,** 1152.

Marks, P. A., and Rifkind, R. A. (1972). *Science* **175,** 955.

Medado, P., Izak, G., and Feldman, S. (1967). *J. Lab. Clin. Med.* **69,** 776.

Medici, P. T., Gordon, A. S., Piliero, S. J., Luhby, A. L., and Yuceoglu, P. (1957). *Acta Haematol.* **18,** 325.

Meineke, H. A., and Crafts, R. C. (1968). *Ann. N. Y. Acad. Sci.* **149,** 208.

Melman, K., and Rosen, S. (1964). *Amer. J. Med.* **36,** 595.

Miller, M. E., Rörth, M., Parving, H., Howard, D., Reddington, I., Valeri, C. R., and Stohlman, F., Jr. (1973). *New Engl. J. Med.* **288,** 706.

Mirand, E. A. (1965). *Invest. Urol.* **2,** 579.

Mirand, E. A. (1968). *Ann. N. Y. Acad. Sci.* **149,** 94.

Mirand, E. A. (1970). *In* "Regulation of Hematopoiesis" (A. S. Gordon, ed.), pp. 635–647. Appleton, New York.

Mirand, E. A., and Gordon, A. S. (1966). *Endocrinology* **78,** 235.

Mirand, E. A., and Murphy, G. P. (1970). *In* "Regulation of Hematopoiesis" (A. S. Gordon, ed.), pp. 495–518. Appleton, New York.

Mirand, E. A., and Murphy, G. P. (1971a). *J. Med.* **2,** 192.

Mirand, E. A., and Murphy, G. P. (1971b). *N. Y. State J. Med.* **71,** 860.

Mirand, E. A., Prentice, T. C., and Slaunwhite, W. R. (1959). *Ann. N. Y. Acad. Sci.* **77,** 677.

Mirand, E. A., Gordon, A. S., and Wenig, J. (1965a). *Nature* (*London*) **206,** 270.

Mirand, E. A., Weintraub, A. H., Gordon, A. S., Prentice, T. C., and Grace, J. T., Jr. (1965b). *Proc. Soc. Exp. Biol. Med.* **118,** 823.

Mirand, E. A., Murphy, G., and Bernardis, L. (1967). *Experientia* **23,** 577.

Mirand, E. A., Murphy, G. P., Steeves, R. A., Weber, H. W., and Retief, F. P. (1968). *Acta Haematol.* **39,** 359.

Mirand, E. A., Gordon, A. S., Zanjani, E. D., Bennett, T. E., and Murphy, G. P. (1972). *Proc. Soc. Exp. Biol. Med.* **139,** 161.

Miyakawa, M., Uno, Y., and Asai, J. (1965). "The Reticuloendothelial System, Morphology, Immunology and Regulation," p. 132. Nissha, Kyoto.

Mizoguchi, H., and Levere, R. D. (1971). *J. Exp. Med.* **134,** 1501.

Mizoguchi, H., and Levere, R. D. (1972). *Proc. Soc. Exp. Biol. Med.* **141,** 310.

Moffatt, D. J., Rosse, C., and Yoffey, J. M. (1967). *Lancet* **ii,** 547.

Morley, A., Quesenberry, P., Garrity, M., and Stohlman, F., Jr. (1971). *Proc. Soc. Exp. Biol. Med.* **138,** 57.

Morrison, J. H., and Toepfer, J. R. (1967). *Amer. J. Physiol.* **213,** 923.

Muirhead, E. E., Leache, B. E., Fisher, J. W., and Kosinski, M. (1968). *Ann. N. Y. Acad. Sci.* **149,** 135.

Murphy, M. J., Jr., Bertles, J. F., and Gordon, A. S. (1971). *J. Cell Sci.* **9,** 23.

Naets, J. P. (1958). *Nature* (*London*) **181,** 1134.

Naets, J. P. (1960a). *Acta Clin. Belg.* **15,** 361.

Naets, J. P. (1960b). *J. Clin. Invest.* **39,** 102.

Naets, J. P. (1963). *In* "Hormones and the Kidney" (P. C. Williams, ed.), pp. 175–186. Academic Press, New York.

Naets, J. P., and Heuse, A. (1962). *J. Lab. Clin. Med.* **60,** 365.

Naets, J. P., and Wittek, M. (1968a). *Blood* **31,** 249.

Naets, J. P., and Wittek, M. (1968b). *Acta Haematol.* **39,** 42.

Naets, J. P., and Wittek, M. (1969). *Amer. J. Physiol.* **217,** 297.

Naets, J. P., and Wittek, M. (1971). *Experientia* **27,** 1468.

Nakao, K., Shirakura, T., Azuma, M., and Maekawa, T. (1962). *Blood* **29,** 754.

Nakao, K., Sassa, S., Wada, O., and Takaku, F. (1968). *Ann. N. Y. Acad. Sci.* **149**, 224.

Nakao, K., Takaku, F., Miura, Y., and Chiba, S. (1971). *In* "The Regulation of Erythropoiesis and Hemoglobin Synthesis" (T. Travnicek and J. Neuwirt, eds.), pp. 65–70. Univ. Karlova, Prague.

Necheles, T. F., and Rai, U. S. (1969). *Blood* **34**, 380.

Necheles, T. F., Sheehan, R. G., and Meyer, H. J. (1968). *Ann. N. Y. Acad. Sci.* **149**, 449.

Nicol, A. G., Conkie, D., Lanyon, W. G., Drewienkiewicz, C. E., Williamson, R., and Paul, J. (1972). *Biochim. Biophys. Acta* **277**, 342.

Niewisch, H., Vogel, H., and Matioli, G. (1967). *Proc. Nat. Acad. Sci. U. S.* **58**, 2261.

Noveck, R. J., and Fisher, J. W. (1971). *Proc. Soc. Exp. Biol. Med.* **138**, 103.

Okamura, H., Udupa, K. B., and Reissmann, K. R. (1971). *Proc. Soc. Exp. Biol. Med.* **136**, 794.

OKunewick, J. P., and Fulton, D. (1970). *Blood* **36**, 239.

Orlic, D., Gordon, A. S., and Rhodin, J. A. G. (1965). *J. Ultrastruct. Res.* **13**, 516.

Orlic, D., Gordon, A. S., and Rhodin, J. A. G. (1968). *Ann. N. Y. Acad. Sci.* **149**, 198.

Ortega, J. A., and Dukes, P. P. (1970). *Biochim. Biophys. Acta* **204**, 334.

Osnes, S. (1958). *Brit. Med. J.* **ii**, 1387.

Ozawa, S. (1967). *Keio J. Med.* **16**, 193.

Pappenheimer, J. R., and Kinter, W. (1956). *Amer. J. Physiol.* **185**, 377.

Paran, M., and Sachs, L. (1968). *J. Cell. Physiol.* **72**, 247.

Paul, J., and Hunter, J. A. (1969). *J. Mol. Biol.* **42**, 31.

Paul, J., Conkie, D., and Freshney, R. I. (1969). *Cell Tissue Kinet.* **2**, 283.

Paul, J., Freshney, I., Conkie, D., and Burgos, H. (1972). *In* "First International Conference on Hematopoiesis. Regulation of Erythropoiesis" (A. S. Gordon, M. Condorelli, and C. Peschle, eds.), pp. 236–244. Il Ponte, Milan.

Paulo, L. G., Roh, B. L., and Fisher, J. W. (1972a). *In* "First International Conference on Hematopoiesis. Regulation of Erythropoiesis" (A. S. Gordon, M. Condorelli, and C. Peschle, eds.), pp. 258–266. Il Ponte, Milan.

Paulo, L. G., Fink, G. D., Roh, B. L., and Fisher, J. W. (1972b). *Proc. Soc. Exp. Biol. Med.* **141**, 806.

Paulo, L. G., Wilkerson, R. D., Roh, B. L., George, W. J., and Fisher, J. W. (1973). *Proc. Soc. Exp. Biol. Med.* **142**, 771.

Pavlovic-Kentera, V., Hall, D. P., Bragassa, C., and Lange, R. D. (1965). *J. Lab. Clin. Med.* **65**, 577.

Perris, A. D., MacManus, J. P., Whitfield, J. F., and Weiss, L. A. (1971). *Amer. J. Physiol.* **220**, 773.

Peschle, C., Sasso, G. F., Mastroberardino, G., and Condorelli, M. (1971a). *J. Lab. Clin. Med.* **78**, 20.

Peschle, C., Sasso, G. F., Rossanigo, F., Mastroberardino, G., and Lipparini, F. (1971b). *Riv. Med. Aeronaut. Spaz.* **34**, 24.

Peschle, C., Zanjani, E. D., Gidari, A. S., McLaurin, W. D., and Gordon, A. S. (1971c). *Endocrinology* **89**, 609.

Peschle, C., Rappaport, I. A., Sasso, G. F., Gordon, A. S., and Condorelli, M. (1972a). *Endocrinology* **91**, 511.

Peschle, C., Sasso, G. F., Rappaport, I. A., and Condorelli, M. (1972b). *J. Lab. Clin. Med.* **79**, 950.

Peschle, C., Sasso, G. F., Rappaport, I. A., Rossanigo, F., Gordon, A. S., and

Condorelli, M. (1972c). In "First International Conference on Hematopoiesis. Regulation of Erythropoiesis" (A. S. Gordon, M. Condorelli, and C. Peschle, eds.), pp. 269–301. Il Ponte, Milan.

Peschle, C., Zanjani, E. D., Sasso, G. F., Rappaport, I. A., Gordon, A. S., and Condorelli, M. (1972d). Scand. J. Haematol. 9, 442.

Peschle, C., Rappaport, I. A., Sasso, G. F., Condorelli, M., and Gordon, A. S. (1973). Endocrinology 92, 358.

Peterson, E. A., and Evans, W. H. (1967). Nature (London) 214, 824.

Piliero, S. J., Medici, P. T., and Gordon, A. S. (1960). Proc. Int. Congr. Int. Soc. Hematol., 7th, Rome, 1958 2, 1.

Pluznik, D. H., and Sachs, L. (1965). J. Cell. Comp. Physiol. 66, 319.

Plzak, L. F., Fried, W., Jacobson, L. O., and Bethard, W. (1955). J. Lab. Clin. Med. 46, 671.

Powsner, E., and Berman, L. (1967). Life Sci. 6, 1713.

Rambach, W. A., Cooper, J. A. D., and Alt, H. L. (1956). J. Lab. Clin. Med. 48, 933.

Rambach, W. A., Alt, H. L., and Cooper, J. A. D. (1957). Blood 12, 1101.

Reisner, E. H., Jr. (1966). Blood 27, 460.

Reissmann, K. R. (1964). Blood 23, 137.

Reissmann, K. R., and Nomura, T. (1962). In "Erythropoiesis" (L. O. Jacobson and M. Doyle, eds.), pp. 71–77. Grune & Stratton, New York.

Reissmann, K. R., and Samorapoompichit, S. (1969). J. Lab. Clin. Med. 73, 544.

Reissmann, K. R., and Samorapoompichit, S. (1970). Blood 36, 287.

Reissmann, K. R., Nomura, T., Gunn, R. W., and Brosius, F. (1960). Blood 16, 1411.

Reissmann, K. R., Diederich, D. A., Ito, K., and Schmaus, J. W. (1965). J. Lab. Clin. Med. 65, 967.

Rifkind, R. A., Chui, D., Djaldetti, M., and Marks, P. A. (1969). Trans. Ass. Amer. Physicians 82, 380.

Robertson, A. L., Jr., Smeby, R. D., Bumpus, F. M., and Page, I. H. (1966). Circ. Res. 23/24, 1.

Rodgers, G. M., George, W. J., and Fisher, J. W. (1971). Pharmacologist 13, 287.

Rodgers, G. M., George, W. J., and Fisher, J. W. (1972). Proc. Soc. Exp. Biol. Med. 140, 977.

Roh, B. L., Paulo, L. G., and Fisher, J. W. (1972a). Amer. J. Physiol. 223, 1345.

Roh, B. L., Paulo, L. G., Thompson, J., and Fisher, J. W. (1972b). Proc. Soc. Exp. Med. 141, 268.

Rosse, W. F., and Waldmann, T. A. (1964a). Blood 24, 739.

Rosse, W. F., and Waldmann, T. A. (1964b). J. Clin. Invest. 43, 1348.

Rosse, W. F., Waldmann, T. A., and Houston, D. E. (1962). Proc. Soc. Exp. Biol. Med. 109, 836.

Safdar, S. H., Krantz, S. B., and Brown, E. B. (1970). Brit. J. Haematol. 19, 435.

Sanchez-Medal, L., Labardini, J., and Loria, A. (1963). Blood 21, 586.

Sanchez-Medal, L., Duarte, L., and Labardini, J. (1970). Blood 35, 721.

Schally, A. V., Arimura, A., and Kastin, A. J. (1973). Science 179, 341.

Schooley, J. C. (1965). Blood 25, 795.

Schooley, J. C. (1966). Proc. Soc. Exp. Biol. Med. 122, 402.

Schooley, J. C., and Garcia, J. F. (1962). Proc. Soc. Exp. Biol. Med. 109, 325.

Schooley, J. C., and Mahlmann, L. J. (1971a). Proc. Soc. Exp. Biol. Med. 137, 1289.

Schooley, J. C., and Mahlmann, L. J. (1971b). Proc. Soc. Exp. Biol. Med. 138, 523.

Schooley, J. C., and Mahlmann, L. J. (1972a). In "First International Conference on Hematopoiesis. Regulation of Erythropoiesis" (A. S. Gordon, M. Condorelli, and C. Peschle, eds.), pp. 167–179. Il Ponte, Milan.

Schooley, J. C., and Mahlmann, L. J. (1972b). Blood 39, 31.

Schooley, J. C., and Mahlmann, L. J. (1972c). Blood 40, 662.

Schooley, J. C., Zanjani, E. D., and Gordon, A. S. (1970). Blood 35, 276.

Schulhof, K., and Mathies, M. M. (1927). J. Amer. Med. Ass. 89, 2093.

Segal, R., Izak, G., and Feldman, S. (1971). Isr. J. Med. Sci. 7, 1017.

Seip, M., Halvorsen, S., Andersen, P., and Kaada, B. R. (1961). J. Clin. Lab. Invest. 13, 553.

Shalet, M., Coe, D., and Reissmann, K. R. (1966). Proc. Soc. Exp. Biol. Med. 123, 443.

Shaw, D. B., and Simpson, T. (1961). Quart. J. Med. 54, 135.

Sherwood, J. B., Robinson, S. H., Bassan, L. R., Rosen, S., and Gordon, A. S. (1972). Blood 40, 189.

Skinner, S. L., McCubbin, J. W., and Page, I. H. (1963). Science 141, 814.

Smith, R. J., and Contrera, J. F. (1972). Proc. Soc. Exp. Biol. Med. 141, 895.

Stephenson, J. R., and Axelrad, A. A. (1971a). Endocrinology 88, 1519.

Stephenson, J. R., and Axelrad, A. A. (1971b). Blood 37, 417.

Stephenson, J. R., Axelrad, A. A., McLeod, D. L., and Shreeve, M. M. (1971). Proc. Nat. Acad. Sci. U. S. 68, 1542.

Stohlman, F., Jr. (1959). Ann. N. Y. Acad. Sci. 77, 710.

Stohlman, F., Jr., and Brecher, G. (1959). Proc. Soc. Exp. Biol. Med. 100, 40.

Stohlman, F., Jr., Ebbe, S., Morse, B. S., Howard, D., and Donovan, J. (1968). Ann. N. Y. Acad. Sci. 149, 156.

Stroebel, C. F., and Fowler, W. S. (1956). Med. Clin. N. Amer. 40, 1061.

Sugiyama, T. (1971). Proc. Nat. Acad. Sci. U. S. 68, 2761.

Sutherland, E. W. (1972). Science 177, 401.

Szalay, K. S., and Gyevac, A. (1967). Life Sci. 6, 925.

Takaku, F., Hirashima, K., and Nakao, K. (1962). J. Lab. Clin. Med. 59, 815.

Takaku, F., Dukes, P. P., and Goldwasser, E. (1964). Endocrinology 74, 968.

Teruel, J. E., and Scaro, J. L. (1971). Acta Physiol. Lat. Amer. 21, 346.

Teruel, J. E., Guidi, E. E., and Scaro, J. L. (1971). Rev. Espan. Fisiol. 27, 83.

Thorbecke, G. J., and Benacerraf, B. (1959). Ann. N. Y. Acad. Sci. 78, 247.

Thorling, E. B. (1972). Scand. J. Haematol., Suppl. 17, 1–166.

Thorling, E. B., and Erslev, A. J. (1972). Brit. J. Haematol. 23, 483.

Thurmon, T. F., Boyer, S. H., Crosby, E. F., Shepard, M. K., Noyes, A. N., and Stohlman, F., Jr. (1970). Blood 36, 598.

Tramezzani, J. H., Morita, E., and Chiocchio, S. R. (1971). Proc. Nat. Acad. Sci. U. S. 68, 52.

Trentin, J. J. (1970). In "Regulation of Hematopoiesis" (A. S. Gordon, ed.), pp. 159–186. Appleton, New York.

Turner, R. W. A., Siminovitch, L., McCulloch, E. A., and Till, J. E. (1967). J. Cell. Physiol. 69, 73.

Van Dyke, D. C., Nohr, L. M., and Lawrence, J. H. (1966). Blood 28, 535.

Van Dyke, D. C., Pollycove, M., and Lawrence, J. H. (1967). Semiannu. Rep. Biol. Med., Donner Lab., Berkeley, Calif., pp. 127–132.

Vittorio, P. V., and Amey, E. A. (1970). Radiat. Res. 44, 434.

Vollmer, E. P., and Gordon, A. S. (1941). Endocrinology 29, 828.

Vollmer, E. P., Gordon, A. S., and Charipper, H. A. (1942). Endocrinology 31, 619.

Wade, J. G., Larson, C. P., Jr., Hickey, R. F., Ehrenfeld, W. K., and Severinghaus, J. W. (1970). *New Engl. J. Med.* **282,** 823.

Wang, F., and Fried, W. (1972). *J. Lab. Clin. Med.* **79,** 181.

Ward, H. P. (1967). *Proc. Soc. Exp. Biol. Med.* **125,** 370.

Ward, H. P., Gordon, B., and Pickett, J. C. (1969). *J. Lab. Clin. Med.* **74,** 93.

Weintraub, A. H., Gordon, A. S., Becker, E. L., Camiscoli, J. F., and Contrera, J. F. (1964). *Amer. J. Physiol.* **207,** 523.

White, W. F., Gurney, C. W., Goldwasser, E., and Jacobson, L. O. (1960). *Recent Progr. Horm. Res.* **16,** 219.

Winkert, J., and Birchette, C. (1969). *12th Annu. Meet. Amer. Soc. Hematol.,* p. 103.

Winkert, J., and Gordon, A. S. (1960). *Biochim. Biophys. Acta* **42,** 170.

Winkert, J., Gordon, A. S., Medici, P. T., Piliero, S. J., Luhby, A. L., and Tannenbaum, M. (1958). *Proc. Soc. Exp. Biol. Med.* **97,** 191.

Winkert, J., Birchette, C., and Wilson, M. (1971). *Res. Commun. Chem. Pathol. Pharmacol.* **2,** 323.

Yoffey, J. M. (1966). "Bone Marrow Reactions," pp. 1–152. Arnold, London.

Zanjani, E. D., and Gordon, A. S. (1971). *Isr. J. Med. Sci.* **7,** 850.

Zanjani, E. D., Contrera, J. F., Cooper, G. W., Wong, K. K., and Gordon, A. S. (1967a). *Proc. Soc. Exp. Biol. Med.* **125,** 505.

Zanjani, E. D., Contrera, J. F., Cooper, G. W., Gordon, A. S., Wong, K. K., and Katz, R. (1967b). *Science* **156,** 1367.

Zanjani, E. D., Cooper, G. W., Gordon, A. S., Wong, K. K., and Scribner, V. A. (1967c). *Proc. Soc. Exp. Biol. Med.* **126,** 540.

Zanjani, E. D., Schooley, J. C., and Gordon, A. S. (1968a). *Life Sci.* **7,** 505.

Zanjani, E. D., Gordon, A. S., Wong, K. K., and McLaurin, W. D. (1968b). *Life Sci.* **7,** 1233.

Zanjani, E. D., Gordon, A. S., Wong, K. K., and McLaurin, W. D. (1969a). *Proc. Soc. Exp. Biol. Med.* **131,** 1095.

Zanjani, E. D., Horger, E. O., III, Gordon, A. S., Cantor, L. N., and Hutchinson, D. L. (1969b). *J. Lab. Clin. Med.* **74,** 782.

Zanjani, E. D., McLaurin, W. D., Gordon, A. S., Rappaport, I. A., Gibbs, J., and Gidari, A. S. (1971). *J. Lab. Clin. Med.* **77,** 751.

Zanjani, E. D., Zalusky, R., and Wasserman, L. R. (1972a). *Clin. Res.* **20,** 878. (Abstr.)

Zanjani, E. D., Zalusky, R., Ross, J., and Wasserman, L. R. (1972b). *Blood* **40,** 967. (Abstr.)

Zanjani, E. D., Gidari, A. S., Peterson, E. N., Gordon, A. S., and Wasserman, L. R. (1973). *In* "Fetal and Neonatal Physiology" (K. S. Comline, K. W. Cross, and P. W. Nathanielsz, eds.), pp. 448–455. Cambridge Univ. Press, Cambridge, England.

Zivny, J., Neuwirt, J., and Borova, J. (1972a). *J. Lab. Clin. Med.* **80,** 217.

Zivny, J., Kolc, J., Neuwirt, J., and Malek, P. (1972b). *Blut* **24,** 174.

Immunology of Gonadal Steroids

MICHEL FERIN, SAM M. BEISER* AND
RAYMOND L. VANDE WIELE

*Departments of Obstetrics and Gynecology, and Microbiology, and the
International Institute for the Study of Human Reproduction,
Columbia University College of Physicians and Surgeons, New York, New York*

I. Introduction

Antibodies against steroids can be elicited by the administration of conjugates in which the steroids or their derivatives are coupled covalently to proteins or polypeptides (Landsteiner, 1945; Lieberman et al., 1959). Different types of procedure for the preparation of these steroid–protein conjugates are shown in Table I. A general description of the methods in use can be found in reviews by Beiser et al. (1968) and by Westphal (1971). Specific details for the preparation and characterization of steroid–protein conjugates are available in the articles of Erlanger et al. (1957, 1959), Goodfriend and Sehon (1958, 1961a), and Gross et al. (1968). Most frequently, the immunogen consists of the steroid coupled to a heterologous protein (a protein foreign to the species being immunized). It is of interest, however, that steroid hormones coupled to homologous proteins also elicit steroid-specific antibodies. In biological studies, the use of such conjugates as immunizing agents decreases the chance of complications due to anaphylaxis. The most commonly used carrier proteins have been: serum albumin of human (HSA), bovine (BSA), or rabbit (RSA) origin, although other proteins such as keyhole limpet hemocyanin (KHL) have been used (Gross et al., 1968). An azo

---

* Deceased September 7, 1972.

TABLE I
TYPES OF PROCEDURES USED TO PREPARE STEROID-PROTEIN CONJUGATES

Steroid reactive group	Derivative	Coupling reaction or reagent
—OH	Hemisuccinate	Mixed anhydride
—OH	Hemisuccinate	Carbodiimide
—OH	Chlorocarbonate	Schötten-Baumann
—OH	Chloroformate	Schötten-Baumann
—OH	Sebacyl chloride	Schötten-Baumann
=O	(O-Carboxymethyl) oxime	Mixed anhydride
=O	Hydrazone	Carbodiimide
=O	Isocyanate	Dioxane bicarbonate pH 10
Phenolic A ring	Azobenzoic acid	Carbodiimide

derivative of 17β-estradiol (estradiol) has been coupled to aminoethyl cellulose (Weliky and Weetall, 1965). Various steroid derivatives have also been conjugated to the methyl ester of tyrosine (Midgley et al., 1971) following the method outlined by Oliver et al. (1968).

II. CHARACTERISTICS OF ANTIBODIES TO STEROIDS

The specificity of any antibody is not absolute and, because of the complexity and heterogenicity of the immune response, may vary from antiserum to antiserum. In particular, when dealing with compounds structurally as closely related as are many steroid hormones, cross-reactions are to be expected and must be carefully studied whenever antisera against steroids are used.

Preliminary testing of antisera can be simply performed using tube precipitation or gel diffusion techniques (Kabat and Mayer, 1961). To eliminate the reaction of antibodies to the carrier, the antisera may be absorbed with unconjugated protein, or preferably the test antigen may consist of the hapten coupled to a protein that does not cross-react with the protein in the immunizing agent. The specificity of sera with significant antibody titers may be further studied by using various hapten-inhibition tests (Lieberman et al., 1959).

The combination of a hapten with an antibody can be measured directly by using labeled haptens, if procedures for separating bound from free hapten are available. A number of such procedures have been developed including equilibrium dialysis, salt precipitation, double-antibody, dextran-coated charcoal, solid-phase and insolubilized antibodies. Various unlabeled haptens can be tested for their capacity to compete with the labeled hapten for the antibody combining site, thus providing data bearing on the specificity of the antibody. Radioimmunoassay procedures which are based on reactions of this type have been discussed in detail in the proceedings of two recent conferences (Diczfalusy, 1970; Peron and Caldwell, 1970). Table II lists various radioimmunoassays for steroid hormones as well as the antigens used for the production of the antibodies used in these assays.

Specificity determinations will, in most cases, indicate that the antisera react not only with the homologous steroid but also cross-react with structurally related steroids. For instance, antibodies to estradiol-17-BSA, while cross-reacting only slightly with neutral steroids, cross-react significantly with other phenolic steroids (Mikhail et al., 1970a,b). There are data, however, that indicate that the problem of cross-reactivity may be overcome in certain instances. The specificity of the antibody appears to be determined primarily by that portion of the steroid molecule farthest from the point of conjugation to protein. Thus antibodies elicited by testosterone-3-BSA, in which the steroid is conjugated through C-3 in the A ring, differ in specificity from antibodies to testosterone-17-BSA in which coupling is via C-17 of the D ring. Antibodies to testosterone-3-BSA are more specific for testosterone and cross-react much less with cortisone, progesterone, and deoxycorticosterone (all of which have identical A rings) than do antibodies to testosterone-17 BSA (Niswender and Midgley, 1970). Figure 1 shows inhibition curves with various steroids in radioimmunoassays using antibodies raised to these two antigens. In a recent investigation (Africa and Haber, 1971), it was proposed to obtain antibodies specific for aldosterone by using a conjugate coupled through the A ring rather than at the D ring. Attempts have also been made to obtain antibodies more specific to estradiol-17β, by attaching the protein via C-3 (Gross et al., 1968) or via C-6 (Exley, 1972; Jeffcoate and Searle, 1972).

Niswender and Midgley (1970) have conjugated BSA to progesterone at the 11 position by using the chlorocarbonate derivative of 11-OH-progesterone, thus leaving both ends available to confer specificity to the antibody.

Another potential method for dealing with the problem of cross-reactions is based on hapten-inhibition studies of homologous and heterologous reactions. The homologous hapten, cortisone-21-hemisuccinate has equal inhibitory activity on the reactions between anti-cortisone-21-BSA and the antigens cortisone-21-BSA and testosterone-17-BSA (Lieberman et al., 1959). On the other hand, the heterologous hapten, testosterone-17-succinate, inhibits the cross-reaction more effectively than it inhibits the homologous reaction. Therefore, it might be possible to synthesize inactive steroids that would reduce cross-reactions without appreciably affecting the homologous reaction.

TABLE II

Some Steroid-Protein Conjugates and Radioimmunoassay Procedures
Used for the Assay of Steroids[a]

Antigen	Separation bound from free	Reference
1. Estrogens		
Estradiol-17-hemisuccinate-BSA	Solid phase	Abraham (1969)
Estradiol-17-hemisuccinate-BSA	Polymerized antibodies	Mikhail et al. (1970a,b)
Estradiol-17-hemisuccinate-BSA	Dextran-coated charcoal	Hotchkiss et al. (1971) Wu and Lundy (1971) Emment et al. (1972)
Estradiol-17-hemisuccinate-BSA	Toluene	Castanier et al. (1972)
Estriol-16-17-dihemi-succinate-BSA	Ammonium sulfate	Gurpide et al. (1971)
Estriol-3-hemisuccinate-HSA	Dextran-coated charcoal	Tulchinsky and Abraham (1971)
2-hydroxyestrone-17-oxime-BSA	Dextran-coated charcoal	Yoshizawa and Fishman (1971)
Estradiol-6-oxime-BSA	Solid phase Dextran-coated charcoal	Exley (1971) Cameron et al. (1972)
2. Progesterone and derivatives		
11-Deoxycortisol-21-hemi-succinate-BSA	Dextran-coated charcoal	Abraham et al. (1971)
Progesterone-3-oxime-BSA	Ammonium sulfate	Furuyama and Nugent (1971)
11α-hydroxyprogesterone-hemisuccinate-BSA	Charcoal Ammonium sulfate	Spieler et al. (1972) Kutas et al. (1972)
17-hydroprogesterone-3-oxime-BSA	Dextran-coated charcoal	Youssefnejadian et al. (1972)
3. Testosterone		
Testosterone-3-oxime-BSA	Ammonium sulfate	Furuyama et al. (1970)
Testosterone-3-oxime-BSA	Dextran-coated charcoal	Collins et al. (1972)
Testosterone-3-oxime-BSA	Double antibody	Ismail et al. (1972)
4. Corticosteroids		
DOC-3-oxime-BSA	Ammonium sulfate	Arnold and James (1971)
Cortisol-21-hemisuccinate-BSA	Dextran-coated charcoal	Ruder et al. (1972)
5. Aldosterone		
Aldosterone-3-oxime-BSA	Florisil	Bayard et al. (1970) Ito et al. (1972)
Aldosterone-3-oxime-BSA	Toluene	Ekins et al. (1972)
Aldosterone-3-oxime-BSA	Charcoal	Farmer et al. (1972)
Aldosterone-3-oxime-BSA	Ammonium sulfate	Mayes et al. (1970)
Aldosterone-18,21-disuccinate-BSA	Florisil	Ito et al. (1972)

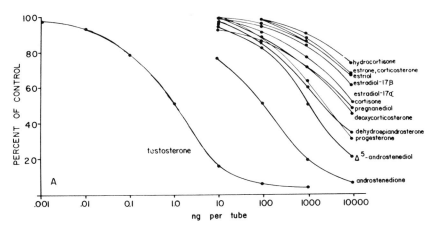

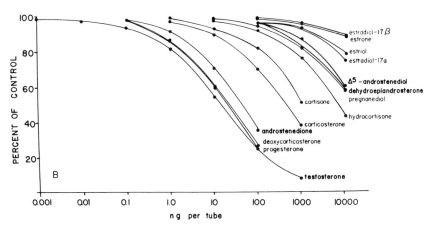

FIG. 1. Inhibition curves with selected steroids in the testosterone-3 radioimmuno-assay (A) and in the testosterone-17 radioimmunoassay (B). From Niswender and Midgley (1970). Reprinted with permission.

[a] Most radioimmunoassays mentioned in this table use a ³H-labeled hormone. In a different approach, steroid-protein conjugates are radioiodinated and the free protein is separated from the bound by a double antibody technique. This method should theoretically offer a higher sensitivity and makes it possible to use reasonable quantities of ³H-labeled hormone as an internal standard to determine recoveries in each sample. For a general discussion of the method, see Midgley et al. (1971). BSA, bovine serum albumin.

III. Use of Antibodies for the Localization of Steroids in Tissues

Antibody methods using fluorescent as well as immunoenzyme techniques have been used successfully for the localization of proteins in tissues. The use of such methods for the localization of steroids presents several problems. Indeed, since steroids are soluble in organic solvents, frozen sections have to be used. Furthermore, haptens do not precipitate when allowed to react with antibodies. However, it is possible that the steroids might be firmly bound to proteins or other cellular components in sufficiently high concentration to make visualization possible. There are only a few published studies in which antibody methods have been used for the detection of steroids in tissues.

Woods and Domm (1966) used anti-testosterone-3-BSA to localize androgens in frozen sections of gonads of domestic fowls and albino rats. Specific-fluorescent droplets were found both intracellularly and extracellularly. The fluorescence was located in the medullary cords and tubules, the rete testis, and the interstitial cells, as well as in the lumina of the medullary tubules. In some fowls, intense fluorescence was strongly correlated with strikingly masculine head furnishings. In the ovaries only slight specific fluorescence was found in the theca interna and the stratum granulosum of developing follicles whereas intense specific fluorescence was present in interstitial cells. Haferkamp et al. (1968) using antibodies to testosterone-3-BSA in a mixed agglutination technique found the antibody in the epithelial cell of rats' seminal vesicles. Goodfriend et al. (1961) used antibodies to estrone-2-carbamido-HSA on frozen sections of rat ovaries and found fluorescence in perifollicular and stromal cells.

Some technical problems inherent in the fluorescence technique are not easy to overcome. Background fluorescence may interfere with interpretation of the results, the fluorescence is not permanent, and good electron microscopy studies are difficult. The peroxidase-labeled antibody technique (Mason et al., 1969; Nakane, 1971) avoids most of these difficulties and should be tried even more because the staining of multiple antigens would permit the simultaneous localization of different hormones. Attention has been given to the problem of specificity in only a limited number of cases. Using antibodies to testosterone-3-BSA, Woods and Domm (1966) did not find any specific fluorescence in the corpus luteum (the site of high progesterone production), in the liver or brain (tissues rich in cholesterol), or in testes of hypophysectomized rats. In further localization experiments, greater attention will have to be attached to problems of specificity—for example, by the use of antisera absorbed with various cross-reagents.

IV. PHYSIOLOGICAL STUDIES USING ANTIBODIES TO STEROIDS

A summary of *in vivo* experiments using antibodies to steroids is shown in Table III. In such experiments, the antibodies are administered directly to the animal (passive immunization) or the animal produces its own antibodies after immunization with the antigen (active immunization).

A. INHIBITION OF EXOGENOUSLY ADMINISTERED HORMONES

1. Antisera to Estrogens

a. Inhibition of the Effect on Uterine Weight Increase. Antisera to estrone and estradiol were used to inhibit the increase in uterine weight seen after the administration of estrone or estradiol in immature intact mice (Neri et al., 1964), immature rats (Goodfriend and Sehon, 1961b; Ferin et al., 1968), and ovariectomized adult rats (Lieberman et al., 1959). In one case, a 6-hour uterine assay was used in which estrone (0.2 μg) and antiestrone were mixed and injected together at one site at the beginning of the experiment. Inhibition of the effects of estrone was obtained. However, the mixing of estrone and the antibody prior to the injection might have led to the formation of a biologically inactive complex. In such biological assays, the antibodies and the hormone should always be injected at different sites. In all other experiments the animals were injected daily for 3 days at separate sites with the steroid and the antiserum, and killed on day 4. In each case, the uterotropic activity of the estrogen was inhibited. An example in which antibodies to estradiol were used to neutralize the biological activity of estradiol in immature rats is shown in Fig. 2. The inhibitory effect of the antiserum is dose dependent, and calculations show that between 17 and 20 antibody combining sites for each molecule of estradiol or estrone are necessary to bring about the neutralization of the estrogenic effect. Notwithstanding this large ratio of antibody sites to molecules of hormone, all biological activity could not be neutralized even when as much as 4.5 times this amount of antiserum is given. It is likely that the association constants between estradiol and its tissue receptor and between estradiol and its antibody are such that a small fraction of the steroid will always remain free and active. On the other hand, it cannot be excluded that the remaining biological activity might be due to the antibody–steroid complex itself.

b. Inhibition of the Effects on the Vaginal Epithelium and Endometrium. In adult ovariectomized rats, stimulation of the glandular tissue of the endometrium as well as cornification of the vaginal epithelium

TABLE III

In Vivo EXPERIMENTS WITH ANTIBODIES TO STEROIDS[a]

Antibodies to	Type of animal	Effect studied	Author
A. Passive immunization			
1. Estrone	Immature rat	Uterotropic effect of estrone (6 hr assay)	Goodfriend *et al.* (1961)
	Immature mice	Uterotropic effect of estrone	Neri *et al.* (1964)
	Ovariectomized rat	Uterotropic effect of estrone	Lieberman *et al.* (1959)
	Guinea pig	Uterine contractions *in vitro*	Goodfriend *et al.* (1961)
2. Estradiol	Immature rat	Uterotropic effect of estradiol	Ferin *et al.* (1968)
	Ovariectomized rat	Uterotropic effect of estradiol	Ferin *et al.* (1968)
	Immature rats	Uptake ^{3}H-estradiol by uterus, ovaries, and pituitary	Ferin *et al.* (1968)
	Immature mice	Uterotropic effect of HCG	Ferin *et al.* (1968)
	Immature rats	Uterotropic effect of HCG	Ferin *et al.* (1968)
	Immature rats	PMS-induced ovulation	Ferin *et al.* (1969a)
	Cyclic hamster	Length of cycle	Caldwell *et al.* (1970)
	Cyclic rat	Ovulation	Ferin *et al.* (1969b)
	Cyclic rat	Prolactin release	Neill *et al.* (1971)
	Cyclic rat	Amine-induced LH release	Raziano *et al.* (1971)
	Pregnant hamster	Nidation	Caldwell *et al.* (1970)
	Pregnant rats	Nidation and maintenance of pregnancy	Raziano *et al.* (1972)
3. Testosterone	Castrated rat	Androgenic-myogenic assay	Lieberman *et al.* (1959) Neri *et al.* (1964)
	Immature rat	Androgenic-myogenic assay	Ferin *et al.* (1968)
	Pregnant rat	Masculine differentiation of male fetus	Goldman *et al.* (1972)
4. Cortisol	Male adrenalectomized mice	Eosinophilic test	Neri *et al.* (1964)
5. Aldosterone	Male adrenalectomized rats	Electrolytic assay	Neri *et al.* (1964)
B. Active immunization			
1. Estradiol-17-BSA	Cyclic hamster	Cycle	Caldwell *et al.* (1970)
	Ovariectomized sheep	LH release	Caldwell *et al.* (1970)

TABLE III (*Continued*)

Antibodies to	Type of animal	Effect studied	Author
	Ovariectomized sheep	Prostaglandin F release	Caldwell *et al.* (1972)
	Cyclic rhesus monkeys	Cycle	Cowchock *et al.* (1972) Ferin *et al.* (1973)
	Rats	Mammary tumors	Caldwell *et al.* (1971)
2. Cholesterol-BSA	Rabbits	Arteriosclerosis	Bailey *et al.* (1964)
3. Testosterone-3-BSA	Rabbits	Serum testosterone ICSH	Thorneycroft (1972)

^a BSA, bovine serum albumin; PMS, pregnant mare serum; HCG, human chorionic gonadotropin; LH, luteinizing hormone.

by estradiol are inhibited by antibodies to estradiol (Ferin *et al.*, 1968).

c. In Vitro Anaphylaxis. Contractions of uterine segments of guinea pigs previously passively sensitized by an intraperitoneal injection of antiserum to estrone-17-HSA were recorded (Goodfriend and Sehon, 1961b). Contraction of the tissue occurs after the addition of the antigen even after desensitization with HSA.

2. Antisera to Testosterone

Male castrated (Lieberman *et al.*, 1959; Neri *et al.*, 1964) or immature rats (Ferin *et al.*, 1968) were treated with testosterone or testosterone propionate for 6 days and sacrificed on day 7. The weight increase of the prostates, seminal vesicles, levator ani, and testes is significantly

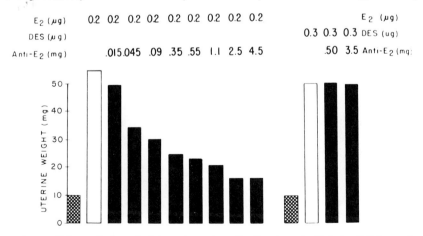

Fig. 2. Effect of the administration of antibodies to estradiol (anti-E$_2$) on the uterotropic activity of 17β-estradiol (E$_2$) and diethylstilbestrol (DES). From Vande Wiele *et al.* (1970).

inhibited by antisera to testosterone. Antisera to testosterone-3-BSA as well as to testosterone-17-BSA were tested and found effective. However, their relative activity was not studied.

3. *Antiserum to Cortisol*

Antiserum to cortisol-21-BSA was tested in a 4-hour eosinophile assay in adrenalectomized male mice (Neri *et al.*, 1964). The antiserum blocks the eosinophilic action of cortisol. However, in order to be active in these acute tests, the antiserum must be administered prior to the cortisol injection.

4. *Antiserum to Aldosterone*

Antiserum to aldosterone-21-BSA was tested in adrenalectomized female rats in an electrolyte assay (Neri *et al.*, 1964). Pretreatment with the antiserum results in a significant increase of the urinary Na:K ratio.

B. *In Vivo* SPECIFICITY OF THE STEROID–ANTIBODY REACTION

Antisera may behave differently in an *in vitro* system, such as a radio-immunoassay, a hapten inhibition test or precipitin test than in an *in vivo* test, and the possibility must be considered that the most specific antiserum, as determined by *in vitro* methods, may not be the best antiserum for use in biological systems. Such antibodies may be directed against a part of the steroid molecule not involved in tissue binding or in hormone activity, in which case the biological activity of the hormone may not be neutralized. In fact, interesting data bearing on the specific portions of steroid hormones involved in tissue binding or in hormone activity might accrue from a comparison of the neutralizing activities of antibodies specific for different portions of the same steroid hormone molecule.

A few preliminary experiments have been carried out to study the specificity of the steroid–antibody reactions under *in vivo* conditions. An example is shown in Fig. 3. Antibodies to testosterone, progesterone, or BSA do not inhibit the uterotropic activity of estradiol. In an androgen assay, antibodies to estradiol do not inhibit the androgenic effect of testosterone (Ferin *et al.*, 1968).

In vitro analysis shows that the binding of diethylstilbestrol to anti-estradiol is less than 0.1% that of estradiol (Tillson *et al.*, 1970). It is therefore not surprising that the uterotropic effect of diethylstilbestrol is not inhibited by antiserum to estradiol (Fig. 2). Thus, diethylstilbestrol can be used to restore estrogenic activity in animals treated with antibodies to estradiol.

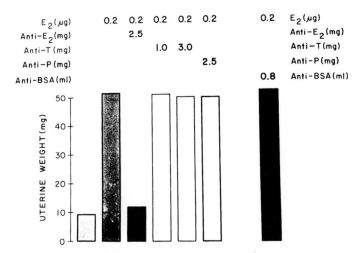

FIG. 3. Effects of antibodies to estradiol (anti-E₂), testosterone (anti-T), progesterone (anti-P), and bovine serum albumin (anti-BSA) on the uterotropic effect of estradiol (E₂).

C. MECHANISM OF ACTION OF ANTIBODIES

Antibodies to estradiol prevent the uptake of tritiated estradiol by the uterus, ovaries, and pituitary (Ferin *et al.*, 1968). So do estrogen antagonists, such as MER-25 and clomiphene citrate. However, these antagonists compete with the estrogen for the receptor sites (Jensen, 1966). On the contrary, even in the presence of large amounts of antibodies to estradiol, estrogenic substances, such as diethylstilbestrol, can still affect the uterine receptor. It is thus probable that the antibodies bind the hapten in the circulation, thereby preventing it from getting to the receptor sites, leaving these sites free.

It is not known whether the estradiol–antibody complex itself possesses some hormonal activity, nor is there information about the metabolism of the estradiol bound to the antiserum. It would be of interest to know whether it is somehow protected from catabolism and thus has a prolonged half-life. Pointing to this possibility is the fact that, in female monkeys immunized with estradiol-BSA or in male rabbits immunized with testosterone-BSA, the level of steroids, measured by radioimmunoassay following extraction from plasma with ether, is quite high (Ferin *et al.*, 1973; Thorneycroft, 1972).

D. INHIBITION OF ENDOGENOUS CIRCULATING HORMONES

In order to use antibodies to steroids to study the role of hormones in various physiological and pathological processes, it must be shown first that these antibodies are able to neutralize the biological activity of the endogenous circulating hormone as well as that of exogenously administered hormone. Experiments in which HCG and antibodies to estradiol were administered to immature female mice and rats indicate this to be so (Ferin *et al.*, 1968). Indeed, as shown on Fig. 4, increases in uterine weight (but not ovarian weight) brought about by the increased estrogen secretion were inhibited by the antibodies.

E. Use of Antibodies to Study the Role of Hormones in Various Physiological and Pathological Processes

The ability of antibodies to neutralize the biological activity of the homologous circulating steroid makes them uniquely useful as tools to study the role of hormones in various physiological processes. The advantages of using antibodies to estrogens, for example, over other experimental methods are evident. Ablation techniques, such as oophorectomy, eliminate complex secretions and in this particular example also eliminate the target organ. In addition, the effect of surgical trauma cannot be overlooked (Schwartz, 1964). Synthetic estrogen antagonists such as MER-25 have complex activities, and their effect may not be due solely to their competitive estrogen antagonism. Owing to the potential difference in threshold to estrogen of various tissues or to the differences in

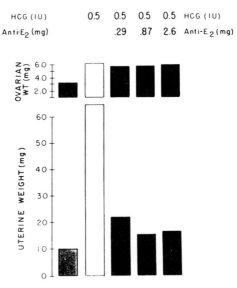

Fig. 4. Effect of human chorionic gonadotropin (HCG) and antibodies to estradiol on ovarian and uterine weights in immature mice. From Vande Wiele *et al.* (1971). Reprinted with permission.

availability of the drug to the receptor, these antagonists might be more effective in one tissue than in another. Antibodies to estradiol, however, have no biological activity other than neutralizing the estrogens in the peripheral circulation, therefore leaving the hormonal receptor sites intact.

Some of the disadvantages of the use of hormonal antisera should not be overlooked. Specificity, one of the main problems, has been mentioned in previous paragraphs. The amount of antiserum that has to be administered to obtain *in vivo* neutralization is high, and supply may be a rate-limiting factor. Toxic or nonspecific effects derived from the injection of large amounts of foreign proteins have not been reported in the literature, but such effects have to be kept in mind. Especially in chronic experiments, appropriate controls must be included to rule out this possibility.

1. Passive Immunization

The studies on passive immunization to steroids reported in the literature deal mainly with the following subjects. First, the role of ovarian hormones on the reproductive cycle, mainly the role of estrogens and progesterone on the cyclic preovulatory release of LH. Second, the relative role of estrogen and progesterone on nidation and on the maintenance of pregnancy. Third, the role of testosterone in the sexual differentiation of the male fetus.

a. Effect on the Cycle. The experiments to be described in this section were designed to support the hypothesis that the surge in estrogen secretion accompanying follicular maturation is the physiological trigger that sets off ovulatory LH release in rats and hamsters. Many experiments, such as the administration of estradiol to 5-day cyclic rats (Everett, 1948) or to immature rats (Hohlweg, 1934), ovariectomy (Schwartz, 1964), or the administration of estrogen antagonists (Shirley et al., 1968) had provided indirect evidence for the role of estrogen. However, studies using antibodies to estradiol and to progesterone have, for the first time, shown direct evidence for this hypothesis.

The experiments were performed in immature rats treated with 10 units (normal ovulation) or 45 units (superovulation) of pregnant mare serum (PMS) (Ferin et al., 1969a) as well as in adult 4-day cyclic female rats (Ferin et al., 1969b). In these animals, luteinizing hormone (LH) release is preceded by a surge in estrogens as measured directly in the blood (Brown-Grant et al., 1970) or as indicated by the "ballooning" of the uterus. If antibodies against estradiol are administered, at the same time as PMS, to immature rats or on the morning of diestrus-2 to cyclic animals, uterine ballooning as well as cornification of the vaginal cells are absent and no ova are found in the fallopian tubes at the expected time. Ovulation is blocked in virtually all animals (Fig. 5). To some degree this effect on ovulation is dose dependent. The specificity of this inhibitory effect on ovulation by antibodies against estradiol was demonstrated in experiments showing that antisera against testosterone or BSA as well as normal sheep serum are ineffective in blocking ovulation. Since several reports indicate that progesterone may also trigger LH release (Everett, 1948), it was of interest to study the effect of antibodies against progesterone upon ovulation in the cyclic rat. In most experiments the injection of antibodies against progesterone failed to inhibit ovulation although uterine ballooning persisted into the morning of estrus, a clear indication that the peripheral effects of progesterone were being suppressed. However, the possibility of a role for derivatives of progesterone cannot be excluded, for the specificity of this particular antiserum could not be tested at the time.

The block in ovulation following the administration of antibodies against estradiol is not permanent. In all cases, ovulation is merely delayed by a period of 24–96 hours—48 hours in the majority of the animals. Because of the short half-life of antibodies in rats (Kabat and Mayer, 1961), it is possible that the secretion of estrogens by a greater number of maturing follicles finally overrides the fading effects of the antiserum, and LH release occurs. All subsequent cycles in these animals were of normal length.

A lengthening in the duration of the cycle in the Golden hamster has also been shown to occur following daily injection of antibodies against estradiol (Caldwell *et al.*, 1970). Although not documented in the study,

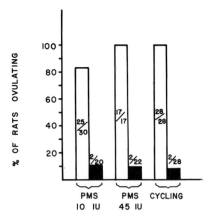

Fig. 5. Percentage of rats ovulating after treatment with antibodies to estradiol of pregnant mare serum (PMS)-treated immature rats or cyclic rats.

the change in length of the cycle might be due to a delay in ovulation as occurs in rats.

The absence of an LH peak, as measured by radioimmunoassay (Ferin *et al.*, 1969b; Neill *et al.*, 1971) (Fig. 6), in the rats in which ovulation has been blocked indicates that the antibodies against estradiol inhibit ovulation by suppressing LH release rather than by a direct effect on the ovary. This is confirmed by the fact that administration of HCG restores ovulation in those treated immature as well as adult animals (Ferin *et al.*, 1969a,b). Antibodies against estradiol administered on diestrus-2 also block the proestrus surge of prolactin (Neill *et al.*, 1971) (Fig. 6).

A final proof of the causative role of estrogens in LH and prolactin

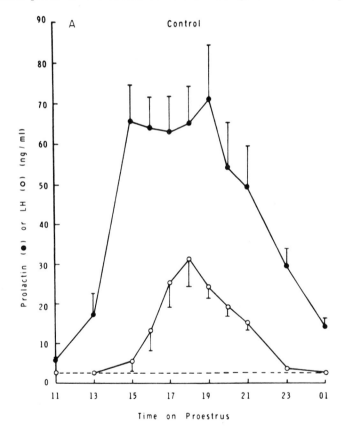

FIG. 6. Mean plasma luteinizing hormone (LH) and prolactin levels at proestrus in rats treated with normal sheep serum (A). Antibodies to estradiol (B). At 10:00 hours of diestrus-2 or with antibodies to estradiol and diethylstilbestrol (C). From Neill *et al.* (1971). Reprinted with permission. See p. 190 for B and C.

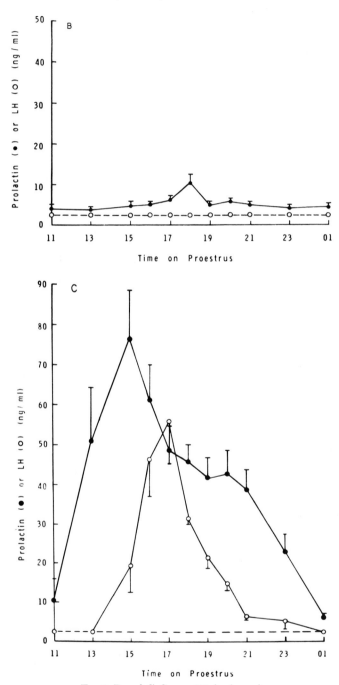

FIG. 6, B and C. See p. 189 for legend.

release was obtained by the demonstration that diethylstilbestrol, an estrogen not inhibited by antibodies against estradiol, restores LH release and ovulation as well as the prolactin surge in most of the "blocked" animals (Fig. 6).

The mechanism by which estrogens trigger the LH or prolactin surges is unknown. It is of interest to note that the activation by estrogens of the neural mechanism for the ovulatory LH release is already completed 12–15 hours prior to the expected onset of the surge. Antibodies to estradiol administered after this period do not block ovulation. Furthermore, in order for this neural activation for LH release to occur, a sustained secretion of estradiol for at least 10 hours is necessary (Kobayashi et al., 1969). This is likely to be the explanation why estrogen restores ovulation only if administered in oil, not in saline.

It is known that monoamines play a role in the regulation of gonadotropin release (Kamberi et al., 1970). Using antibodies against estradiol, it has been shown that the release of LH and ovulation induced by intraventricular monoamine administration is probably estrogen dependent (Raziano et al., 1971). Indeed, rats treated with antibodies against estradiol on diestrus-2 fail to ovulate following intraventricular injection of L-DOPA or L-epinephrine, even though these amines are effective in restoring ovulation in rats in which it was blocked with pentobarbital (Fig. 7).

The results outlined in this paragraph strongly support the hypothesis that, both in the immature animal treated with PMS and in the adult

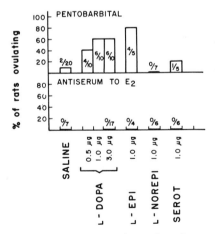

FIG. 7. Percentage of animals ovulating after intraventricular injection of L-DOPA, L-epinephrine, L-norepinephrine, or serotonin in rats in which luteinizing hormone (LH) release was blocked by pentobarbital (upper) or by antibodies to estradiol (lower).

cyclic rat, estrogens serve as a trigger that sets off preovulatory LH release.

b. Effect on Nidation. The results of experiments using antibodies against estradiol or progesterone in the pregnant rat support existing evidence implicating progesterone and estrogens in the processes leading to implantation (Raziano *et al.*, 1972). Indeed, neutralization of the circulating progesterone or estrogens by antibodies on days 3 or 4 of gestation, but not on day 5, results in delayed implantation (Fig. 8). In all the antiserum-treated groups, free intrauterine ova are found on day 6 at a time implantation has already occurred in the control animals. Other procedures disrupting the secretion of the ovarian steroids, e.g., hypophysectomy or castration, have similarly to be performed before the evening of day 4 in order to block implantation (Zeilmaker, 1963). Furthermore, early progesterone will induce implantation in such animals only if supplemented by estrogen at the end of it (Psychoyos, 1970). Results from experiments with antibodies in rats confirm the existence of such a sequential interplay of protesterone and estrogens. On the contrary, in the hamster antibodies against estradiol have no effect on implantation (Caldwell, 1970) and indeed, in ovariectomized hamsters, implantation occurs quite normally after progesterone treatment alone (Harper, 1970).

Of great interest is the observation that, in animals in which implantation is delayed by antibodies against progesterone, there is a greatly increased rate of resorption of the implanted ova. These long-term

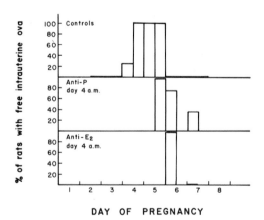

Fig. 8. Percentage of rats with free intrauterine ova. Control rats (upper), rats treated with antibodies to progesterone (anti-P) (middle), and rats treated with antibodies to estradiol (anti-E₂) (lower). The antibodies were injected on the morning of day 4 of pregnancy.

effects must be assumed to be secondary to the hormonal disturbance at the time of implantation, since antibodies are generally not effective beyond 48 hours. Whether they are due to the direct and specific inhibition of progesterone by the antiserum or to temporary estrogen predominance (as evidenced by the appearance of basal cells in the vaginal smear) remains uncertain. This observation raises the possibility that fetal abnormalities, seen in the later stages of pregnancy, may be attributed to a hormonal imbalance at the time of implantation.

 c. *Effect on the Maintenance of Pregnancy.* In a series of experiments, antibodies against estradiol or against progesterone were administered at various times during pregnancy in the rat (Raziano *et al.*, 1972). A single injection of antibodies against progesterone on day 11 results in a complete resorption of the fetuses in all the animals (Fig. 9). Treatment with antibodies against estradiol also produces complete resorption, but only in 40% of the animals, showing the lesser role played by the estrogens during this part of pregnancy. Indeed, in anti-LH-treated rats progesterone replacement, but not estrogens alone, can reverse the effects of the antiserum. Treatment with antisera against progesterone or estrogens did not alter the length of gestation in animals which delivered viable fetuses.

 d. *Effect on the Sexual Differentiation of the Male Fetus.* In order to define the role of androgens on masculine differentiation in the male fetus, antibodies against testosterone-3-BSA were injected into pregnant rats from days 13 to 20 of pregnancy (Goldman *et al.*, 1972). The results indicated that the antiserum against testosterone reduces the anogenital

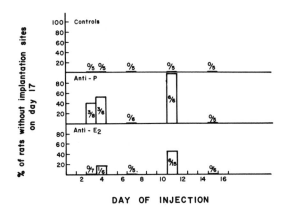

Fig. 9. Percentage of rats in which complete resorption of the fetuses has occurred by day 17 of pregnancy. Control rats (upper), rats treated with antibodies to progesterone (anti-P) (middle), and rats treated with antibodies to estradiol (anti-E₂) (lower). The antibodies were injected on different days as indicated.

distance and the testicular weight of the male fetuses, while not affecting the genitalia of female fetuses. Further work with antisera against other steroids is clearly indicated.

2. Active Immunization

Active immunization with steroid-protein conjugates has been carried out in rats, hamsters, sheep, rabbits, monkeys, and humans.

a. Effects of Immunization against Estrogens upon the Reproductive Cycle. Rhesus monkeys (Cowchock *et al.*, 1972; Ferin *et al.*, 1973) and hamsters (Caldwell *et al.*, 1970) were immunized with estradiol-17-BSA, and the effects on the cycle were observed. In the monkey, doses of 1.5–6.0 mg of the antigen were used. The antigen was mixed with Freund's adjuvant, and the usual immunization schedule consisted of four weekly injections followed by boosters every 6 weeks. The antiestradiol titers were measured using the principle of radioimmunoassay for estradiol and expressed as percent of ³H-estradiol protein bound at a dilution of 1:100 of the antiserum. In all animals, antibodies appeared after the priming period. An increase in titers was seen approximately 10–12 days after each booster injection (Fig. 10).

To follow the effect of immunization on the reproductive cycles, vaginal smears were taken and the levels of progesterone or "progestins" were determined. As soon as antibodies were produced, the animals ceased to ovulate as indicated by the absence of cyclic variation in progesterone or "progestins" levels (Fig. 10). Cyclic variations in the vaginal smears

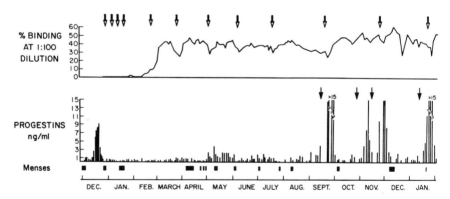

Fig. 10. Effects of immunization to estradiol-17-bovine serum albumin of a rhesus monkey. Upper panel: Antiestradiol titers as measured by a radioimmunoassay at 1:100 dilution of the antiserum. The arrows indicate the time of injection of the antigen (3 mg). Lower panel: Plasma levels of "progestins" as determined by a protein-binding assay. The arrows indicate the time of injection of diethylstilbestrol (250 μg).

were absent as well. In most monkeys, the interval between menses became irregular. These studies corroborate those reported in previous paragraphs in which passive immunization with antibodies against estradiol was employed, and add further evidence to the theory that the ovulatory surge is triggered by the changing levels of estrogens in the circulation. If so, it should be possible to induce a LH surge, in these immunized monkeys, by the administration of diethylstilbestrol. Figure 11 indicates that this is indeed so, the LH release occurring approximately 24–38 hours after the injection of the estrogen. In ovariectomized ewes immunized against estradiol-17β, diethylstilbestrol similarly induces a LH surge (Caldwell *et al.*, 1970).

In such immunized monkeys and hamsters, the ovaries were characterized by multiple cystic follicles. This fact is presumably due to chronic stimulation of the ovaries by the high levels of gonadotropins. Such chronic hyperstimulation is reflected by an increased secretion of steroids by the gonads, which explains the high levels of steroids generally found in most animals actively immunized to estrogens (Ferin *et al.*, 1973) or androgens (Thorneycroft, 1972) (Nieschlag *et al.*, 1973).

b. Effects of Immunization against Estrogens on Tumors. In rats actively immunized with estradiol-17-BSA, the time of onset of mammary tumor growth, as well as the survival time, is significantly increased (Caldwell *et al.*, 1971). The animals with the highest titers have the longest survival period.

c. Effects of immunization against cholesterol on arteriosclerosis. Rabbits were actively immunized with cholesterol–esters–BSA, and the effect

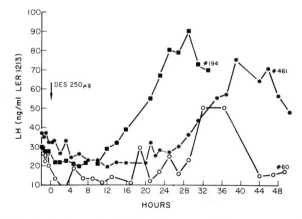

FIG. 11. Level of plasma luteinizing hormone (LH), as measured by a radioimmunoassay, after the injection of 250 μg of diethylstilbestrol (DES) to three rhesus monkeys immunized to estradiol-17-bovine serum albumin.

of immunization on arteriosclerosis was studied (Bailey *et al.*, 1964). In immunized rabbits fed cholesterol, the intensity of arteriosclerotic plaques in the thoracic aorta is significantly less than in control animals maintained on the same diet.

d. *Immunization against Steroids in Humans.* The capability of humans to respond to steroid–protein conjugates has been studied to a limited extent in patients with metastatic breast and bladder tumors (Veenema *et al.*, 1959). Such patients are usually considered to be poor responders to an antigenic stimulus, and any positive response may therefore be considered highly significant. Estrone-17-RSA, estrone-17-HSA, testosterone-17-RSA, testosterone-17-HSA, testosterone-3-RSA, and testosterone-3-HSA were used as antigens. These antigens were mixed either with alum precipitates or with incomplete Freund's adjuvant. Approximately half of the subjects responded with significant antibody production as measured by a quantitative precipitin reaction. Selected sera were tested for specificity by the hapten inhibition technique. In all cases where this was done, the homologous hapten inhibited the reaction.

These results demonstrate the capacity of humans to respond to antigenic stimulus with the formation of antisteroid antibodies. Insufficient data are available to differentiate between the response to the antigens as alum precipitates or in incomplete Freund's adjuvants.

V. Summary and Conclusions

The first comprehensive publication (Erlanger *et al.*, 1959) describing the production of antibodies against steroids, by the administration of steroid–protein conjugates, dates back to 1959, yet it is only in the last few years that the potentialities of this approach have been at least partially explored. The realization that steroid antibodies could be used in radioimmunoassay systems finally led to a surge of interest in the production of steroid antibodies; at the present time, hardly a month goes by without the publication of a new radioimmunoassay for steroids. These methods, which are sensitive down to the picogram level, have revolutionized several areas in reproductive endocrinology by making it possible to measure fluctuations in steroid levels at intervals of a minute or less.

Even now, many of the possible uses of steroid antibodies have not been fully explored. In their original study, Lieberman *et al.* (1959) were attracted by the therapeutic possibilities of immunization with steroids. For instance, they hoped to forgo surgical castration by actively immunizing the patient against either testosterone or estrogens. Many other applications come easily to mind. In the field of contraception, active immunization with estrogen conjugates could cause lasting anovulation.

Whenever desired, this condition could then be reversed by the administration of synthetic estrogens not inhibited by antibodies. Antibodies to progesterone could also be used to terminate unwanted pregnancies. There are obvious, significant limitations to this immunological approach in man, but the possibility of their use has been clearly demonstrated in animals. Finally, a plea is in order for an increased use of steroid-antibodies to study the role of hormones in various endocrine processes. Since antibodies have no biological activity other than by their capacity to inactivate the homologous hormone in the peripheral circulation, they have unique advantages over other methods by which inactivation of a hormone is sought. Examples in which such an approach has led to clarification of mechanisms controlling reproductive processes, such as the role of estrogens on the ovulatory LH surge and the role of estrogen and progesterone on implantation and pregnancy, have been discussed in this chapter. In other fields there have been many attempts to exploit this approach. Even the scanty data discussed above (effects on tumor growth, on arteriosclerosis, etc.) clearly indicate that the broadening of the use of steroid antibodies should prove very rewarding.

REFERENCES

Abraham, G. E. (1969). *J. Clin. Endocrinol. Metab.* **29,** 866.

Abraham, G. E., Swerdloff, R., Tulchinsky, D., and Odell, W. D. (1971). *J. Clin. Endocrinol. Metab.* **32,** 619.

Africa, B., and Haber, E. (1971). *Immunochemistry* **8,** 479.

Arnold, M. L., and James, V. H. T. (1971). *Steroids* **18,** 789.

Bailey, J. M., Bright, R., and Tomar, R. (1964). *Nature (London)* **201,** 407.

Bayard, F., Beitins, A., Kowarski, A., and Migeon, C. (1970). *J. Clin. Endocrinol. Metab.* **31,** 1.

Beiser, S. M., Butler, V. P., and Erlanger, B. F. (1968). *In* "Textbook of Immunopathology" (P. A. Miesher and H. J. Muller-Eberhard, eds.), pp. 15–24. Grune & Stratton, New York.

Brown-Grant, K., Exley, D., and Naftolin, F. (1970). *J. Endocrinol.* **48,** 295.

Caldwell, B. (1970). *In* "Immunologic Methods in Steroid Determination" (F. G. Peron and B. V. Caldwell, eds.), p. 221. Appleton, New York.

Caldwell, B. V., Scaramuzzi, R. J., Tillson, S. A., and Thorneycroft, I. H. (1970). *In* "Immunologic Methods in Steroid Determination" (F. G. Peron and B. V. Caldwell, eds.), pp. 183–198. Appleton, New York.

Caldwell, B. V., Tillson, S. A., Esber, H., and Thorneycroft, I. H. (1971). *Nature (London)* **231,** 118.

Caldwell, B. V., Tillson, S. A., Brock, W., and Speroff, L. (1972). *Prostaglandins* **1,** 217.

Cameron, E. H. D., and Jones, D. A. (1972). *Steroids* **20,** 737.

Castanier, M., Grenier, J., and Scholler, R. (1972). *J. Steroid Biochem.* **3,** 305.

Collins, W. P., Mansfield, M. D., Alladina, N. S., and Sommerville, I. F. (1972). *J. Steroid Biochem.* **3,** 333.

Cowchock, S., Ferin, M., Dyrenfurth, I., Carmel, P., Zimmerman, E., Brinson, A., and Vande Wiele, R. L. (1972). *In* "Gonadotropins" (B. Saxena, C. G. Beling, and H. M. Gandy, eds.), pp. 87–97. Wiley, New York.

Diczfalusy, E. (1970). "Steroid Assay by Protein Binding. Karolinska Symposia on Research Methods in Reproductive Endocrinology." Stockholm.

Ekins, R. P., Newman, G. B., Piyasena, R., Banks, P., and Slater, J. D. (1972). *J. Steroid Biochem.* **3,** 289.

Emment, Y., Collins, W. P., and Sommerville, I. F. (1972). *Acta Endocrinol. (Copenhagen)* **69,** 567.

Erlanger, B. F., Borek, F., Beiser, S. M., and Lieberman, S. (1957). *J. Biol. Chem.* **228,** 713.

Erlanger, B. F., Borek, F., Beiser, S. M., and Lieberman, S. (1959). *J. Biol. Chem.* **234,** 1090.

Everett, J. W. (1948). *Endocrinology* **43,** 389.

Exley, D. (1972). *J. Steroid Biochem.* **3,** 497.

Exley, D., Johnson, M. W., and Dean, P. D. G. (1971). *Steroids* **18,** 605.

Farmer, R. W., Roup, W. G., Pellizzai, E. D., and Fabre, L. F. (1972). *J. Clin. Endocrinol. Metab.* **34,** 18.

Ferin, M., Zimmering, P., Lieberman, S., and Vande Wiele, R. L. (1968). *Endocrinology* **83,** 565.

Ferin, M., Zimmering, P. E., and Vande Wiele, R. L. (1969a). *Endocrinology* **84,** 893.

Ferin, M., Tempone, A., Zimmering, P. E., and Vande Wiele, R. L. (1969b). *Endocrinology* **85,** 1070.

Ferin, M., Dyrenfurth, I., Cowchock, S., and Vande Wiele, R. L. (1973). *Endocrinology* (in press).

Furuyama, S., and Nugent, C. A. (1971). *Steroids* **17,** 663.

Furuyama, S., Mayes, D. M., and Nugent, C. A. (1970). *Steroids* **16,** 415.

Goldman, A. S., Baker, M. K., Chen, J. C., and Wieland, R. (1972). *Endocrinology* **90,** 716.

Goodfriend, L., and Sehon, A. H. (1958). *Can. J. Biochem. Physiol.* **36,** 1172.

Goodfriend, L., and Sehon, A. H. (1961a). *Can. J. Biochem. Physiol.* **39,** 941.

Goodfriend, L., and Sehon, A. H. (1961b). *Can. J. Biochem. Physiol.* **39,** 961.

Goodfriend, L., Leznoff, A., and Sehon, A. H. (1961). *Can. J. Biochem. Physiol.* **39,** 967.

Gross, S. J., Campbell, D. H., and Weethall, H. H. (1968). *Immunochemistry* **5,** 55.

Gurpide, E., Giebenhain, M. E., Tseng, L., and Kelly, W. G. (1971). *Amer. J. Obstet. Gynecol.* **109,** 897.

Haferkamp, O., Vogel, W., Bultman, B., Andrezejewski, C. Z., and Tonutti, E. (1968). *Klin. Wochenschr.* **46,** 557.

Harper, M. J. (1970). *Anat. Rec.* **167,** 225.

Hohlweg, W. (1934). *Klin. Wochenschr.* **13,** 92.

Hotchkiss, J., Atkinson, L. E., and Knobil, E. (1971). *Endocrinology* **89,** 177.

Ismail, A. A., Niswender, G. D., and Midgley, A. R. (1972). *J. Clin. Endocrinol. Metab.* **34,** 177.

Ito, T., Woo, R., Haning, R., and Horton, R. (1972). *J. Clin. Endocrinol. Metab.* **34,** 106.

Jeffcoate, S. L., and Searle, J. E. (1972). *Steroids* **19,** 181.

Jensen, E. (1966). *Proc. Can. Cancer Res. Conf.* **6,** 143.

Kabat, E. A., and Mayer, M. M. (1961). "Experimental Immunochemistry." Thomas, Springfield, Illinois.

Kamberi, I. A., Mical, R. S., and Porter, J. C. (1970). *Endocrinology* **87**, 1.

Kobayashi, F., Hara, K., and Miyake, T. (1969). *Endocrinol. Jap.* **16**, 501.

Kutas, M., Chung, D., Bartoj, D., and Castro, A. (1972). *Steroids* **20**, 697.

Landsteiner, K. (1945). "Specificity of Serological Reactions." Harvard Univ. Press, Cambridge, Massachusetts.

Lieberman, S., Erlanger, B. F., Beiser, S. M., and Agate, F. J. (1959). *Recent Progr. Horm. Res.* **15**, 165.

Mason, T. E., Phifer, R. F., Spicer, S. S., Swallow, R. A., and Dresein, R. E. (1969). *J. Histochem. Cytochem.* **17**, 563.

Mayes, D., Furuyama, S., Kem, D. C., and Nugent, C. A. (1970). *J. Clin. Endocrinol. Metab.* **30**, 682.

Midgley, A. R., Niswender, G. D., Gay, V. L., and Reichert, L. E. (1971). *Recent Progr. Horm. Res.* **27**, 235.

Mikhail, G., Wu, C. H., Ferin, M., and Vande Wiele, R. L. (1970a). *In* "Immunologic Methods in Steroid Determination" (F. G. Peron and B. V. Caldwell, eds.), pp. 113–126. Appleton, New York.

Mikhail, G., Wu, C. H., Ferin, M., and Vande Wiele, R. L. (1970b). *Steroids* **15**, 333.

Moore, P. H., Jr., and Axelrod, L. R. (1972). *Steroids* **20**, 199.

Nakane, P. K. (1971). *In* "Research Methods in Reproductive Endocrinology, Karolinska Symposia" (E. Diczfalusy, ed.), No. 3, pp. 190–204. Stockholm.

Neill, J. D., Freeman, M. E., and Tillson, S. A. (1971). *Endocrinology* **89**, 1448.

Neri, R. O., Tolksdorf, S., Beiser, S. M., Erlanger, B. F., Agate, F. J., and Lieberman, S. (1964). *Endocrinology* **74**, 593.

Nieschlag, E., Usadel, K. H., Schwedes, U., Kley, H. K., Schöffling, K., and Krüskemper, H. L. (1973). *Acta Endocr. Suppl.* **173**, 116.

Niswender, G. D., and Midgley, A. R. (1970). *In* "Immunologic Methods in Steroid Determination" (F. G. Peron and B. V. Caldwell, eds.), pp. 149–174. Appleton, New York.

Oliver, G. C., Parker, B. M., Brasfield, D. L., and Parker, C. W. (1968). *J. Clin. Invest.* **47**, 1035.

Peron, F. G., and Caldwell, B. V. (1970). "Immunologic Methods in Steroid Determination." Appleton, New York.

Psychoyos, A. (1970). *In* "Advances in the Biosciences" (E. Raspe, ed.), Vol. 4, pp. 275–287. Pergamon, Oxford.

Raziano, J., Cowchock, S., Ferin, M., and Vande Wiele, R. L. (1971). *Endocrinology* **88**, 1516.

Raziano, J., Ferin, M., and Vande Wiele, R. L. (1972). *Endocrinology* **90**, 1133.

Ruder, H. J., Guy, R. L., and Lipsett, M. B. (1972). *J. Clin. Endocrinol.* **35**, 219.

Schwartz, N. B., (1964). *Amer. J. Physiol.* **207**, 1251.

Shirley, B., Wolinsky, J., and Schwartz, N. B. (1968). *Endocrinology* **82**, 959.

Spieler, J. M., Webb, R. L., Saldarini, R. J., and Coppola, J. A. (1972). *Steroids* **19**, 751.

Thorneycroft, I. H. (1972). Society for the Study of Reproduction, Fifth Annual Meeting, Abstr. No. 48.

Tillson, S. A., Thorneycroft, I. H., Abraham, G., and Caldwell, B. V. (1970). *In* "Immunologic Methods in Steroid Determination" (F. G. Peron and B. V. Caldwell, eds.), pp. 127–148. Appleton, New York.

Tulchinsky, D., and Abraham, G. E. (1971). *J. Clin. Endocrinol. Metab.* 33, 775.

Vande Wiele, R. L., Bogumil, J., Dyrenfurth, I., Ferin, M., Jewelewicz, R., Warren, M., Rizkallah, T., and Mikhail, G. (1970). *Rec. Prog. Horm. Res.* 26, 63.

Vande Wiele, R. L., Ferin, M., Raziano, J., Dyrenfurth, I., and Mikhail, G. (1971). *Res. Steroids* 4, 171.

Veenema, R., Beiser, S. M., Erlanger, B. F., and Lieberman, S. (1959). Unpublished observations.

Weliky, N., and Weetall, H. H. (1965). *Immunochemistry* 2, 293.

Westphal, U. (1971). Monographs on Endocrinology. Steroid–Protein Interactions, Vol. 4. pp. 446–462. Springer-Verlag, Berlin-New York.

Woods, J. E., and Domm, L. V. (1966). *Gen. Comp. Endocrinol.* 7, 559.

Wu, C. H., and Lundy, L. E. (1971). *Steroids* 18, 91.

Yoshizawa, I., and Fishman, J. (1971). *J. Clin. Endocrinol. Metab.* 32, 3.

Youssefnejadian, E., Florensa, E., Collins, W. P., and Sommerville, I. F. *Steroids* 20, 773.

Zeilmaker, G. H. (1963). *Acta Endocrinol. (Copenhagen)* 44, 355.

Hormonal Control of Ovoimplantation*

ALEXANDRE PSYCHOYOS

Centre National de la Recherche Scientifique, Laboratoire de Physiologie de la Reproduction, Hôpital de Bicêtre, 94-Bicêtre, France

I. INTRODUCTION

The mammalian ovum undergoes several "trials" after its release from the ovarian follicle. The ovum must be fertilized as soon as possible after release, otherwise it will degenerate within a few hours. It must then migrate or be transported through the oviduct within a definite interval, for if it arrives either too early or too late into the uterus it will encounter a hostile (toxic) environment. During the period of oviduct transit, the ovum must cleave and reach the morula stage of differentiation before it can coparticipate with the uterus in the initiation of implantation. Tubal or oviduct transit in most mammalian species occupies the first 3–4 days postfertilization (Andersen, 1927; Hertig *et al.*, 1954; Blandau, 1961; De Feo, 1967; Humphrey, 1968; Harper and Chang, 1971). In contrast, the interval between the arrival of the fertilized ovum into the uterus and the moment of its implantation is quite variable and depends not only on the species but also on the physiological state of the female. This interval can normally be on the order of 1–2 days, as in the rat, guinea pig, and man, or it may be of a longer duration

* Dedicated to the memory of Jean-Jacques Alloiteau and David Kirby.

as it normally is in the rabbit (4 days) and cat (13 days). In several species, a normal delay in implantation occurs which extends the preimplantation interval to several months. During delayed implantation, the ovum remains in the uterus as a blastocyst in a state of dormancy or diapause. No matter what the duration of the preimplantation interval may be, ovoimplantation requires that the uterus first undergo a series of changes which lead to what will be called a "receptive" phase of implantation.

The details of the mechanisms by which the ova of each species implant are varied and numerous (Amoroso, 1952; Boyd and Hamilton, 1952). In some species, the ovum increases in volume as a blastocyst which fills the luminal space of the uterus, as is the case for the rabbit, carnivores, and some species of monkeys. The blastocysts of other species remain as small bodies which are progressively embraced or enclosed by the epithelium of the uterine lumen (in the mouse and rat), or the blastocyst may actively invade the uterine mucosa, as in the guinea pig, chimpanzee, and man. It has been estimated that in man more than 30% of the embryos fail to implant for various reasons. Ovoimplantation for each species is an extremely complicated series of phenomena which requires a strict synchrony between embryonic and uterine events. The establishment and maintenance of embryo-maternal contact pose many problems at differing levels of analysis, such as histocompatibility and immunological tolerance, which go beyond the author's scope for critical discussion. What will be presented below is a personal viewpoint of ovo-endometrial interactions which focuses on the endocrinological states which initiate or arrest ovoimplantation.

It has been known for some time that the ovaries and the pituitary gland or the hormones thereof are indispensable for the occurrence of ovoimplantation. The coparticipation of these glands in establishing the endocrinological states involved in implantation is general for all species, with the curious exception of the armadillo, in which ovariectomy advances the time of implantation. The essential role of the corpus luteum for the initiation of pregnancy has been known since the classical studies of Fraenkel and Cohn (1902), Loeb (1908a,b), and Bouin and Ancel (1910). Loeb (1908a,b) reported that an endometrial response he considered as being a *deciduoma* could be induced by "indifferent stimuli" and that this response appeared to be similar to the endometrial response or *decidua* formation occurring during implantation. The fact that the stimuli which induced deciduoma were apparently "indifferent stimuli" suggested to Loeb that the uterus was "prepared" for decidua formation by a substance originating from the corpora lutea. Twenty years later, Weichert (1928) obtained deciduomata in castrated rats and guinea pigs treated with extracts of corpora lutea, and Allen and Corner (1929) found an active principle, called progesterone, in luteal extracts which maintained pregnancy in ovariectomized rabbits.

Progesterone was thought to be the only hormonal requirement for ovoimplantation in all mammalian species until the early 1960s. During that period, experiments were reported that clearly established that the *initiation* of ovoimplantation in the rat and mouse requires estrogen and that estrogen is effective only when administered to ovariectomized animals which previously were subjected to a regimen of daily progesterone administration. The results of these experiments and others concerning the hormonal control of implantation will be discussed in detail. These data are synthesized into conceptual generalizations about sequential phases and states of uterine receptivity which are viewed as models for future investigation. The involvement of estrogen in the development of uterine receptivity for implantation remains unproved in most mammalian species, when the test of its absence is based on the effects of ovariectomy on nidation (Courrier and Jost, 1939; Orsini and Meyer, 1959; Deanesly, 1963; Hafez, 1963; Orsini and Psychoyos, 1965; Buchanan, 1969; Harper *et al.*, 1969). It is the author's opinion that most mammalian species, other than the mouse and rat, have not been critically studied with respect to extraovarian sources of estrogens (e.g., the adrenals) and in particular with respect to the chronology of antecedent hormonal interactions during the estrous cycle preceding fertilization, which may prepare the uterus for subsequent implantation. It is hoped that the models of phases and states of uterine receptivity herein presented will aid in extending our understanding of the control mechanisms regulating nidation.

II. BIOLOGY OF OVOIMPLANTATION

A. TIMING OF EVENTS OF EARLY PREGNANCY

Information is now available that permits one to follow the temporal sequence of events during early pregnancy in the rat with high precision (De Feo, 1967; Psychoyos, 1967a, 1973). Spermatozoa are normally present at the site of fertilization before the release of follicular ova, and the time of ovulation can be considered as the beginning of pregnancy. Ovulation occurs "spontaneously" around 2 AM on the day of estrus if the animals have been housed under a 14-hour photoperiod of controlled illumination from 6 AM to 8 PM daily (Everett, 1964). Under these conditions, the ovarian or estrous cycle of the rat is shortened to 5 days, with estrous behavior recurring every sixth day. If a female is mated on this day, the act of coitus shunts the animal out of the estrous cycle through

neurogenic alteration of the hypothalamohypophyseal controls on prolactin (LTH) secretion. Circulating LTH prolongs diestrus, i.e., the
interval of progesterone secretion by corpora lutea cells; LTH-stimulated
corpora lutea function for several days longer than the corpora lutea
of nonmated animals (Alloiteau and Mayer, 1967).

A hormonal status analogous to that of the early stages of a normal
pregnancy can be obtained by conditions which either prolong or simu-
late progestational diestrus. Diestrus in the rat can be extended for up to
12 days by naturally occurring events or to several months by experimental intervention and animals subjected to such conditions are commonly referred to as being pseudopregnant (Long and Evans, 1922;
De Feo, 1967). Exactly what is meant by this term is usually qualified
in the literature of reproduction by each investigator of the phenomenon.
However, a common element of all states of pseudopregnancy, induced
by whatever means, is the early domination of the reproductive system
by progesterone. For the purposes of the present review, the timing of
events in pregnancy and pseudopregnancy will be operationally defined.
The first day (day 1) of normal pregnancy in the rat is designated as
the day of detection of spermatozoa in a vaginal smear. For animals
made pseudopregnant, the second day (day 2) of pseudopregnancy is
designated as the day of the first detection of large numbers of leukocytes
in a vaginal smear.

Ovum transport through the rat oviduct takes about 90 hours. Fertilized ova enter the uterus at the morula stage of development on the
evening of day 4 of pregnancy and develop during the night to the
blastocyst stage (De Feo, 1967; Psychoyos, 1967a). On the morning of
day 5, the blastocysts are round vesicles about 100 μ in diameter, con-
sisting of a layer of cytotrophoblast cells which encloses a fluid filled
cavity (the blastocoele) and an inner mass of enlarged cells. Since the
latter is known to give rise to the future embryo, it is also termed the
embryonic cell mass and that region of the trophoblast to which the
inner cell mass is attached is referred to as the embryonic pole of the
blastocyst.

On the morning of day 5 of pregnancy, blastocysts are still surrounded
by a zona pellucida and are distributed within the uterine lumen along
the length of the uterine horns. On or about noon of this day, the zona-
encapsulated blastocysts are consistently found to lie free *in utero,* with
the embryonic pole of the blastocyst directed toward the antimesometrial
surface of the uterine lumen (Psychoyos, 1967a). Between noon and
4 PM of day 5, the zona pellucida disappears, presumably by a lytic
process whose mechanism is unclear (Dickman and Noyes, 1961;
Alloiteau and Psychoyos, 1966; Dickman, 1969). Zona-free blastocysts
flushed from uteri after 4 PM are smaller in size than the zona-encap-

sulated blastocysts of the morning and the older blastocysts appear contracted with their blastocoel markedly reduced in volume (Psychoyos, 1967a). Histological examination of uteri fixed late on this afternoon shows that although the contracted blastocysts still lie free *in utero*, they are compressed between the mesometrial and antimesometrial surfaces of the uterine lumen, due to an edematous swelling of the endometrial stroma (Psychoyos, 1966c, 1967b). The occurrence of a transient phase of endometrial edema is a phenomenon characteristic of preimplantation in a variety of mammals, including man (Noyes *et al.*, 1950).

During the 4 days that fertilized ova take to develop and pass through the fallopian tubes, the uterine endometrium is progressing to an implantation "receptive phase" under the guidance of ovarian hormones. An essential component of endometrial "receptivity" is the development of the potential for a decidual transformation reaction (Shelesnyak, 1960; De Feo, 1967; Finn, 1971). The earliest known response of a "receptive" endometrium to any kind of deciduogenic stimulus is an increase in the permeability of the endometrial capillaries to macromolecules (Psychoyos, 1966c, 1967a). Capillary permeability can be demonstrated by intravenous injection of macromolecular colorants (Evans' Blue,

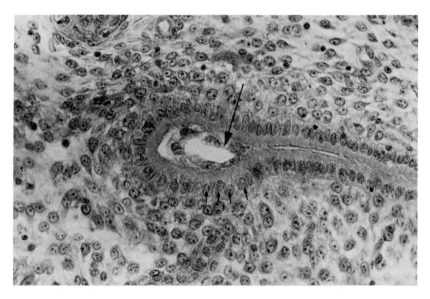

Fig. 1. Transverse section of a rat uterus through a region which exhibited a "blue spot" after dye injection at 5 PM on day 5 of pregnancy. Edema of the endometrial stroma has obliterated the uterine lumen and compressed the blastocyst (arrow) against the epithelial surface of the uterus. Note the basal position of the nuclei of the luminal epithelial cells (arrows).

Geigy Blue, or Pontamine Blue); e.g., blue areas or spots are apparent on the outer surface of the uterus within 15 minutes after the injection of these dyes into rats on day 6 of pregnancy (Psychoyos, 1966a, 1970). After the application of experimental deciduogenic stimuli to pseudopregnant animals, these colorants can be seen to leave the circulation in certain areas of the uterine stroma within about 2 hours after stimulation (Psychoyos, 1973). Injection of dye into pregnant rats first produces blue spots in the endometrial stroma on the late afternoon of day 5 at precisely the sites where the blastocysts are in apposition with the luminal epithelium (Psychoyos, 1966c, 1970). The existence of a short interval of uterine sensitivity to deciduogenic stimuli (Kraicer and Shelesnyak, 1959; Shelesnyak and Kraicer, 1960) has been demonstrated to be maximal in the rat around noon of day 5 of pregnancy (De Feo, 1963a) (Fig. 2).

Profound morphological changes are occurring within the cells of the luminal epithelium simultaneously with the above endometrial events.

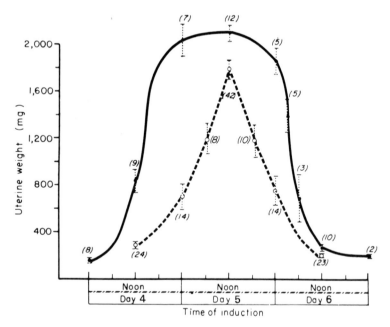

Fig. 2. Comparison of the onset, magnitude and decline of uterine sensitivity for deciduoma formation initiated by trauma or chemical inducers. Uterine weights were measured 120 ± 0.25 hours after application of the stimuli. Numbers in parentheses are the number of uteri weighed; days 4 to 6 correspond to the days of pseudopregnancy enumerated by the method of counting described above in the text. —, Scratch trauma; ---, chemical inducers. Adapted from De Feo (1963b).

The nuclei of the simple columnar epithelial cells are located in the apical half of the cells on the morning of day 5 (Allen, 1931; Psychoyos, 1966c; Potts, 1969). The nuclei change position around noon and come to lie close to the basal plasma membrane. Each nucleus now occupies a position within the cell that until noon was occupied by a cluster of large lipid droplets (Alden, 1947). Although the basal location and ultra-structural characteristics of these droplets are distinctive, no precise information exists as to the process by which they disappear from the cytoplasm. What is clear is that around noon of day 5 when the lipid droplets are no longer identifiable, the apical cytoplasm of these cells has a spongy appearance due to the presence of numerous small vacuoles (Psychoyos, 1966c; Potts, 1969).

Ultrastructural studies have provided suggestive information about the sequence of events during the final stages of preimplantation. Around noon of day 5 of pregnancy the surface of the blastocyst approaches the tips of the microvilli on the luminal epithelial cells to within a distance of about 1 μ (Potts, 1969; Tachi et al., 1970). The epithelial microvilli become flattened and stubby in profile by the afternoon and a new epi-thelial surface structure appears in the form of a bulbous cytoplasmic projection. Scanning electron microscopy (Figs. 3 and 4) reveals that three-dimensionally these projections have the appearance of a "mush-room" (Psychoyos and Mandon, 1971a,b; Nilsson, 1972). Only one such structure is present on any given epithelial cell for a limited period; by day 6 of pregnancy, these projections have disappeared and the epithelial cells once again bear ordered microvilli (Psychoyos, unpublished data). The blastocyst and epithelial cells come into close contact late on the afternoon of day 5, when the epithelial cells have lost their microvilli (Fig. 4). The first sites of adhesion or close contact between the two occur on the surface of the "mushroomlike" structures (Tachi et al., 1970). The surface of the blastocyst is interdigitated around these com-plex epithelial surface structures during the night of day 5. By noon of day 6 the invasion stage of preimplantation has begun, with the first indications of the insinuation of cytoplasmic projections of the tropho-blast cells into and between the epithelial cells (Enders and Schlafke, 1967, 1969; Tachi et al., 1970).

B. Initiation of Ovoimplantation

Early proponents of theories on the initiation of ovoimplantation were divided between the notions that either the ovum or the endometrium was the sole active agent in initiating implantation. Current opinion occupies the middle ground, as expressed by Fawcett (1950), that both the blastocyst and the endometrium have overlapping and mutually

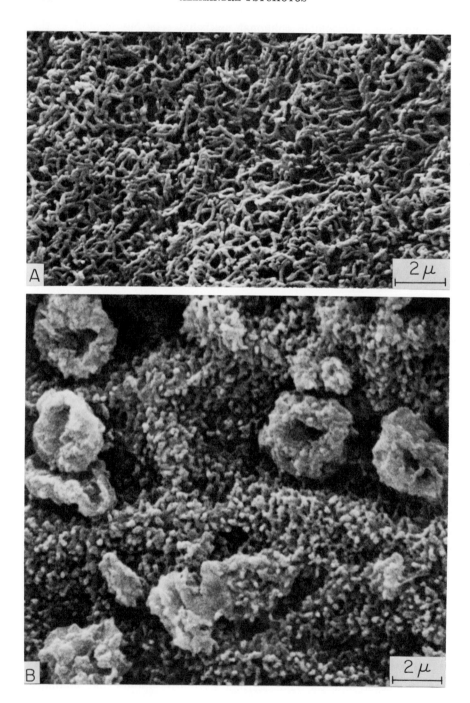

supporting roles with neither being chiefly responsible for initiating implantation. The question remains as to what are the means by which the blastocyst and uterus become cooperative partners in initiating implantation. Blandau (1949) was the first to distinguish an early stage of preimplantation contact between the rat blastocyst and uterine epithelium and proposed that the decidualization of the underlying endometrial stroma was induced during this contact. Blastocysts are known to have unique properties which enable them to induce decidualization that are not possessed by ova at preblastocyst stages of development (Alden and Smith, 1959) or by blastocysts with nonviable blastomeres (Segal and Nelson, 1958). Although the decidualizing stimuli provided by the blastocyst is stage dependent, there need be no species-specific stimulus. The blastocysts of a variety of species can induce decidualization in the mouse uterus (Kirby, 1970), but in the rat there is no corresponding information as to whether there is a species specificity.

Time-lapse cinematography of rat blastocysts cultured *in vitro* has revealed certain possible mechanisms by which the rat blastocyst could inform the uterus of its presence. Blastocysts recovered on noon of day 5 of pregnancy exhibit a series of repetitive contractions and dilatations during the first 35–40 hours *in vitro*. The contraction phase of this sequence occurs over a 1-minute interval during which the blastocyst is reduced in size to a cell mass about 70 μ in diameter. The blastocyst then dilates to about 150 μ in diameter by a progressive increase in volume of the blastocoel. The dilatation phase of the cycle takes some 6 hours, after which spontaneous contractions recur and the dilatation of the blastocoel begins again (Borgese and Cassini, 1963; Cole and Paul, 1965; Bitton-Casimiri *et al.*, 1970) (Fig. 5).

It is important to note that after the first sequence of contractions *in vitro*, one large or several smaller droplets of a viscous refractile fluid are seen on the outer surface of the contracted blastocysts. This fluid appears to have been squeezed out of the blastocoel during the contraction phase (Bitton-Casimiri *et al.*, 1971). The droplets are pushed against the inner surface of the zona pellucida by the expanding blastocyst and can be seen to emerge subsequently into the culture medium through apparent local ruptures in the zona. A hypothesis has been advanced that

---

Fig. 3. (A) Scanning electron micrograph of the epithelial surface of the uterine lumen obtained from a rat killed at 3 PM on day 4 of pregnancy. The micrograph reveals the complex interdigitation of microvilli projecting from the luminal surface of the epithelial cells. (B) Scanning electron micrograph of the luminal surface of the uterus of a rat killed at 3 PM on day 5 of pregnancy. Note the "mushroomlike" protrusions on the surface of individual epithelial cells and the reduction in length of the microvilli on the other epithelial cells. From Psychoyos and Mandon (1971b).

Fig. 4. Scanning electron micrograph of the uterine surface and a portion of a blastocyst of a rat killed at 5 PM on day 5 of pregnancy. Note the "imprints" on the "mushroomlike" projections indenting the surface of the trophoblast cells. The sample was prepared for observation by separating the apposed faces of the uterine lumen, which resulted in fragmentation of the blastocyst. Imprints of the "mushroomlike" projections on the surface of the blastocyst are indicated by arrows; MP, the "mushroomlike" projections on the surface of individual uterine epithelial cells.

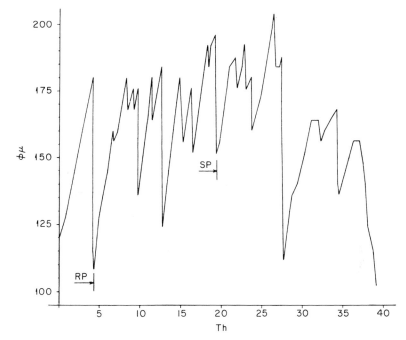

FIG. 5. An example of the variation in diameter of a cultured blastocyst during sequential expansion and contraction phases recorded by time-lapse cinematography. The blastocyst was recovered from a uterus at 4 PM on day 5 of pregnancy and cultured 40 hours *in vitro*. RP, spontaneous rupture of the zona pellucida; SP, emergence of the blastocyst from the zona pellucida; Th, hours *in vitro*; $\phi\mu$, diameter of blastocyst in microns. From Bitton-Casimiri *et al.* (1971).

these droplets contain chemical factors involved in the induction of decidualization (Psychoyos, 1967a; Bitton-Casimiri *et al.*, 1971). This proposal finds support in the observation that living blastocysts whose blastocoels have been filled with trophoblast cells are noncontractile and incapable of inducing decidualization (Gardner, 1971).

Although the blastocoel may contain decidualizing factors, there are at least two additional means by which blastocysts may induce decidualization. The first of these is by mechanical stimulation of the uterine epithelium during the successive cycles of blastocyst contraction and expansion. The second is by trophoblast invasion of the uterine epithelium. Six-day-old rat blastocysts do not exhibit cyclic contractions if placed *in vitro* but will implant normally on transfer to the uteri of rats in day 6 of pseudopregnancy (Bitton-Casimiri *et al.*, 1970; Psychoyos, 1970). It is known that chemical and mechanical inducers are no longer capable of initiating decidualization on day 6 of pseudopregnancy and that deciduoma can be induced at this time only by direct injury of the uterine epithelium (De Feo, 1967). There thus appear to be "fail-safe" programs in the sequence of events of early implantation which ensure that at least one of several operative mechanisms will initiate endometrial decidualization.

The luminal epithelium of the uterus appears to be an indispensable intermediate between the blastocyst and the endometrium. Whether the epithelial cells function as transducers which amplify and relay deciduogenic information or whether these cells are induced to release a unique epithelial stimulus for decidualization is open to speculation and further investigation. What is clear at this point is that disruption of the integrity of the luminal epithelium by traumatic stimuli will induce endometrial decidualization, whereas injury of the endometrium alone is without effect (Fainstat, 1963); and that the ability of traumatic stimuli to induce an endometrial response is completely abolished if the luminal surface of the uterus is exposed to $-20°C$ for 2–3 minutes (Ferrando and Nalbandov, 1968).

Efforts to identify chemical factors responsible for decidualization have focused particular attention on histamine (Chambon and Lefrein, 1952; Shelesnyak, 1957). The introduction of histamine into the lumen of the rat uterus on day 5 of pseudopregnancy induces massive decidualization whereas direct application of histamine antagonists suppresses deciduoma formation (Shelesnyak, 1957). A variety of compounds with differing pharmacological activities have been found to induce deciduomata when instilled into the uterine lumen during the period of optimal sensitivity (De Feo, 1963b, 1967; Psychoyos, 1967a) and compounds with no antihistaminic activity but with inhibitory effects on capillary permeability also prevent deciduoma formation (Psychoyos, 1967a). The latter data highlight the central fact that an increase in vascular permeability appears to be a *sine qua non* condition for decidualization and indicate that the role histamine or other vasoactive amines may play in decidualization must not be overlooked.

We are far from knowing what occurs between the time the epithelium is "informed" and the capillary networks of the endometrial stroma increase in permeability. The lag time between the application of an experimental decidualizing stimulus and the first indications of stromal capillary permeability is on the order of 2–3 hours (Psychoyos, 1973). The autonomous regulation of capillary permeability is known to be dependent on the activation of histidine decarboxylase in mast cells which lie in close proximity to the vascular endothelia (Schayer, 1963). Activation of this enzyme and the synthesis of histamine is induced by intravenous administration of a number of drugs with lag times of 2–3 hours. The coincidence in these induction lag-times suggests that histidine decarboxylase activation and/or synthesis may be involved in the vascular permeability changes which lead to decidualization. That the synthesis of histamine or other vasoactive amines *in situ* may be involved in decidualization is indicated by the following kind of experiment: in rats in which the luminal surface of the uterus has been exposed to $-20°C$ for 2–3 minutes, the intraluminal instillation of histamine induces decidualization, whereas traumatic stimuli are ineffective (Ferrando and Nalbandov, 1968).

Since the discovery by Loeb (1908a,b) that the decidual reaction can be experimentally induced, this phenomenon has been the subject of numerous biological investigations (Shelesnyak, 1962; De Feo, 1967; Finn, 1971). A new organ with specific functions is formed within an interval of 2–3 days which offers the cell biologist a model system for the study of the processes of intercellular communication and cell differentiation. The molecular biology of the decidual reaction has also yet to be worked out in any detail. The hard facts are limited to demonstrations of a tremendous increase in RNA synthesis in the uterus during decidualization (Shelesnyak and Tic, 1963a,b; Glasser, 1972), the blocking effect of actinomycin D on this increase (Sananès and Psychoyos, 1970), the appearance of decidua specific proteins (Yoshinaga, 1972), and an interesting demonstration that crude RNA extracts of decidualized tissue will induce decidualization after intraluminal instillation (Psychoyos, 1969a).

Evidence for induced gene activation associated with the initiation of decidualization and the synthesis of RNA coding for decidua specific proteins have yet to be established, although the studies of Glasser and O'Malley (1970) offer a promising approach to the latter. These authors compared the synthesis of rapidly labeled proteins and nuclear RNA by decidual tissues taken from progesterone treated rats with labeling profiles of protein and nuclear RNA obtained from the uteri of untreated and estrogen-treated, ovariectomized animals. Reported differences in labeling in this type of comparison were interpreted to indicate that RNA transcription occurs in response to progesterone treatment (Glasser, 1972). However, these data give no information on the specificity of induced RNA transcription in that no comparison of the labeling profiles of protein and nuclear RNA was made for progesterone-treated animals, before and after the induction of decidualization.

The first endometrial cells to differentiate into decidual cells are located in the stroma subjacent to the luminal epithelium of the uterus (Krehbiel, 1937; De Feo, 1967). Decidualization of stromal cells appears to spread progressively toward the basal zone of the mucosa. The mechanisms by which differentiation is sequentially induced in cells located progressively farther from the uterine epithelium is unknown (Marcus, 1970). One can speculate that the epithelium induces the first population of decidualizing stromal cells to differentiate and that these cells in turn relay a deciduogenic "message" to noninduced stromal cells. The induction of deciduoma has not received the attention of developmental biologists, and one has no idea of the nature of the "heterogenetic" interactions between epithelium and stroma or of the possible roles of cell migration and "homogenetic" or assimilatory transmission mechanisms (Saxen and Saksela, 1971) in the spread of decidual cell differentiation. It is known that the subepithelial endometrial stromal cells are never seen to divide in the absence of a deciduogenic stimulus; that these cells remain in G_2 of the cell cycle until induced; and, that thymidine-^{3}H incorporation first occurs in this cell population following induction (Galassi, 1968). We know nothing of whether the epithelium represses the division of stromal cells through a G_2 arrest, of whether the "informed" epithelium ceases to repress cell division or on the contrary promotes cell division as the first step in decidual induction. Answers to this type of consideration offer a promising approach to the analysis of the cell biology of decidualization.

III. Hormonal Aspects of Ovoimplantation

A. Ovarian Hormone Requirements for Implantation

At present the rat is the species in which the hormonal requirements for ovoimplantation are best known. The first systematic studies undertaken to determine these requirements only date from some 25 years ago. Until then attention had been focused on the phenomenon of delayed implantation which occurs in rodents during lactation. Lataste (1891) was the first to observe that pregnancy in the *Muridae* could be prolonged for several days in suckling females and that the duration of the prolongation varied according to the number of young being nursed. His postulation that an arrest of embryonic development occurred after the ova had reached the uterus has been amply confirmed. The prolongation of pregnancy during lactation is now known to be due to an extension of the prenidatory period during which fertilized ova at the blastocyst stage are held in a state of diapause within the uterus (Enzmann *et al.*, 1932; Baevsky, 1963; McLaren, 1968).

The hormonal basis for delay of implantation by lactation was investigated as soon as purified ovarian hormones became available. However, the results of these early studies were confusing, in that both progesterone and estrogen when administered alone were reported to shorten the duration of delayed implantation in animals nursing large litters (Krehbiel, 1941a; Weichert, 1941, 1942; Courrier and Baclesse, 1955). That the efficacy of progesterone in shortening the duration of delay was not due to a deficiency in progesterone secretion during lactation was indicated by the fact that the uterus of lactating females would decidualize on traumatic stimulation. However, the threshold for this response was higher than in normal pregnancy. Krehbiel (1941b) showed by electrical stimulation that the stimulus intensity required to induce deciduoma in lactating rats was higher than the intensity required during normal pregnancy. We now know that the short period of optimal sensitivity to a decidualizing stimulus exhibited during normal pregnancy is postponed in lactating animals until a time just prior to actual implantation (Brumley and De Feo, 1964). It was later shown by Bloch (1958) that the efficacy of progesterone in shortening the duration of lactation delay was dependent on the presence of the ovaries. If rats were ovariectomized during lactation delay, progesterone administration had no effect in terminating the arrest of implantation.

Chambon (1949) demonstrated for the first time that delayed implantation would also occur in nonlactating rats if the animals were ovariectomized on day 2 of pregnancy. Canivenc and Laffargue (1956) subsequently ovariectomized rats on day 4 of pregnancy and found that implantation was delayed even when as much as 10 mg of progesterone was administered per day following ovariectomy. Cochrane and Meyer (1957) likewise found that progesterone treatment did not prevent implantation delay in animals ovariectomized on day 3 of pregnancy. However, they were unable to obtain consistent results of delay when ovariectomy was performed on day 4. Canivenc et al. (1956) reported that implantation delay did not occur in animals ovariectomized on day 2 of pregnancy, even if treated with progesterone. The basis for these apparent contradictions was explained through the observation that if one took special care in performing the ovariectomies to remove all ovarian tissue, ovariectomy on any day up to noon of day 4 of pregnancy resulted in delayed implantation, even when progesterone treatment followed the operation (Psychoyos and Alloiteau, 1962). Implantation could only be induced by the additional administration of estradiol (Psychoyos, 1962; Nutting and Meyer, 1963). These results were further supported by experiments (Psychoyos, 1961, 1966a) in which blastocysts were transferred to the uteri of virgin hosts which were ovariectomized and treated with progesterone. The transferred blastocysts were obtained from normal pregnant females on the morning of day 5, on the afternoon of this day when the endometrial "blue reaction" first occurs and on the morning of day 6 when invasive giant cells are present on the surface of the blastocyst. Whatever the age or developmental stage of the transferred blastocysts, implantation did not occur until estrogen was administered. These results leave no doubt that estrogen is indispensable for the induction of nidation in the rat.

The state of uterine preparation for implantation has classically been assayed by testing the endometrium for a decidual response following some form of physical stimulation. With the exception of a few studies like those of Krehbiel (1941b) most decidualizing stimuli employed were traumatic, produced either by passing a thread along the uterine lumen or by scratching the endometrial walls. As discussed above, the endometria of ovariectomized rats receiving progesterone and of lactating animals exhibiting implantation delay respond to this type of stimulus by deciduoma formation (Mayer, 1959). On the basis of this fact, progesterone was considered to be a sufficient hormonal requirement for the development of the endometrial potential for decidualization. Certain drugs were subsequently found to induce decidualization in pseudopregnant rats on intraluminal instillation or intraperitoneal injection (e.g., pyrathiazine), but only when applied during a short period of optimal sensitivity on day 5 of pseudopregnancy (Shelesnyak and Kraicer, 1960; De Feo, 1963a). These inducers were not effective in inducing decidualization in ovariectomized animals which received postoperative progesterone, and it was found that deciduoma formation could be induced only when estrogen was coadministered with progesterone (Courrier and Psychoyos, 1960; Yochim and De Feo, 1963; Shelesnyak and Kraicer, 1963). Shelesnyak (1960) was the first to suggest that the transient period of optimal uterine sensitivity to drug inducers of decidualization was dependent on estrogen. To explain the chronological precision of the onset and duration of this interval of sensitivity, he postulated the existence of an ovarian "estrogen surge" and proposed that the onset of this "surge" corresponded to the time on day 4 when the proestrus rise in estrogen would have occurred in these animals had they not been in progestation. Titration of the amount of estradiol required to induce implantation in ovariectomized, progesterone-treated rats revealed that the minimal effective dose of estradiol was of the order of 30–50 ng if given subcutaneously and 3–5 ng if given locally to the uterus (Table I). The latter could be reduced to 2 ng if progesterone (50 μg) was coinjected with the estradiol (Psychoyos, 1961, 1966a). Under these conditions, the "blue reaction" of the endometrium to dyes injected 24 hours after the coinjection of these hormones was comparable to the endometrial "blue reaction" of a normal pregnancy on the afternoon of day 5. Evidence that an estrogen intervention must occur late in the afternoon of day 4 of normal pregnancy in order for implantation to occur on day

TABLE I

EFFECT OF VARIOUS DOSES OF 17β-ESTRADIOL IN INDUCING IMPLANTATION IN RATS
OVARIECTOMIZED EARLY IN PREGNANCY AND TREATED WITH PROGESTERONE[a]

Dose (ng)	Percentage of animals showing implantations
10 s.c.[b]	0
25 s.c.	42.8
50 s.c.	87.5
100 s.c.	100
2.5[c]	0
5[c]	75
2.5 + progesterone 500 ng[c]	54.5
Progesterone 500 ng[c]	0

[a] From data of Psychoyos (1961, 1966a).
[b] s.c. = Subcutaneous injection.
[c] Local injection into the periuterine fat.

5 was offered by the results of ovariectomies performed on the evening of day 4 of pregnancy. Implantation occurred normally in these animals after progesterone administration, whereas implantation failed to occur in animals ovariectomized before noon on day 4, unless estrogen was coinjected with progesterone (Psychoyos, 1960; Zeilmaker, 1963). Similar results have been obtained with pseudopregnant animals ovariectomized either in the morning or during the late afternoon of day 4 of pseudopregnancy. Animals ovariectomized on the morning of day 4 did not exhibit sensitivity to drug inducers of decidualization when tested the next day unless they were injected with estrogen on the afternoon of day 4 (Shelesnyak et al., 1963).

B. HYPOTHALAMOHYPOPHYSEAL CONTROL OF IMPLANTATION

Ovoimplantation has proved to involve a more complex set of phenomena than initially supposed. Information on the development of the endometrial potential for decidualization and its hormonal conditioning argued for the intervention of higher control mechanisms in timing the sequence of events in early pregnancy. Ball (1940) demonstrated that coitus is in fact the starting point for the establishment of progestation. Implantation does not occur if coital stimulation is insufficient owing to the failure of the corpora lutea to maintain a progestational hormonal status. Prolactin (LTH) secretion is essential in the rat for luteal cell maintenance and progesterone secretion (Astwood, 1941; Alloiteau and Mayer, 1967). LTH release by the anterior pituitary of the rat, as in many other species, is under negative hypothalamic control (Meites et *al.*, 1963; Nicoll *et al.*, 1970) exerted by the release of prolactin inhibiting factor (PIF). The hypothalamus ceases to secrete PIF after coital stimulation, and hypophyseal secretion of LTH thereby occurs. Pregnancy is terminated, i.e., implantation fails to occur, under certain circumstances in which the hypothalamus resumes PIF secretion. This occurs when progestational females are placed in the proximity of alien males (Bruce, 1961). Olfactory stimuli emanating from the males initiate the resumption of PIF secretion, and the corpora lutea degenerate in the absence of LTH.

The role of the hypothalamohypophyseal axis in controlling the secretion of estrogen required for ovoimplantation has been explored in numerous studies. For the purposes of presentation, results on hypophyseal and hypothalamic control of estrogen secretion will be discussed in turn. Hypophysectomy induces a delay in implantation which can be interrupted only by simultaneous injection of progesterone and estrogen (Cohrane and Meyer, 1957). Hypophysectomized rats treated daily with highly purified LTH do not implant ova, even though their corpora lutea show signs of typical luteotropic stimulation; implantation occurs normally in these animals when FSH and LH are combined with the daily LTH treatment (Ahmad *et al.*, 1969). Alloiteau (1961) showed that hypophysectomy during the evening of day 3 of pregnancy blocks blastocyst implantation in progesterone-treated animals, but that implantation occurred normally with progesterone treatment if the operation was performed on the afternoon of day 4. Zeilmaker (1963) compared the time limits when hypophysectomy and ovariectomy would no longer result in delayed implantation in progesterone-treated animals and concluded that ovoimplantation requires the release of gonadotropins around noon of day 4 of pregnancy—i.e., about 7–8 hours before the end of the interval when ovariectomy can induce delayed implantation. Madhwa *et al.* (1968) showed that a minimal dose of anti-LH antisera injected at 10 AM on day 4 of pregnancy will produce delayed implantation which can be counteracted by subsequent estrogen administration. These data allow one to conclude that the estrogen required for ovoimplantation on day 5 of pregnancy is in turn dependent on the release of LH around noon of day 4 of pregnancy. The question is: How is LH release initiated at this precise time?

Everett (1954, 1956a,b, 1964) demonstrated in a series of classic experiments that hypophysectomy and isografting of the anterior pituitary under the kidney capsule assured the continuous release of LTH by the isograft. This conclusion was based on the fact that for periods of up to 2 months the uteri of these animals would decidualize on traumatic stimulation, and it was inferred that sufficient levels of progesterone were being produced by the ovaries due to LTH secretion by the pituitary isograft. When pituitary isografting was performed during progestation, however, nidation did not occur unless estrogen or LH was administered (Everett, 1956a; Meyer *et al.*, 1958; Alloiteau *et al.*, 1963; McDonald *et al.*, 1967). The disconnection of the anterior pituitary from the hypothalamus allowed the graft to stimulate corpora luteal progesterone production, but not that of estrogen. Pituitary isografts are now known to exhibit a deficiency in LH and FSH secretion due to the absence (low concentration) of hypothalamic releasing factors (FSHRF and LRF) required for the synthesis and secretion of FSH and LH (Schally, 1970; McCann, 1970). Likewise, lesions of the median eminence inflicted on the first 2 days of pregnancy result in delayed implantation which can be reversed by estrogen, whereas the lesion is without effect on implantation if the operation is performed on day 4 (Gale and McCann, 1961). LTH secretion by the anterior pituitary is enhanced by median eminence lesions while the synthesis and secretion of FSH and LH are suppressed (McCann and Friedman, 1960).

It is currently accepted that the suckling stimulus influences the hypophyseal-hypothalamic axis in a way analogous to the above operations by suppression of the negative hypothalamic control on LTH secretion and by inhibition of the release of FSH and LH (Rothchild, 1960). However, a prolactin-stimulating activity has also been detected in median eminence extracts from rats (Nicoll *et al.*, 1970), the existence of which could explain the rapid discharge of prolactin occurring in response to the suckling stimulus (Everett, 1964; Grosnevor *et al.*, 1967). Suckling stimulation sufficient to decrease estrogen levels to values lower than required for egg implantation probably is realized in the rat only when more than three young are being suckled—although no chemical data exist on this point. When the number of young nursed is fewer than three there is no delay in implantation in lactating animals (Mayer, 1959). The intensity of the suckling stimulus also influences the duration of the implantation delay, which is proportional to the number of suckling pups (Lataste, 1891; Brumley and De Feo, 1964). Implantation delay induced by suckling reveals the time parameters involved in the hypothalamic and hypophyseal control of the estrogen secretion required for normal ovoimplantation. If female rats nursing a standard litter of 10 pups are separated from the litter before 1 PM of day 4, implantation delay does not occur, whereas if the separation is effected 3 hours later, implantation is delayed by 1 day (Zeilmaker, 1964). These observations clearly indicate that estrogen release on the evening of day 4 is dependent on hypothalamic-hypophyseal events, which under the stimulus of suckling may occur later on day 4 than indicated by the critical time limits established for hypophysectomy to induce implantation delay. This suggests that the suckling stimulus may interfere with the ovarian secretion of estrogen by a mechanism other than the blockade of the release of hypophyseal LH. Does suckling induce the release of a hypothalamic or hypophyseal factor which inhibits ovarian estrogen secretion in response to LH? A factor which also must be taken into consideration is the effect of melanocyte-stimulating hormone (MSH) on ovarian function. Pituitary MSH activity has been reported to be decreased by suckling, an observation suggesting that release of this hormone is induced by neurogenic stimulation (Taleisnik and Orias, 1966; Deis and Orias, 1968). MSH has also been found to inhibit the ovarian ovulatory response to exogenous LH (Psychoyos, 1966d). Such data need to be explored further to determine the role of MSH in the blockade of estrogen secretion induced by suckling.

The operation of a biological clock or circadian rhythm in the neurohypophyseal control of ovoimplantation is indicated by the use of tranquilizers which induce delayed implantation. Daily treatment of progestational animals with certain tranquilizers induces delayed implantation which is not dependent on exogenous progesterone and can be terminated by estrogen administration (Psychoyos, 1968). The pharmacological "isolation" of the hypothalamus from the anterior pituitary induced by these drugs maintains luteal progesterone secretion through the continual release of LTH. A single injection of the tranquilizer trifluoperazine (TFP) on day 3 of pregnancy postpones ovoimplantation by 24 hours to day 6 of pregnancy. TFP injection on day 3 of pregnancy also advances the critical limit for ovariectomy to induce delayed implantation to day 5, instead of day 4, of pregnancy; ovariectomy before noon of day 5 maintains the animals in pseudopregnancy until estrogen is administered, whereas animals ovariectomized during the late afternoon of day 5 implant their ova on day 6, with progesterone alone (Table II).

It is of interest to note that nidation is consistently postponed by 24 hours regardless of whether the drug was injected at 10 AM or 8 PM on day 3. Animals injected over this 10-hour period showed a positive endometrial "blue reaction" precisely on the early afternoon of day 6 of pregnancy. Injection of the drug over the same interval on day 4 had no effect on the time course of implantation, which occurred normally on day 5 of pregnancy (Psychoyos, 1963c, 1968). The same results were obtained when atropine was injected according to this schedule (Schlough, 1969). Atropine and TFP are known to inhibit the ovulatory rise of LH when administered before 2–4 PM on the day of proestrus, either day 4

TABLE II

POSTPONEMENT OF THE TIME LIMITS FOR AN OVARIECTOMY, INDUCING DELAY
IN PREGNANT RATS, BY PRETREATMENT WITH TRIFLUOPERAZINE (TFP)[a]

Treatment by TFP on day 3 (12 noon) of pregnancy	Day of ovariectomy	Percentage of rats showing delay
−	4 (9 AM–12 noon)	95
−	4 (7 PM–8 PM)	56
−	5 (10 AM–12 noon)	0
+	5 (10 AM–12 noon)	100
+	5 (7 PM–8 PM)	37
+	6 (10 AM–12 noon)	0

[a] From data of Psychoyos (1963c, 1968).

or 5, depending on the duration of the estrous cycle (Everett, 1964; Psychoyos, 1968). The failure of these drugs to affect implantation when injected on day 4 of pregnancy indicates that their blockade of the release of LH is only partial and that the levels of LH required for the preparations for implantation are much less than those involved in the initiation of ovulation (Schwartz and Talley, 1968). Bindon (1969a) investigated the time limits for the effectiveness of TFP in inducing a delay in implantation and found that the drug had to be given before 12

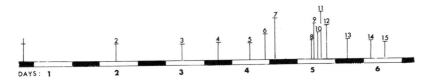

FIG. 6. Timing of sequential preimplantation events in the rat. The 14-hour photoperiod of each day (6 AM to 8 PM) is indicated by the clear bar and the 10-hour dark period by the shaded bar. The numbered vertical lines indicate the time of (1) ovulation and fertilization; (2) the first cleavage and (3) second cleavage divisions of the egg; (4) the end of the period when tranquilizers and (5) hypophysectomy can induce implantation delay; (6) entry of the morula-stage egg into the uterus; (7) the end of the period during which ovariectomy induces implantation delay; (8) the initiation of endometrial edema; (9) attachment (loose) of the blastocyst to the antimesometrial surface of the uterine epithelium; (10) the onset of uterine sensitivity for decidualization; (11) the loss of the zona pellucida; (12) the endometrial "blue reaction" on injection of dyes becomes positive; (13) the end of the period of optimal sensitivity for decidualization; (14) the appearance of endometrial decidual cells; (15) the "final" attachment of the blastocyst to the uterine epithelial cells and the initiation of trophoblast invasion of the endometrium.

midnight of day 3 of pregnancy for TFP to delay implantation. The limit of TFP's effectiveness in inducing implantation delay corresponds to the interval during the night of day 3 of pregnancy, when a significant increase occurs in pituitary FSH output (Bindon, 1969b).

The hypothalamic-hypophyseal axis is clearly the operative control during early pregnancy, not only for the maintenance of corpora luteal function, but also for determining the time of nidation through the release of estrogen (Psychoyos, 1964). Two chronologically sequential events appear to be critical. The first is the secretion of FSH during an interval following 12 midnight on day 3 of pregnancy. The second is the secretion of LH some 12 hours later around the early afternoon of day 4. These two events program the secretion of ovarian estrogen on the evening of day 4 of pregnancy.

IV. Effects of Ovarian Hormones on Ovoendometrial Relationships

A. Morphological and Metabolic Changes

The possibility of suspending embryo-maternal interactions prior to implantation and to reinitiate them at will offers an invaluable model for the analysis of the factors involved in ovoimplantation. In the absence of the hormonal conditions required for the evolution of ovoendometrial interactions, the two partners remain in a preimplantation state of pre-attachment for an indefinite period. Blastocysts in the preimplantation stage are normally found with their embryonic pole in close association with the antimesometrial epithelium of the uterine lumen. When implantation is delayed for prolonged periods, the blastocysts are enclosed between the apposed walls of the uterus (Psychoyos, 1966c, 1967a). The uterine epithelium during delayed implantation is covered by short regular microvilli (Potts and Psychoyos, 1967a; Mayer et al., 1967; Potts, 1969). On certain of the epithelial cells there also exist large protrusions of the plasma membrane that have been described as being "sea-anemone-like" in shape (Psychoyos and Mandon, 1971a). The plasma membranes of the arrested blastocyst and uterine epithelium are usually separated from one another by distances on the order of 1μ and the trophoblast cells on the surface of the arrested blastocyst have the occasional microvillous projection (Potts and Psychoyos, 1967a; Bergstrom and Nilsson, 1970). It is important to note for the discussion below that, during the normal preimplantation stage and in delayed implantation, the basal cytoplasm of the uterine epithelial cells has a localized cluster of large lipid droplets and that similar-appearing lipid droplets or inclusions are found scattered in the cytoplasm of the trophoblast cells. The nucleoli of the latter are dense and prominent, and the nuclear membrane is indented by numerous infoldings (Potts and Psychoyos, 1967a; Potts, 1967, 1969).

Histochemical studies have shown that the RNA content of the blastocyst and uterine epithelial cells is minimal during implantation delay (Psychoyos, 1966c). Intraluminal instillation of radioactive precursors gives no indication of the synthesis of DNA, RNA, or protein in either the blastocysts or epithelial cells of the uteri of ovariectomized, progesterone-treated rats (Prasad et al., 1968). Weitlauf and Greenwald (1965, 1967, 1968) studied in utero protein synthesis in mouse blastocysts and found that the incorporation of methionine-^{35}S increases in the blastocyst between days 4 and 5 of normal pregnancy and that in lactation delay the increase in incorporation into the blastocyst only occurs when implantation is imminent. They also found that blastocysts in mice ovariectomized and treated with progesterone early in pregnancy did not incorporate labeled methionine until protein synthesis was induced by the administration of estrogen.

The surface morphology of the uterine epithelial cells is dependent on the hormonal status of the animal. If rats are ovariectomized during the estrous cycle and treated with estrogen, the microvilli of the uterine epithelial cells increase in length and frequency on the cell surface (Fainstat and Chapman, 1965; Ljungkvist, 1971). The surface morphology described above for the uterine epithelium in delayed implantation is true for animals that have been ovariectomized early in pregnancy and treated daily with progesterone. If at any time during the delay, estrogen is injected, the surface character of the epithelial cells changes within 8–10 hours after estrogen administration (Potts, 1969; Nilsson, 1970; Ljungkvist, 1971). The tentacular projections of the "sea anemone-like" structures enlarge and apparently fuse together (Psychoyos, unpublished) to form a bulbous "mushroomlike" structure which protrudes from the epithelial cell surface (Psychoyos and Mandon, 1971a,b). The surfaces of the blastocyst and epithelium come into contact at sites of apposition between the trophoblast cells and the "mushroomlike" surface projections. Within 18 hours after estrogen injection, the microvilli of both the trophoblast and epithelial cells have become flattened, and by 24 hours the plasma membranes of the two cell types are seen to run parallel over the surface of the "mushroomlike" structures and over the remainder of the epithelial interface, which now no longer bears microvilli (Potts and Psychoyos, 1967a; Potts, 1969). The lipid droplets in both the epithelial and trophoblast cells disappear within 18 hours after estrogen injection, and the nucleoli of the trophoblast cells become diffuse (Potts and Psychoyos, 1967a) ; RNA synthesis in both the blastocyst and uterus is stimulated by estrogen, as is a marked increase in the incorporation of amino acids (Psychoyos, 1966c; Prasad *et al.*, 1968; Dass *et al.*, 1969; Mohla *et al.*, 1970; Tachi *et al.*, 1972).

B. Lysis of the Zona Pellucida

Under the combined effects of estrogen and progesterone, the endometrium arrives at the phase of implantation "receptivity." The lysis of the zona pellucida *in utero* is one of the events that signals the existence of the "receptive" phase (Dickman and Noyes, 1961; Alloiteau and Psychoyos, 1966; Dickman, 1969; McLaren, 1970a). Normally the zona pellucida is "shed" during the early afternoon of day 5 of pregnancy, and no trace is subsequently found of the zona. During implantation delay induced by ovariectomy or hypophysectomy, the blastocysts remain encapsulated within the zona for 2–3 days beyond day 5 post coitum. The delayed blastocyst emerges from the zona on its own by "hatching" and the abandoned zona pellucida persists in the lumen of the uterus for several days. The "hatching" process has been recorded *in vitro* by cinematography and the shed zona retains its morphological identity for extended periods *in vitro* under the usual conditions of pH employed for blastocyst culture (Cole, 1967; Bitton-Casimiri *et al.*, 1970). Blastocysts in delayed implantation which are surrounded by a zona pellucida are found free of the zona within 24 hours after estrogen administration to ovariectomized rats maintained on progesterone (Psychoyos, 1966b; Alloiteau and Psychoyos, 1966). The mechanism of zona lysis in these animals appears to be the same as that occurring during normal pregnancy, in that zonae pellucidae are not recoverable.

The existence of a specific zona lysin has been postulated, but remains as yet undemonstrated. It is known that the exposure of rat blastocysts to medium of pH 3.5–4.0 results in the complete lysis or dissociation of the zona pellucida within a few minutes (Dickman, 1969) and that brief exposure at these pH levels has no effect on the subsequent viability and development of the blastocyst *in utero* (Brun and Psychoyos, 1972). These findings suggest that zona lysis could occur *in utero* by transient acidosis of the blastocyst's environment. This is also supported by the observation that a discreet lowering of the pH of the fluid within the uterine lumen occurs on day 5 of pregnancy, during the interval when zona lysis is known to occur normally (McLaren, 1970b). One can imagine that local ionic changes occur at the interface between the blastocyst and uterine epithelium during the preimplantation stage which lead to zona lysis. *In vitro*, one can induce a local lysis or dissolution of the zona of 5-day blastocysts by placing a microdrop of acidified medium (pH 3.7) in contact with the zona. Over a period of about 2 minutes, the zona swells and progressively dissolves, beginning at the initial point of contact with the microdrop. Zona dissolution stops due to the buffering action of the culture medium and a portion of the zona is left intact (Brun and Psychoyos, 1972). Histochemical studies have demonstrated that a marked increase in ATPase activity occurs on the surface of the luminal epithelial cells during the period of transition to the phase of uterine "receptivity" (Christie, 1966). In addition to the role this enzyme may play in the processes of active transport, ATPase could also be associated with a mechanism of pH lowering at the epithelial cell interface.

V. Effects of Ovarian Hormones on Endometrial Receptivity

A. Hormonally Induced Changes in Endometrial Receptivity

Fertilized ova can develop *in vitro* in relatively simple media (Whitten, 1956; Cole and Paul, 1965; Bitton-Casimiri and Psychoyos, 1968; Brinster, 1969) and proliferate in several extrauterine sites in the absence of ovarian control (Fawcett *et al.*, 1947; Runner, 1947; Kirby, 1960, 1963a,b, 1965; Bland and Donovan, 1965). Chang (1950) first showed, however, that intrauterine development of the fertilized ovum requires a precise synchrony between the stage of ovum development and that of the corpora lutea. The transfer of rabbit ova to pseudopregnant rabbits was unsuccessful if the asynchrony between the age of the fertilized ova and the age of the host uterus was more than 1 or 2 days. In the rat, the 5-day blastocyst survives in the uterus of pseudopregnant animals which are 3 or 4 days pseudopregnant by remaining in diapause until the host uterus becomes receptive to implantation on day 5 of pseudopregnancy. However, 5-day blastocysts never implant when transferred to animals that are 6 or more days pseudopregnant (Dickman and Noyes, 1960; Psychoyos, 1966a). Extensive studies of this phenomenon in the rat by Noyes *et al.* (1963) have shown that the end of day 5 is a critical period during which the uterine milieu becomes hostile (toxic) to unimplanted blastocysts as well as to ova in preblastocyst stages of development. The 5-day blastocyst degenerates and is expelled via the vagina when transferred to pseudopregnant uteri after day 5 (Psychoyos, 1966a). The phase of uterine receptivity occurring on day 5 of normal pregnancy and pseudopregnancy appears to be invariably followed by a state of "nonreceptivity" manifested by the loss of the endometrial potential for deciduoma formation and the hostility of the uterine milieu to unimplanted ova. Both the "receptive" phase and "nonreceptive" state can be interpreted as being expressions of the same biphasic phenomenon induced by a precise temporal sequence of hormonal conditioning. Any procedure which postpones the completion of this conditioning by the evening of day 4 allows the endometrium to remain in a "neutral state."

The capacity for endometrial decidualization is retained in this state, with no apparent time limits—although sensitivity to decidualizing stimuli is reduced. Blastocysts remain viable in a dormant state in such uteri for periods which can be extended to several months (Psychoyos, 1966a, 1967a, 1969b, 1973).

The existence of "neutral" and "nonreceptive" uterine states with an intervening phase of "receptivity" is an interpretation based on numerous findings, in particular those concerning conditions under which one can experimentally induce two asynchronous sets of deciduomata or implantations. Peckham and Greene (1947, 1950) succeeded in obtaining two sets of deciduomata in lactating animals and in animals which were ovariectomized on day 4 of pregnancy and treated with progesterone, but were unable to obtain this result in animals ovariectomized on day 5 of pregnancy. They attributed this failure as being due to the presence of implanting embryos in the uterus on day 5. We can now see that in the first case their animals were ovariectomized before the realization of hormonal conditions which shift the endometrium from the "neutral" state to the "receptive" phase and that their failure to induce "second set" deciduomata after ovariectomy of day 5 can be attributed to the fact that the uteri were then in a "nonreceptive" state. Asynchronous implantations have been reported to occur spontaneously in lactating animals (Weichert, 1940), in hypophysectomized rats with pituitary autografts (Cochrane et al., 1962), and in pregnant rats treated with tranquilizers (Psychoyos, 1968). Asynchronous implantation can be experimentally induced during lactation delay by local uterine injection of progesterone or estrogen (Canivenc et al., 1953; Yoshinaga, 1961). Either hormone will induce the implantation of a "first set" of embryos at the site(s) of hormone injection, while the implantation of the "second set" occurs "spontaneously" elsewhere in the uterus. The hormonal status of lactating animals differs from that of ovariectomized animals in that there is enough endogenous estrogen circulating in the former to act synergistically with the topically injected progesterone to induce implantation (Psychoyos, 1966a).

Sequential implantation "sets" can also be obtained in animals ovariectomized in pregnancy and treated with progesterone (Psychoyos, 1966a, 1967b). Implantation of the "first set" was obtained by local uterine injection of estradiol (5 ng) and of the "second set" by the systemic injection of 100 ng of estradiol. The age difference between the two sets of fetuses depends on the interval between the estradiol injections. When the interval exceeded 6 days, "second set" implantation no longer occurred in the uterine horn which had received topical estradiol, but did occur in the contralateral control horns which had not received estradiol on the first injection. If the systemic injection of estradiol was delayed by more than 10 days, "second set" implantation did not occur in the control horns. The reasons for these failures are unknown. Asynchronous implantation also occurs during delayed implantation induced by tranquilizers or by the operations of hypophysectomy and pituitary autografting early in pregnancy (Alloiteau *et al.*, 1963; Psychoyos *et al.*, 1966). In these cases it is not necessary to induce the "second set" implantations. Implantation of the latter occurs spontaneously 6 days after topical estradiol induction of the "first set," presumably due to estrogen secretion stimulated by placental gonadotropins of the "first set" embryos.

A local phase of implantation "receptivity" appears to be induced by topical application of estrogen, the rest of the uterine endometrium remaining in a "neutral" state until estrogen is made available to it. The notion that the uterus passes through two successive states of "receptivity" during the course of implantation is based on the following type of experiment (Psychoyos, 1969b): Estrogen (25–100 ng) is given systematically on day 5 post coitum to animals that (1) have one uterine horn rendered sterile by ligation of the uterotubal junction prior to mating, and (2) are ovariectomized early in pregnancy and treated with progesterone. Laparotomy is performed on day 8 to verify the occurrence of implantations in the normal horn and donor blastocysts are transferred into the sterile horn. A second dosage of estradiol (100 ng) is injected on the following day (day 9) and the animals are laparotomized 3 days later. The number of implantation sites in the normal horns is found to increase with increasing amounts of estradiol injected on day 5; conversely, the number of implantation sites of donor blastocysts is inversely proportional to the amount of estradiol injected on day 5. The interpretation of this decrease is that, by increasing the concentration of estrogen administered on day 5, the extent of the uterine endometrium in the "neutral" state decreases in both the sterile and normal horns and that implantation "receptivity" induced in the endometrium by the first dose of estrogen is followed by a "nonreceptive" state in which the endometrium is hostile to blastocysts.

B. HORMONAL CONDITIONING OF ENDOMETRIAL RECEPTIVITY

All available information concerning the evolution of the "receptive" phase and "nonreceptive" endometrial state indicates that they are a consequence of the action of estrogen on a uterus primed by progesterone (Rothchild and Meyer, 1942; Psychoyos, 1963a, 1966a; De Feo, 1967; Meyers, 1970; Rossi-Cartoni and Bignami, 1969). The phase of "receptivity" follows a precise time course after the administration of estrogen to ovariectomized rats which have previously received a regimen of

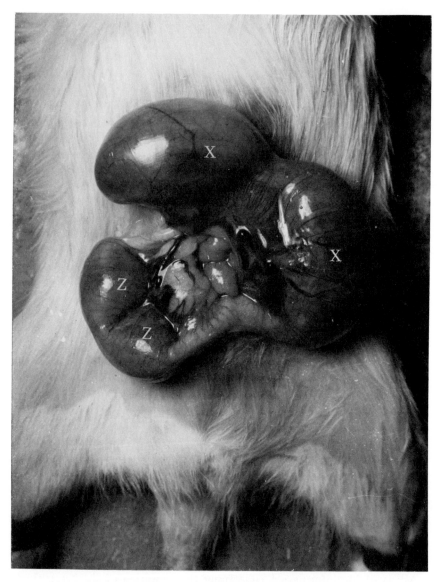

FIG. 7. Asynchronous implantation in a progesterone-treated rat, ovariectomized early in pregnancy. Laparotomy on day 21 post coitum. Implantation of two fetuses (X) at term in the right uterine horn was induced by subcutaneous injection of 50 ng of estradiol on day 5 post coitum; the left horn was rendered sterile prior to coitus by tubal ligation. Two fetuses (Z) have developed from blastocysts transferred into the left horn on day 9 post coitum. Implantation of the "second set" embryos was induced by subcutaneous injection of 100 ng of estradiol on day 10 post coitum.

progesterone treatments. The biphasic changes in endometrial receptivity normally are initiated on the evening of day 4 of pregnancy by an ovarian estrogen intervention. Is the chronological precision of the estrogen intervention due to a particular set of ovarian events occurring on this evening? Estimations of estrogen secretion during the estrous cycle and early pregnancy have been made by intravaginal bioassay (Yoshinaga et al., 1969; Waynforth et al., 1972) and by radioimmunoassay (Shaikh and Abraham, 1969; Shaikh, 1971). These studies show that during the estrous cycle a detectable peak amount of estrogen appears at about noon of each day in the ovarian venous plasma. During day 4 through day 5 of the cycle, i.e., on the day before proestrus and including the day of proestrus, the estrogen content of the ovarian venous plasma does not decline on the afternoon of day 4 of the cycle; rather the ovarian estrogen output continues to increase and reaches a maximal level of 9–11 ng of estrogen per ovary per hour on the noon of proestrus (Yoshinaga et al., 1969). This phenomenon of a continued rise in estrogen levels does not occur on the afternoon of day 4 of pregnancy; rather, the 24-hour periodicity in estrogen secretion continues with a decline in estrogen on the afternoon of day 4 from a peak level of 2 ng of estrogen per ovary per hour in ovarian venous plasma (Yoshinaga et al., 1969). A transient increase in circulating estradiol levels also occurs early in the afternoon of day 4 of pregnancy, with a peak value of 303 pg of estradiol per milliliter of plasma. Plasma estradiol levels decline during that afternoon to a low of 113 pg of estradiol per milliliter from 10 PM to 12 midnight of day 4 (Shaikh, 1971). These findings are consistent with an expected tendency of the ovary to increase its estrogen output on day 4 of pregnancy and with the persistence of diurnal variation in the secretion of estrogen involved in the induction of nidation. The highly sensitive and specific method of gas chromatography with electron capture detection demonstrates that the peaks in circulating estrogen on days 3 and 4 of pregnancy are quantitatively similar (Fig. 8) (Nimrod-Zmigrod et al., 1972). Therefore, it is difficult to explain the precise timing of the changes leading to endometrial "receptivity" and "nonreceptivity" on the basis of differences in estrogen levels on day 4 vs day 3 of pregnancy.

Safeguard mechanisms appear to operate to prevent the occurrence of asynchrony in ovoendometrial interactions which could result from fortuitous variations in circulating estrogen levels. One should note that while the peak values of estrogen normally appear in plasma around noon of day 4 of pregnancy, it is only on the evening of this day that the ovaries are no longer necessary for nidation. A prerequisite must be fulfilled during the afternoon of day 4 which allows endogenous estrogen to act. What is this prerequisite? In pregnant rats ovariectomized on day 4 of pregnancy and started on a daily regimen of progesterone treatment beginning immediately after the operation, exogenous estrogen induces implantation at the normal time on day 5 when it is administered on the evening of day 4, but has no effect if given on that morning. In the latter case, estrogen can induce implantation when given on the morning of day 4, if an intact animal is started on a progesterone regimen on the first day of pregnancy and is ovariectomized as above on day 4 (Psychoyos, 1966a). The capacity of the endometrium to respond to estrogen appears to be dependent on the length of time the uterus or the reproductive system is exposed to progesterone. There are numerous data which show clearly that estrogen can be effective in inducing the endometrial changes leading to the "receptive" phase and "nonreceptive" state, only after a period of preparation of the endometrium by progesterone treatment for about 48 hours (Psychoyos, 1966a, 1967a, 1969b, 1973; Harper 1968; Martin and Fin, 1969, 1970). Thus, in pregnant rats ovariectomized on day 2 and treated daily with both estrogen and progesterone starting on day 5 post coitum, the endometrial "blue reaction" cannot be evoked earlier than the third day after the beginning of hormone treatment (Psychoyos, 1966a). Similarly, animals ovariectomized on the day after the day of estrus and treated daily with both ovarian hormones show the same timing in the onset, the magnitude of response and loss of sensitivity for deciduoma formation as intact pseudopregnant animals (Yochim and De Feo, 1963). Dickman (1972) has concluded from a certain type of experiment that only 24 hours of progesterone priming is sufficient or "compatible" with nidation. In his study, females in the estrous cycle were ovariectomized, and 30 days after the operation progesterone was administered for the first time. Twenty-four hours after this injection, donor blastocysts were transferred to the uteri of these animals, and a regimen of progesterone and estrogen administration was begun. The animals were autopsied 15 days after the transfer, and fetuses were found to be present in the uteri. On the basis of this finding, Dickman concluded that 24 hours of progesterone priming is sufficient for estrogen to initiate implantation and interpreted the experiment as indicating that the first dose of estrogen in the combined hormone treatment was a so-called "nidatory" estrogen. It is important to note that there was no indication in these data of the precise developmental stage of the embryos on autopsy. When in fact did the blastocysts implant relative to the first progesterone administration? Another interpretation of these data is possible which is consistent with other findings: namely, the transferred blastocysts may have implanted only after the second combined hormone administration, not after the first as assumed by Dickman.

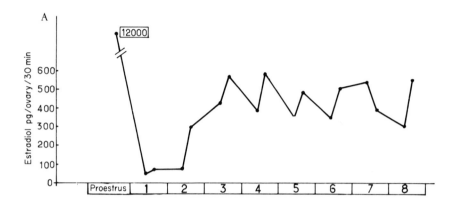

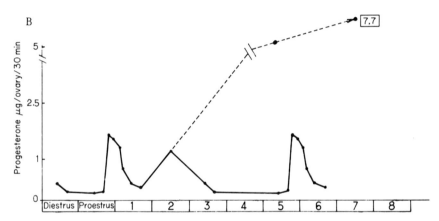

Fig. 8. Secretion rate of 17β-estradiol and progesterone into the ovarian venous blood of rats. (A) Ovarian secretion of 17β-estradiol in proestrus and during the first week of pregnancy. For proestrus, blood was collected for 30 minutes beginning at 3 PM and the values represent the estradiol content of blood collected from two animals. For pregnancy, each point represents the mean of five analyses; each analysis was done on a combined sample of blood from three animals. From the data of Nimrod-Zmigrod et al. (1972). (B) Ovarian secretion of progesterone during the estrous cycle and the first week of pregnancy. For the estrous cycle (●—●), each point indicates the mean of values obtained for 8–10 animals sacrificed at the indicated times (data of Uchida et al., 1969). For pregnancy (●- - -●), each point is the mean value of analyses for 5 animals (data of Hashimoto et al., 1968).

Progesterone blood levels during the estrous cycle show the following sequence (Eto et al., 1962; Feder et al., 1968; Hashimoto et al., 1968; Uchida et al., 1969; Roser and Bloch, 1969; Hashimoto and Wiest, 1969): On day 5 of the cycle, the day of proestrus, there is a high burst of pre-ovulatory progesterone circulating for a short interval. Progesterone levels are almost nonexistent the next day during estrus (day 1 of a cycle), and progesterone levels start to rise again by the afternoon of the first day of diestrus (day 2) to reach peak values on day 3, followed by a decline to low values on day 4 of the cycle. The decline in progesterone blood levels does not occur on day 3 of early pregnancy or pseudopregnancy (Fajer and Barraclough, 1967; Hashimoto et al., 1968; Wiest, 1970), rather the blood levels persist at values approximate to those of day 3 of the estrous cycle with a tendency to gradually increase for the next several days (Fig. 8). According to this schema, the 48 hours of progesterone preparation of the endometrium is normally achieved by the evening of day 4 of pregnancy. If estrogen is also available at this moment the basic hormone requirements for the induction of implantation are satisfied and result in the appearance of the "receptive" phase of endometrial receptivity at about noon of day 5 and thence to the "nonreceptive" state on day 6.

Certain aspects of the timing of the onset of the "receptive" phase and "nonreceptive" state of endometrial receptivity are indicated in the following experiments (Psychoyos, 1969b, 1970). Donor blastocysts implant in the uteri of virgin rats treated with various progesterone–estrogen sequences if the blastocysts are transferred within 24 hours after the injection of estrogen, which completes the basic hormonal sequence initiating the "receptive" phase. If the blastocysts are transferred later than 24 hours after this estrogen injection, implantation fails to occur (Table III).

Similarly, prepubertal rats can be induced to ovulate by a 48-hour

TABLE III

IMPLANTATION OF BLASTOCYTS TRANSFERRED TO VIRGIN OVARIECTOMIZED RATS, PRETREATED WITH THE OVARIAN HORMONES AT DIFFERENT SEQUENCES[a,b]

	Treatment[c] prior to transfer on day 5					Percentage of blastocysts implanted
Days:	1	2	3	4	5	
	—	—	P	P	PE	44
	P	P	P	P	PE	71
	P	P	P	PE	P	66
	P	P	PE	P	P	0
	P	P	PE	P	PE	0
	—	—	PE	P	PE	63

[a] From data of Psychoyos (1969b).
[b] The basic progesterone-estrogen sequence is underlined.
[c] P, progesterone, 5 mg subcutaneously (s.c.); E, 17β-estradiol, 100 ng s.c.

treatment with PMS followed by HCG which induces ovulation about 12 hours after injection. If progesterone is administered for 3 days, beginning on the first day of injection of PMS, the presence of progesterone for 48 hours preceding a fertile coitus completely blocks implantation (Psychoyos, 1963b). In this case, the basic sequence of progesterone (exogenous) and estrogen (endogenous at proestrus) completes the hormonal conditions initiating endometrial receptivity when the ova are still in the oviduct and the uterus is in the "nonreceptive" state when the ova enter the uterus on the evening of day 4 of pregnancy. The daily administration of progesterone during early pregnancy, beginning on the day of proestrus or estrus, has no effect on implantation unless estrogen is given systemically or locally to the uterus on or before day 3 of pregnancy (Table IV) (Psychoyos, 1970; Yoshinaga and Greep, 1971). In this example, as in the above case, completion of the basic progesterone-estrogen sequence prior to the arrival of ova into the uterus creates an asynchrony in embryomaternal relations. Uterine sensitivity for deciduoma formation is advanced in the same manner as endometrial receptivity for implantation. If rats are treated with progesterone beginning on the day of estrus, rendered pseudopregnant post coitum, and injected with estrogen on day 3, the optimal endometrial response for deciduoma formation by trauma is obtained on day 4—one day in advance of the usual interval of optimal sensitivity (Yoshinaga and Greep, 1970).

A contraceptive effect of progesterone, independent of its inhibition

TABLE IV

EFFECT ON OVOIMPLANTATION OF SEQUENTIAL TREATMENT OF NORMAL RATS
WITH A PROGESTERONE DERIVATIVE AND ESTRADIOL[a]

Day of treatment[b]						Mean number of implantation sites in rats showing nidation
	Day of pregnancy			Number of rats treated	Percentage of rats showing nidation	
Proestrus	Day 1 (estrus)	Day 2	Day 3			
—	—	—	E	5	100	9.6
—	P	P	—	5	100	9.0
—	P	P	E	12	40	7.6
P	P	—	—	8	87	9.1
P	P	—	E	8	25	5.5
P	P	P	—	5	100	8.2
P	P	P	E	10	20	1.0

[a] From unpublished data of A. Psychoyos.

[b] P = 2.5 mg of a progesterone derivative given subcutaneously (s.c.); activity of this derivative is 75% of the activity of progesterone, as based on the Clauberg test in rabbits. E = 100 ng of 17β-estradiol given s.c.

TABLE V

EFFECT OF A SINGLE INJECTION OF ESTRADIOL OR OF AN INTERRUPTION OF THE PROGESTERONE TREATMENT ON THE UTERINE CAPACITY FOR DECIDUALIZATION BY TRAUMA OF OVARIECTOMIZED, PROGESTERONE-TREATED RATS[a]

Day:	Daily treatment[b] before trauma										Percentage of animals with decidual response	Uterine weight of the traumatized cornua[c] (mg ± SE)
	1	2	3	4	5	6	7	8	9	10		
	P	P	PE	Tr							100	540 ± 17
	P	P	PE	P	Tr						12.5	146 ± 18
	P	P	P	P	Tr						100	513 ± 80
	P	P	P	P	P	P	P	P	P	Tr	100	507 ± 89
	P	P	PE	P	P	P	P	P	P	Tr	0	101 ± 5
	P	P	PE	—	P	P	P	Tr			0	112 ± 2
	P	P	PE	—	—	P	P	P	Tr		87.5	425 ± 23
	P	P	PE	—	—	—	P	P	P	Tr	87.5	398 ± 70

[a] From data of Meyers (1970).

[b] P, progesterone 2.5 mg s.c.; E, 17β-estradiol 200 ng; Tr, trauma.

[c] 96 Hours after trauma.

of ovulation, has been demonstrated in human beings with small dosages of progestins given daily orally (Martinez-Manautou et al., 1966) or contained in silastic capsules implanted subcutaneously (Croxatto et al., 1969). Progestins given during the preovulatory period interfere with normal implantation in the rabbit (Chang, 1969) and a contraceptive action of progesterone contained in silastic capsules placed directly in the uterine cavity has been demonstrated in the rabbit (Vickery et al., 1970), the rhesus monkey, and the human being (Scommegna et al., 1970).

Meyers (1970) showed that maintenance of the "nonreceptive" state of endometrial receptivity requires daily progesterone administration. Maintenance was tested only up to 11 days after the onset of "nonreceptivity" in these experiments, but presumably the uterus can be kept in this state for an indefinite period (Table V). Meyers also found that if the progesterone regimen was stopped for a minimal interval of 72 hours, the endometrium redevelops its progestational potential. The latter finding is important, for it shows that in the absence of progesterone the uterus passes through a recovery phase after which progesterone treatment can reinitiate the "neutral" state of endometrial receptivity.

C. Summary of the Information on Endometrial Receptivity

A model of the relationships between hormonally induced events and the phases and states of endometrial receptivity is presented in a symbolic representation (Fig. 9) which summarizes the available information on the sequential endometrial events (Cooper and Psychoyos, 1973). The first events begin at a point of departure designated as P→, which represents the initiation of a series of uterine changes leading to the "neutral" state of endometrial receptivity. These changes are progesterone dependent and require at least 48 hours of progesterone administration before the "neutral" state is established. Animals can be maintained indefinitely in this state by a regimen of daily progesterone treatment. If at any time, designated as E/, estrogen administration is superimposed once on the progesterone regimen, a second series of uterine events are initiated which lead to the establishment of the "nonreceptive" state. A "receptive" phase of endometrial receptivity exists for a few hours midway between E/ and the establishment of the "nonreceptive" state. Maintenance of the "nonreceptive" state requires continued progesterone administration. If this is terminated at any time when the uterus is in either the "neutral" or "nonreceptive" states, progesterone arrest for a minimal period of 72 hours returns the uterus to a condition where the readministration of progesterone leads to the reestablishment of the "neutral" state. In the diagram, the arrest of progesterone treatment is

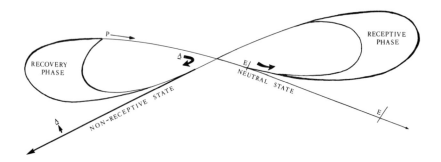

Fig. 9. A Möbius strip of uterine receptivity to ovoimplantation in ovariectomized rats. The cycle: If a regimen of daily progesterone administration is begun
at point P→, within 48 hours the uterus is established in a neutral state of receptivity equivalent to the uterine state of delayed implantation. Implantation is
initiated by estrogen, given once as E/, which induces a brief phase of uterine receptivity to ova, followed by a state of nonreceptivity or toxicity to ova. The
maintenance of the nonreceptive state requires continued progesterone administration. If at any time the progesterone regimen is terminated (A), within 72 hours
the uterus will pass through a recovery phase which allows the neutral state of
receptivity to be reestablished by a second regimen of progesterone administration.
The indefinite nature of the potential duration of the neutral and nonreceptive
states is indicated by lines projecting off the cyclic strip. The short-circuit cycle:
If progesterone administration is terminated (A) when the uterus is in the neutral
state, the uterus will pass through the recovery phase and return to a point where
the reinitiation of progesterone administration reestablishes the neutral state. From
G. W. Cooper and A. Psychoyos (1973), unpublished data.

designated as A and the interval of return of the uterus to a state of
progestational potential is referred to as the recovery phase. Under the
conditions of a normal pregnancy, P→ is initiated late on day 2 and leads
to the establishment of the "neutral" state on the evening of day 4.
E/ is realized on the evening of day 4, with the "nonreceptive" state
following some 36–48 hours later. The transient phase of "receptivity"
occurs during a brief interval around mid day of day 5 of pregnancy.

VI. Hormone Recognition and Transcriptional Events

The control of endometrial receptivity appears to be essentially
realized by hormone interactions based on the time relationship between
the secretion of progesterone and estrogen. We are now at a critical point
in our understanding, when it is just becoming apparent how endometrial
functions, effected by the synergistic or antagonistic relationship of progesterone and estrogen (Courrier, 1950), are manifested at the molecular
level.

Recognition of ovarian hormones by the endometrial cells is now known to be due to the existence of specific intracellular macromolecular components. The presence of estradiol receptors in the uterine cytosol fractions of castrated and immature animals is well established, and a nuclear estradiol receptor, whose formation is dependent on the presence of both estradiol and the cytoplasmic estradiol receptors, has been demonstrated (Talwar et al., 1964; Toft and Gorski, 1966; Jensen et al., 1968; Gorski et al., 1968; Baulieu et al., 1972). The transfer of estradiol into the cell nucleus is followed by binding of the hormone to these nuclear receptor components. An estradiol–nuclear receptor complex is known to be capable of attaching to an acceptor site(s) on the nuclear chromatin; attachment appears to induce the transcription of messenger RNA coding for the synthesis of a specific protein. According to current suggestions, this protein activates a nucleolar RNA-polymerase, which in turn amplifies the synthesis of ribosomal RNA. Cyclic changes in the concentration of estradiol-receptor sites in cytosol preparations of rat uteri (Mešter et al., 1970) have been demonstrated during the estrous cycle, with a maximum occurring in late diestrus (Feherty et al., 1970). An increase in cytoplasmic receptor sites is also observed by day 3 of pregnancy in the endometrium and the levels of these receptors plateau until day 6, when the levels begin to decline (Mešter et al., 1973). Cytoplasmic estrogen receptors remain at constant low values after ovariectomy at estrus or the day after estrus and can be increased by treatment with either estrogen (Feherty et al., 1970) or progesterone (Mešter et al., 1973).

Macromolecular components have been found in uterine cytosol fractions which show high affinity binding for progesterone (Milgrom and Baulieu, 1970; McGuire and De Della, 1971; Milgrom et al., 1971, 1972; Feil et al., 1972). If one extrapolates from what is known about transcriptional events and the synthesis of a specific protein called avidin induced by progesterone in the chicken oviduct (O'Malley et al., 1969), it is to be expected that progesterone-receptor complexes should induce the synthesis of specific proteins in mammalian endometria as well. Progesterone-binding components in rat uterine cytosol fractions show variations during the estrous cycle with a maximum at proestrus. Increase in the levels of these components appears to be estrogen dependent; ovariectomy "destroys" these components, but restoration to levels characteristic for normal animals follows estrogen stimulation (Feil et al., 1972). The cytoplasmic levels of progesterone binding macromolecules are markedly decreased during diestrus, presumably owing to the increase in circulating progesterone at diestrus. A decrease in these binding components has been shown to occur in the guinea pig after progesterone administration. Diestrus of the luteal phase of the cycle in the guinea pig lasts for more than 12 days. During this interval, uterine proges-

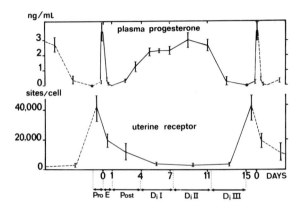

FIG. 10. Comparison of plasma progesterone levels (ng/ml) and the number of progesterone-receptor sites per uterine cell during the estrous cycle of the guinea pig. Pro, proestrus; E, estrus; Post, postestrus; D_i, diestrus. From Milgrom et al. (1972).

terone-receptor components remain low in cytosol fractions and are found to increase at proestrus (Milgrom et al., 1972) (Fig. 10).

It is interesting that the starting point for progesterone preparation of the "neutral" state begins on the day on which progesterone binding components reach a nadir in the endometrial cytoplasm. This fact could indicate that the macromolecular binding components have an antagonistic effect on the induction of the "neutral" state by progesterone. With this interpretation in mind, it is interesting that the high cytoplasmic levels of these binding components are present during proestrus and decline after a transitory preovulatory rise of circulating progesterone. This rise is correlated with the postestrous decrease in the cytoplasmic levels of progesterone-receptor components. Does the decline in cytoplasmic receptors allow the endometrium to respond to progesterone 2 days later by the evolution of the "neutral" state of receptivity? Evidence that this is indeed the case, that a saturation or destruction of progesterone binding components is requisite, is offered by the fact that the preovulatory rise of progesterone, though quantitatively higher than the progesterone levels attained during early pregnancy on the evening of day 2, is unable to induce the initiation of endometrial changes leading to the "neutral" state. For this to occur, exogenous progesterone is needed—indicating that in proestrus the progesterone requirements indicated as P→ in Fig. 9 are much greater than those needed on day 2 of pregnancy.

The proestrus rise in progesterone binding components appears to be induced by estrogen released on the day preceding proestrus. Estrogen presumably acts by inducing *de novo* synthesis of these progesterone binding macromolecules which in turn cancel or prevent the preovulatory rise in progesterone secretion from having an effect P→ leading to the "neutral" state of receptivity. Preovulatory progesterone is involved, as discussed above, in the decline in cytoplasmic progesterone-receptor levels. A decline in these levels appears to be a requisite condition for the initiation of the "neutral" state of endometrial receptivity by rising progesterone levels on day 2 of pregnancy. The fact that the basic progestrone–estrogen sequence leading to "receptivity" and the "non-receptive" state commences on the evening of day 2 of pregnancy appears to result from progesterone—estrogen interactions which have been acting at the molecular level since the day preceding proestrus. This molecular interplay of hormones and receptors is also under command of the hypothalamic-hypophyseal axis through the controlled release of pituitary hormones responsible for ovulation and the sequential preovulatory rises in estrogen and progesterone secretion.

Most of the uterine changes occurring after the completion of the basic progesterone–estrogen sequence (P→, E/) also occur in uteri stimulated by estrogen alone. These changes include histamine release, a decrease in the number of mast cells, an increase in intrauterine eosinophilic leukocytes, endometrial vasodilatation, edema, and increases in precursor incorporation into ribonucleic acid and proteins (Shelesnyak and Kraicer, 1963; Marcus and Shelesnyak, 1967; Lobel *et al.*, 1965a,b; De Feo, 1967; Segal and Scher, 1967; Heald and O'Grady, 1970; Glasser, 1972). However, the changes specific to the "receptive" endometrium and in particular those exhibited by the luminal epithelium, require the combined action of progesterone and estrogen. These changes include the loss of the large cytoplasmic lipid droplets by the epithelial cells and the blastocyst, ultrastructural surface changes, as well as uterine changes which permit the blastocyst to develop and the zona pellucida to undergo lysis.

Why is estrogen effective in inducing endometrial "receptivity" only after the "neutral" state is established by progesterone? The level of incorporation of radioactive estradiol by the endometrium of ovariectomized rats is known to be dependent on the regimen of progesterone treatment prior to estradiol administration (Fig. 11) (Psychoyos *et al.*, 1968). Recent autoradiographic studies (Tachi *et al.*, 1972) have shown that uteri in the "neutral" state, i.e., in ovariectomized, progesterone-treated animals, bind tritiated estradiol in the endometrial stromal cells, while the luminal epithelial cells remain unlabeled. Smith *et al.* (1970) reported that progesterone treatment promotes estrogen binding by uterine stromal cells and inhibits or fails to promote estrogen incorporation into the epithelial cells. Estrogen induction of DNA-dependent RNA

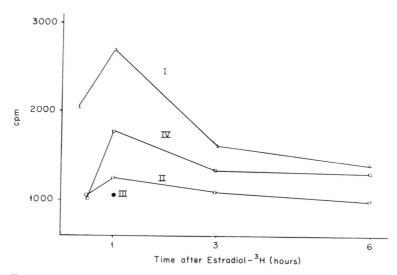

Fig. 11. Total incorporation of estradiol-³H (O-³H) into the endometrium of ovariectomized rats. The animals treated with various sequences of unlabeled estradiol (O) and progesterone (P) were injected with 0.1 μg of estradiol-³H and sacrificed after 1, 3, or 6 hours. Major changes in incorporation of label were noted within 1 hour. Incorporation by animals in Group III is considered as the baseline value, in which estradiol-³H was given 48 hours after a single injection of unlabeled estradiol. Treatment sequence: I, — — PO P PO-³H; II, P P PO P PO-³H; III, — — O — O-³H; IV, P P P P PO-³H. After Psychoyos *et al.* (1968).

synthesis prior to the manifestation of the "receptive" phase is suggested by the ability of actinomycin D to suppress uterine sensitivity for the decidual response (Glasser, 1965, 1972). However, it has not yet been possible to demonstrate that qualitatively different RNAs are synthesized by the rat uterus during the prenidatory period (Heald *et al.*, 1972) (Fig. 12); although such has been reported to occur in the rabbit endometrium at the time of egg implantation (Vittorelli *et al.*, 1967). In our laboratory, recent experiments have shown that progesterone induces a 2-fold increase in uridine incorporation (pulse labeling) into nuclear RNA fractions within 4 hours after injection and that after 9 hours pulse-labeling incorporation occurs at the same rate in the control and experimental animals (Sananès *et al.*, 1973). Glasser and O'Malley (1970) found a specific RNA fraction to be synthesized by decidual tissue under progesterone stimulation. Estrogen stimulates the rate of incorporation of uridine into uterine RNA to a greater degree in ovariectomized progesterone-treated animals than in animals which have not received progesterone after ovariectomy (Psychoyos, 1969a, 1970)

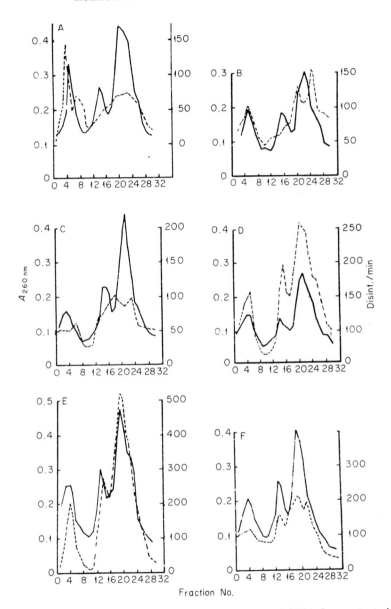

Fig. 12. Distribution of radioactivity in phenol-extracted RNA from rat uteri at different stages of pregnancy, following a 1-hour pulse of uridine-^{3}H. Days of pregnancy: (A) day 2; (B) day 3; (C) day 4; (D) day 5; (E) day 6, the implantation area, and (F) the interimplantation area. Curves: —, absorbance at 260 nm of fractions collected after sucrose gradient centrifugation; -----, disintegrations per minute. From Heald *et al.* (1972).

TABLE VI

EFFECT OF PROGESTERONE PRETREATMENT ON THE INCORPORATION *in Vivo*
OF TRITIATED URIDINE INTO UTERINE NUCLEAR RNA
(PULSE LABELING 10 MINUTES PRIOR TO SACRIFICE)[a]

	Regimen of treatment[b] of ovariectomized rats prior to sacrifice on day 5					Percent of incorporation of controls (treated with estrogen alone)
Day:	1	2	3	4	5	
	—	—	—	—	PE	157
	—	—	—	P	PE	74
	—	—	P	P	· PE	93
	—	P	P	P	PE	259
	P	P	P	P	PE	268

[a] From data of Psychoyos (1970).

[b] On day 5 the animals received progesterone 90 minutes prior to sacrifice, with estrogen administered 30 minutes before sacrifice. P, progesterone, 5 mg s.c. in sesame oil; E, 17β-estradiol, 10 μg i.p. in propylene glycol.

(Table VI). The rate of uridine incorporation induced by estrogen administration varies according to the duration of the pretreatment with progesterone, being greatest after 48 hours of pretreatment. This quantitative difference in the stimulation of RNA synthesis by estrogen may also be indicative of qualitative differences in the RNA synthesized before and after the completion of the 48-hour progesterone priming period, but direct evidence on this point is not available at present. It is amply apparent that our present knowledge is seriously deficient in the correlation of functional uterine conditions with transcriptional and translational events. However, it is at the molecular level that the study of the mechanisms of ovoimplantation must now be approached.

VII. REPRESSION AND ACTIVATION OF THE BLASTOCYST

The uterus is a hostile environment for the fertilized ovum except during an interval of a few hours when the uterine environment promotes the development of the blastocyst and actively participates in initiating the process of implantation. Is it paradoxical that the uterus is usually hostile to ova considering the invasive potential of the trophoblast cells? The complex mechanisms that control the synchrony of ovoendometrial evolution protect the blastocysts from the uterus and the uterus from the blastocysts. The ovum at any stage of development degenerates *in utero* if the development of the uterus is asynchronously in advance of that of the ovum. If the ovum reaches the uterus when the endometrium has yet to become receptive, it either will degenerate or its growth will be arrested at the blastocyst stage until the endometrium becomes receptive. Ovum degeneration occurs in most species after early ovariectomy without progesterone replacement therapy and may occur during lactation, as is usually the case in the rabbit (Courrier, 1945). However, in a large variety of species a delay in the manifestation of endometrial receptivity is accompanied by blastocyst diapause (Canivenc, 1960; Enders, 1967; Short and Hay, 1965; Daniel and Krishnan, 1970).

Extensive studies have been undertaken during the past several years to determine whether uterine control of the proliferation and survival of the fertilized ovum, and in particular the blastocyst, is exerted by factors which either promote or inhibit ovum development. A specific protein (uteroglobin), whose synthesis is hormone sensitive, has been identified by Beier (1968). Uteroglobin appears to be identical to a protein called blastokinin, which has been isolated from rabbit uteri during early pregnancy (Fig. 13). Blastokinin has been reported to promote blastulation and blastocyst development *in vitro* (Krishnan and Daniel, 1967). However, the evidence offered for such an effect is not particularly convincing. Any culture medium enriched in serum proteins favors *in vitro* development of the blastocyst and proteinaceous components of the uterine secretion appear to have an analogous nonspecific effect. Rat blastocysts cultured in the presence of any one of four main protein fractions obtain by Sephadex G-200 column fractionation of rat uterine flushings show an increase in metabolic activity, as judged by the uptake and incorporation of RNA precursors (Psychoyos *et al.,* 1973). However, the possibility does exist that uterine proteins may be involved in a specific way to assure blastocyst totipotency in development. Kirby (1965) demonstrated a favorable effect of the progestational uterine environment on the normal development of embryonic mouse tissues. Tubal ova, up to the morula stage, give rise to trophoblastic tissue only when transferred to ectopic sites, such as under the kidney capsule. The same is true for ova which have developed up to the blastocyst stage within the oviducts. However, if such blastocysts are first transferred to a receptive uterus and then to an ectopic site, the blastocysts give rise to embryonic as well as trophoblastic tissues.

The metabolic activity of the ovum during the early cleavage stages differs from that of the blastocyst (Weitlauf and Greenwald, 1967). Incorporation of RNA and protein precursors *in vitro* is minimal up to the morula stage and rises sharply at the blastocyst stage (Mintz, 1965; Monesi and Salfi, 1967). Radiolabeling and extraction of RNA synthesized *in utero* by rabbit ova has shown that total RNA synthesis changes little during the tubal life of the embryo. RNA synthesis at the 2-cell stage is predominately tRNA (71% of uridine incorporation is into low

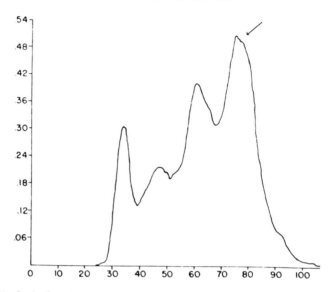

Fig. 13. Sephadex G-200 gel filtration of the uterine fluid of rabbits on day 5 of pregnancy. The fraction which corresponds to blastokinin is indicated by the arrow. From Daniel and Krishnan (1970).

molecular weight RNA). Ova exhibit a 1000-fold increase in RNA synthesis after entering the uterus. The synthetic pattern in the blastocyst shows a predominance of ribosomal RNA synthesis (71%) and DNA-like RNA (21%) (Greenslade et al., 1972). Rat and mouse blastocysts in the uteri of lactating females and animals undergoing experimentally induced delay do not show high levels of RNA and protein synthesis. Rat blastocysts from normal pregnancies (Weitlauf and Greenwald, 1965; Psychoyos, 1967b; Prasad et al., 1968; Sanyal and Meyer, 1970) incorporate DNA, RNA, and protein precursors in vitro, whereas blastocysts obtained from lactating or experimentally delayed animals do not incorporate these precursors during the first few hours in vitro after recovery from these uteri (Gulyas and Daniel, 1969; Psychoyos and Bitton-Casimiri, 1969; Jacobson et al., 1970). Dormant blastocysts begin to incorporate uridine after some 12 hours in vitro (Fig. 14), and RNA synthetic activity gradually increases until the incorporation values plateau around the twentieth hour of culture (Psychoyos et al., 1973; Psychoyos and Bitton-Casimiri, 1969). Likewise, the cells of dormant blastocyst proliferate on transfer to the anterior chamber of the eye or under the kidney capsule, whereas blastocysts which remain in a uterus in delay continue to be in diapause (Kirby, 1967; Psychoyos, 1967b).

What are the uterine conditions that induce diapause? Presumably

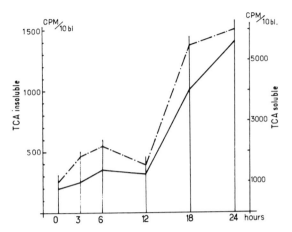

FIG. 14. Uptake and incorporation *in vitro* of uridine-^{3}H by rat blastocysts (bl) in diapause after varying periods of culture. Blastocysts in diapause were recovered on day 8 from rats ovariectomized on day 2 of pregnancy and treated daily with 5 mg of progesterone. The blastocysts were cultured at 37°C in Eagle's L medium, supplemented with 1.0% fetal calf serum, under an atmospheric mixture of 5% CO_2 and 95% air. The blastocysts were pulse labeled for 45 min with uridine-^{3}H at 100 μCi/ml and then extracted with 5% trichloroacetic acid (TCA); radioactivity of both the TCA-soluble ($-\cdot-$) and TCA-insoluble ($-$) fractions was measured.

either an active inhibition is exerted on the blastocyst by the endometrium, or the uterine environment is deficient in certain essential metabolites under the hormonal conditions causing delayed implantation. The latter alternative was proposed by Gwatkin (1966) on the basis of his finding that the outgrowth *in vitro* of mouse blastocyst cells required the presence of essential amino acids in culture medium. In their absence, the blastocysts remained in a state of diapause *in vitro* comparable to that occurring *in utero* under conditions of delay. Blastocyst diapause could thus result from a selective restriction of essential metabolites in the uterine fluid. However, the concentrations of essential amino acids in the luminal fluid of uteri in delay have been found to be at higher values than in the luminal fluid of normal uteri during early pregnancy (Gwatkin, 1969). Weitlauf and Greenwald (1968) showed that labeled methionine injected into mice in delay is secreted into the uterine lumen and is incorporated by normal 5-day blastocysts which were transferred to the uterus just prior to the injection of methionine. The incorporation of methionine gradually declined and stopped after prolonged exposure of these blastocysts to the luminal environment of the delayed uterus (Weitlauf, 1969).

Brambell (1937) and Whitten (1958) have suggested that diapause of

the blastocyst during delayed implantation is due to an inhïbitory uterine factor. In our laboratory, studies on the identification of a blastocyst
inhibitory factor were begun in 1966. The initial studies were determinations of the effects of a supernatant of homogenates of the uteri of
ovariectomized-progesterone treated rats on blastocyst RNA synthesis
in vitro (Psychoyos, 1969b; Psychoyos and Bitton-Casimiri, 1969).
These supernatants were found to inhibit the *in vitro* uptake of uridine
by normal rabbit and rat blastocysts. The inhibitory effect was abolished
by heating at 80°C for 10 minutes and was markedly decreased in uterine homogenates prepared from animals which had received estrogen 4
hours prior to sacrifice. More recently, we have been studying the inhibitory activity of uterine flushings on the incorporation *in vitro* of
uridine into blastocyst RNA (Psychoyos *et al.*, 1973). Blastocyst RNA
synthesis has been estimated 22 hours after placement of the blastocysts
in culture by pulse labeling with uridine for 45 minutes and extracting
the TCA-soluble and TCA-insoluble radioactivity. The uterine flushings
have been obtained just prior to assay *in vitro* by flushing 1.0 ml of
culture medium sequentially through 3 or 4 uteri. The protein concentration of the flushings are estimated and adjusted in all samples to
160 μg/ml. Two hours before uridine pulse labeling, the cultured blastocysts have been transferred to uterine flushing culture medium. The
animals whose uteri were flushed have been in various hormonal
conditions.

Flushings of the uteri of ovariectomized animals, either untreated or
treated with progesterone, or from animals sacrificed on one of the first
4 days of pregnancy have given similar results. All culture media containing uterine flushings inhibit both the total uptake of uridine (TCA-
soluble label) and the synthesis of RNA (incorporation of label into
TCA-insoluble RNA) to values about 50% less than the controls. The
inhibitory activity of flushings obtained from the uteri of animals on the
second day of pregnancy is less than the activity of flushings obtained
on days 3 and 4 of pregnancy. Likewise, the inhibitory activity of uterine
flushings from untreated ovariectomized animals was less than that of
the flushings obtained from the uteri of ovariectomized, progesterone-
treated animals.

The administration of estradiol to ovariectomized, progesterone-
treated rats 1 hour before sacrifice completely abolished the inhibitory
activity of the uterine flushings. The finding that was unexpected was
that if the uteri were flushed 18 hours after estradiol administration the
inhibitory activity was markedly increased and blocked more than 90%
of the uridine uptake of cultured blastocysts. The flushings of the uteri
of 5-day pseudopregnant rats had similar high inhibitory activity and

those of uteri on day 6 or 7 of pseudopregnancy completely inhibited uridine uptake by blastocysts (Fig. 15). Most blastocysts incubated in the latter flushing culture media degenerate within 2 hours of exposure. If these media are diluted 1:10, the uptake of uridine by blastocysts is still inhibited and the incorporation of label into RNA is 50% of the controls. A parallel decrease in inhibitory activity on dilution of flushing culture media obtained from ovariectomized, progesterone-treated rats and from animals sacrificed on day 6 or 7 of pseudopregnancy is observed, which indicates that the chemical identity of the inhibitory factor(s) may be identical in both cases. It can be suggested that the same component in these uterine secretions could be responsible for either the maintenance of blastocysts in diapause during delayed implantation or for the death of the blastocysts in a uterus which is in the state of "nonreceptivity" and that the quantity of the factor(s) varies according to the hormonal status of the animal.

The isolation and identification of inhibitory factors or components in uterine secretions are currently being pursued in our laboratory. It was initially thought that the inhibitory components were proteins, but fractionation of uterine secretions on Sephadex G-200 columns gave at least four protein fractions, all of which stimulated the metabolic activity of blastocysts *in vitro* and the inhibitory activity of unfractionated

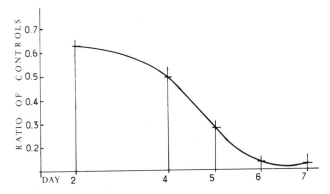

Fig. 15. Incorporation of uridine-^{3}H by normal 5-day rat blastocysts pulse labeled for 45 minutes with uridine-^{3}H at 100 μCi/ml after hour 22 of culture. The blastocysts were cultured as described for Fig. 14 for the first 20 hours *in vitro*. The culture medium was then replaced by a culture medium which had been flushed through three uteri of rats on one of the indicated days of pregnancy (abscissa). The protein content of the flushed media was adjusted to 160 μg/ml and the blastocysts were incubated for 2 hours in these media prior to addition of uridine-^{3}H. The incorporation of uridine-^{3}H into trichloroacetic acid-insoluble RNA of blastocysts exposed to uterine flushings is expressed as the ratio of incorporation of label into the RNA of these blastocysts to that of control blastocysts.

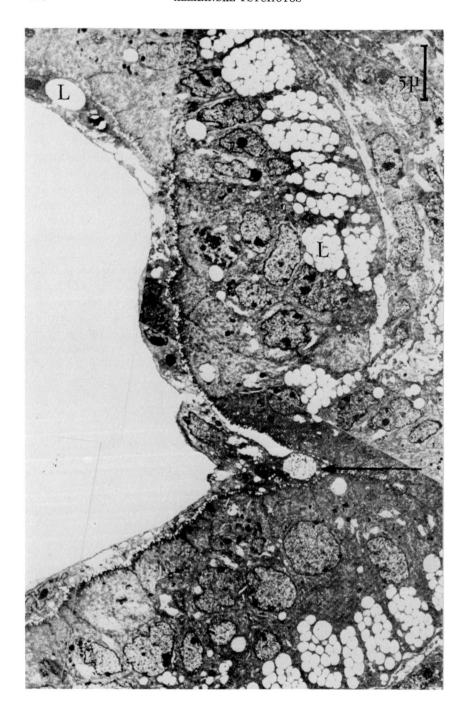

uterine secretions was found to be dialyzable. Our most recent studies have shown that the inhibitory activity in uterine secretions can be recovered in alcohol:ether or in methanol extracts of uterine flushings and that the extracts contain lipid components which have inhibitory activity toward blastocysts *in vitro*.

In 1939 Susanne Bloch postulated that delayed implantation in the mouse was due to the failure of an osmiophilic secretion "radiating from the nuclei of the epithelial cells to migrate through the epithelium." She considered this lipid material to be a nutritional factor that was withheld from the blastocyst by its failure to migrate into the uterine lumen. We now know that at the precise moment when the process of ovoimplantation is initiated an abundant lipid material stored in the basal cytoplasm of the epithelial cells is dispersed and reappears within these cells after a few hours. Droplets of lipid material are found in the cytoplasm of blastocyst cells during diapause. Electron micrographs of mouse blastocysts (Potts and Psychoyos, 1967b) indicate clearly that lipid material is accumulated by trophoblast cells during implantation delay (Fig. 16). This suggests that, contrary to Bloch's interpretation, the diapause blastocyst has access to, and is influenced by, lipid components of epithelial origin. The accumulation of lipid droplets in the cytoplasm of roe deer blastocysts in diapause has recently been reported (Aitken et al., 1973), with the significant observation that activation of the diapause blastocyst is accompanied by the disappearance of stored lipid droplets in both the blastocyst and uterine epithelial cells. Are lipid factors present in these droplets which repress blastocyst metabolic activity?

The onset of ovoendometrial interactions which lead to implantation occurs at the time of disappearance of stored lipid droplets in both the blastocyst and epithelial cells. Are the lipid droplets secreted into the uterine lumen, or are they metabolized by processes of which we know little or nothing? The fact that the blastocyst inhibitory activity of uterine flushings increases (see above) during the interval of endometrial receptivity for implantation suggests that secretion into the uterine lumen is one of the pathways of disappearance of these lipid droplets. If

---

FIG. 16. A montage of electron micrographs of consecutive fields of a transverse section through a diapausing mouse blastocyst and the surrounding uterine epithelium on day 6 post coitum. Implantation delay was induced by ovariectomy on day 3 of pregnancy with daily treatment with 2 mg of progesterone. The arrow indicates a cytoplasmic extension of a trophoblast cells inserted between a fold in the epithelium of the uterine lumen. Note the clusters of lipid droplets (L) in the basal cytoplasm of the epithelial cells and the scattered lipid droplets within the trophoblast cells of the blastocyst. From Potts and Psychoyos (1967b).

this is true, how is it that the blastocyst escapes from the toxic effects of these factors? During the optimal interval of ovoendometrial interaction, the rat blastocyst is embraced by the uterine epithelium over its entire circumference. Does this embrace "shield" the blastocyst from the lipids (toxic factors) secreted into the uterine lumen?

One can suggest that the same factor(s) which repress blastocyst metabolic activity also repress the endometrial stromal cells. We know that the optimal time for the induction of deciduoma formation in the rat coincides with the time of endometrial receptivity for ovoimplantation (see the above discussion on the induction of decidualization). How are epithelial lipids involved in the repression of both the endometrial and blastocyst cells? For obvious reasons of ignorance, much of the above has been expressed as questions couched in metaphorical language. We are now at a point where we must search for a molecular language to express the occurrence of repression and activation of ovoendometrial interactions. If a key to these phenomena lies in the components of the uterine epithelial lipids, can we express our future explanations in terms of membrane permeability and the release or binding of membrane-associated molecules?

ACKNOWLEDGMENTS

I am deeply grateful to my friend Dr. George Cooper for his stimulating discussions and his invaluable contribution in the development of the ideas and models presented in this article and also for his efficacious cooperation in the labor involved in the preparation of the manuscript.

The research of the author's laboratory has been supported by the Ford Foundation and The Population Council of New York; et Le Centre National de la Recherche Scientifique, France.

REFERENCES

Ahmad, N., Lyons, W. R., and Papkoff, H. (1969). *Anat. Rec.* **164**, 291.
Aitken, R. J., Burton, J., Hawkins, J., Kerr-Wilson, R., Short, R. V., and Steven, D. H. (1973). *J. Reprod. Fert.* **34**, 481.
Alden, R. H. (1947). *Anat. Rec.* **97**, 1.
Alden, R. H., and Smith, J. (1959). *J. Exp. Zool.* **142**, 215.
Allen, W. M. (1931). *Anat. Rec.* **48**, 65.
Allen, W. M., and Corner, G. W. (1929). *Amer. J. Physiol.* **88**, 340.
Alloiteau, J. J. (1961). *C. R. Acad. Sci.* **253**, 1348.
Alloiteau, J. J., and Mayer, G. (1967). *Arch. Anat. Microsc. Morphol. Exp.* **56**, Suppl. 3/4, 189.
Alloiteau, J. J., and Psychoyos, A. (1966). *C. R. Acad. Sci., Ser.* D **262**, 1561.
Alloiteau, J. J., Psychoyos, A., and Acker, G. (1963). *C. R. Acad. Sci.* **256**, 4284.
Amoroso, E. C. (1952). *In* "Marshall's Physiology of Reproduction" (A. S. Parkes, ed.), Vol. 2, p. 127. Longmans, Green, New York.
Andersen, D. H. (1927). *Amer. J. Physiol.* **82**, 557.
Astwood, E. B. (1941). *Endocrinology* **28**, 309.

Baevsky, U. B. (1963). In "Delayed Implantation" (A. C. Enders, ed.), p. 141. Univ. of Chicago Press, Chicago, Illinois.
Ball, J. (1940). Amer. J. Physiol. 130, 471.
Baulieu, E. E., Alberga, A., Raynaud-Jammet, C., and Wira, C. R. (1972). Nature (London), New Biol. 236, 236.
Beier, H. (1968). Biochim. Biophys. Acta 160, 289.
Bergstrom, S., and Nilsson, O. (1970). J. Reprod. Fert. 23, 339.
Bindon, B. M. (1969a). J. Endocrinol. 43, 225.
Bindon, B. M. (1969b). J. Endocrinol. 44, 349.
Bitton-Casimiri, V., and Psychoyos, A. (1968). C. R. Acad. Sci. Ser. D 267, 762.
Bitton-Casimiri, V., Brun, J. L., and Psychoyos, A. (1970). C. R. Acad. Sci., Ser. D 270, 2979.
Bitton-Casimiri, V., Brun, J. L., and Psychoyos, A. (1971). J. Reprod. Fert. 27, 461.
Bland, K. P., and Donovan, B. T. (1965). J. Reprod. Fert. 10, 189.
Blandau, R. J. (1949). Anat. Rec. 104, 331.
Blandau, R. J. (1961). In "Sex and Internal Secretions" (W. C. Young, ed.), Vol. 2, p. 791. Williams & Wilkins, Baltimore, Maryland.
Bloch, S. (1939). J. Endocrinol. 1, 399.
Bloch, S. (1958). Experientia 14, 447.
Borgese, E., and Cassini, A. (1963). In "Cinemicrography in Cell Biology" (G. G. Rose, ed.), p. 274. Academic Press, New York.
Bouin, P., and Ancel, P. (1910). J. Physiol. Pathol. Gen. 12, 1.
Boyd, J. D., and Hamilton, W. J. (1952). In "Marshall's Physiology of Reproduction" (A. S. Parkes, ed.), Vol. 2, p. 1. Longmans, Green, New York.
Brambell, F. W. R. (1937). Amer. J. Obstet. Gynecol. 33, 942.
Brinster, R. (1969). Advan. Biosci. 4, 199.
Bruce, H. M. (1961). J. Reprod. Fert. 2, 138.
Brumley, L. E., and De Feo, V. J. (1964). Endocrinology 75, 883.
Brun, J. L., and Psychoyos, A. (1972). J. Reprod. Fert. 30, 489.
Buchanan, G. D. (1969). J. Reprod. Fert. 18, 305.
Canivenc, R. (1960). In "Les Fonctions de Nidation Utérine et leurs Troubles" (G. Masson, ed.), p. 33. Masson, Paris.
Canivenc, R., and Laffargue, M. (1956). C. R. Acad. Sci. 242, 2857.
Canivenc, R., Drouville, C., and Mayer, G. (1953). C. R. Acad. Sci. 237, 1036.
Canivenc, R., Laffargue, M., and Mayer, G. (1956). C. R. Soc. Biol. 150, 2208.
Chambon, Y. (1949). C. R. Soc. Biol. 143, 753.
Chambon, Y., and Lefrein, H. (1952). C. R. Soc. Biol. 146, 821.
Chang, M. C. (1950). J. Exp. Zool. 114, 197.
Chang, M. C. (1969). Endocrinology 84, 356.
Christie, G. A. (1966). J. Reprod. Fert. 12, 279.
Cochrane, R. L., and Meyer, R. K. (1957). Proc. Soc. Exp. Biol. Med. 96, 155.
Cochrane, R. L., Prasad, M. R. N., and Meyer, R. K. (1962). Endocrinology 70, 228.
Cole, R. J. (1967). J. Embryol. Exp. Morphol. 17, 481.
Cole, R. J., and Paul, J. (1965). Preimplantation Stages Pregnancy, Ciba Found. Symp. p. 82.
Cooper, G. W., and Psychoyos, A. (1973). Unpublished data.
Courrier, R. (1945). "Endocrinologie de la Gestation." Masson, Paris.
Courrier, R. (1950). Vitam. Horm. (New York) 8, 179.
Courrier, R., and Baclesse, M. (1955). Reunion Endocrinologistes Langue Fr., Paris, 1955 p. 1.

Courrier, R., and Jost, A. (1939). *C. R. Soc. Biol.* **130**, 1162.
Courrier, R., and Psychoyos, A. (1960). *C. R. Acad. Sci.* **250**, 2486.
Croxatto, H., Diaz, S., Vera, R., Ethart, M., and Atira, P. (1969). *Amer. J. Obstet. Gynecol.* **105**, 1135.
Daniel, J. C., and Krishnen, R. S. (1970). *J. Exp. Zool.* **172**, 267.
Dass, C. M., Mohla, S., and Prasad, M. R. (1969). *Endocrinology* **85**, 528.
Deanesly, R. (1963). *In* "Delayed Implantation" (A. C. Enders, ed.), p. 253. Univ. of Chicago Press, Chicago, Illinois.
De Feo, V. J. (1963a). *Endocrinology* **72**, 305.
De Feo, V. J. (1963b). *Endocrinology* **73**, 488.
De Feo, V. J. (1967). *In* "Cellular Biology of the Uterus" (R. M. Wynn, ed.), p. 192. Appleton, New York.
Deis, R. P., and Orias, R. (1968). *J. Physiol. (London)* **197**, 47.
Dickman, Z. (1969). *Advan. Reprod. Physiol.* **4**, 187.
Dickman, Z. (1972). *J. Endocrinol.* **53**, 327.
Dickman, Z., and Noyes, R. W. (1960). *J. Reprod. Fert.* **1**, 197.
Dickman, Z., and Noyes, R. W. (1961). *Fert. Steril.* **12**, 310.
Enders, A. C. (1967). *In* "Cellular Biology of the Uterus" (R. M. Wynn, ed.), p. 151. Appleton, New York.
Enders, A. C., and Schlafke, S. (1967). *Amer. J. Anat.* **120**, 185.
Enders, A. C., and Schlafke, S. (1969). *Amer. J. Anat.* **125**, 1.
Enzmann, E. V., Saphir, N. R., and Pincus, G. (1932). *Anat. Rec.* **54**, 325.
Eto, T. H., Masuda, H., Suzuki, Y., and Hoshi, T. (1962). *Kachiku Hanshoku Kenkyukai-Shi* **8**, 34.
Everett, J. W. (1954). *Endocrinology* **54**, 685.
Everett, J. W. (1956a). *Anat. Rec.* **124**, 287.
Everett, J. W. (1956b). *Endocrinology* **58**, 786.
Everett, J. W. (1964). *Physiol. Rev.* **44**, 373.
Fainstat, T. (1963). *Amer. J. Anat.* **112**, 337.
Fainstat, T., and Chapman, G. B. (1965). *Amer. J. Obstet. Gynecol.* **112**, 852.
Fajer, A. B., and Barraclough, C. A. (1967). *Endocrinology* **81**, 617.
Fawcett, D. W. (1950). *Anat. Rec.* **108**, 71.
Fawcett, D. W., Wislocki, G. B., and Waldo, C. M. (1947). *Amer. J. Anat.* **81**, 413.
Feder, H. H., Resko, J. A., and Goy, R. W. (1968). *J. Endocrinol.* **41**, 563.
Feherty, P., Robertson, D. M., Waynforth, U. B., and Kellie, A. E. (1970). *Biochem. J.* **120**, 837.
Feil, P. D., Glasser, S., Toft, D. O., and O'Malley, B. W. (1972). *Endocrinology* **91**, 738.
Ferrando, G., and Nalbandov, A. V. (1968). *Endocrinology* **83**, 933.
Finn, C. A. (1971). *Advan. Reprod. Physiol.* **5**, 1.
Fraenkel, L., and Cohn, F. (1902). *Anat. Anz.* **20**, 294.
Galassi, L. (1968). *Develop. Biol.* **17**, 75.
Gale, C. C., and McCann, S. M. (1961). *J. Endocrinol.* **22**, 107.
Gardner, R. L. (1971). *Advan. Biosci.* **6**, 279.
Glasser, S. R. (1965). *Proc. 6th Panamer. Congr. Endocrinol., Mexico, 1964. Excerpta Med. Found. Int. Congr. Ser.* **99**, 335.
Glasser, S. R. (1972). *In* "Reproductive Biology" (H. Balin and S. Glasser, eds.), p. 115. Excerpta Med. Found., Amsterdam.
Glasser, S. R., and O'Malley, B. W. (1970). *Endocrine Soc., 52nd Meet., 1970* Abstr. No. 120.

Gorski, J., Toft, D., Shyamala, G. S., Smith, D., and Notides, A. (1968). *Recent Progr. Horm. Res.* **24**, 45.

Greenslade, F. C., McCormack, J. J., and Hahn, D. W. (1972). *Annu. Meet. Soc. Study Reprod., 5th, East Lansing, 1972* Abstr. No. 121.

Grosnevor, C. E., Mena, F., Dhariwal, A. P. S., and McCann, S. M. (1967). *Endocrinology* **81**, 1021.

Gulyas, B. J., and Daniel, J. C. (1969). *Biol. Reprod.* **1**, 11.

Gwatkin, R. B. L. (1966). *J. Cell. Physiol.* **68**, 335.

Gwatkin, R. B. L. (1969). *J. Fert.* **14**, 101.

Hafez, E. S. E. (1963). *Proc. Soc. Exp. Biol. Med.* **114**, 604.

Harper, M. J. K. (1968). *Anat. Rec.* **162**, 433.

Harper, M. J. K., and Chang, M. C. (1971). *Advan. Reprod. Physiol.* **5**, 167.

Harper, M. J. K., Doud, D., and Elliot, A. (1969). *Biol. Reprod.* **1**, 253.

Hashimoto, I., and Wiest, W. G. (1969). *Endocrinology* **84**, 873.

Hashimoto, I., Hendricks, D. M., Anderson, L. L., and Melampy, R. M. (1968). *Endocrinology* **82**, 333.

Heald, P. J., and O'Grady, J. E. (1970). *Biochem. J.* **117**, 65.

Heald, P. J., O'Grady, J. E., O'Hare, A., and Vass, M. (1972). *Biochim. Biophys. Acta* **262**, 66.

Hertig, A. T., Rock, J., Adams, E. C., and Mulligan, W. J. (1954). *Carnegie Inst. Wash., Contrib. Embryol.* **35**, 199.

Humphrey, K. W. (1968). *J. Endocrinol.* **40**, 267.

Jacobson, M. A., Sanyal, M. K., and Meyer, R. K. (1970). *Endocrinology* **86**, 982.

Jensen, E. V., Suzuki, Y., Kawashima, T., Stumpf, W., Jungblut, P., and DeSombre, E. (1968). *Proc. Nat. Acad. Sci. U. S.* **59**, 632.

Kirby, D. R. S. (1960). *Nature (London)* **187**, 707.

Kirby, D. R. S. (1963a). *J. Anat.* **97**, 119.

Kirby, D. R. S. (1963b). *J. Reprod. Fert.* **5**, 1.

Kirby, D. R. S. (1965). *Preimplantation Stages Pregnancy, Ciba Found. Symp.* p. 325.

Kirby, D. R. S. (1967). *J. Reprod. Fert.* **14**, 517.

Kirby, D. R. S. (1970). *In* "Ovoimplantation, Human Gonadotropins and Prolactin" (P. O. Hubinont, F. Leroy, C. Robyn, and P. Leleux, eds.), p. 86. Karger, Basel.

Kraicer, P. F., and Shelesnyak, M. C. (1959). *C. R. Acad. Sci.* **248**, 3213.

Krehbiel, R. H. (1937). *Physiol. Zool.* **10**, 212.

Krehbiel, R. H. (1941a). *Anat. Rec.* **81**, 43.

Krehbiel, R. H. (1941b). *Anat. Rec.* **81**, 67.

Krishnan, R. S., and Daniel, J. C. (1967). *Science* **158**, 490.

Lataste, M. F. (1891). *C. R. Soc. Biol.* **9**, 21.

Ljungkvist, I. (1971). Abstr. Dissertations, No. 111. Fac. Med. Uppsala Univ., Uppsala.

Lobel, B. L., Tic, L., and Shelesnyak, M. C. (1965a). *Acta Endocrinol. (Copenhagen)* **50**, 469.

Lobel, B. L., Tic, L., and Shelesnyak, M. C. (1965b). *Acta Endocrinol. (Copenhagen)* **50**, 517.

Loeb, L. (1908a). *J. Amer. Med. Ass.* **50**, 1897.

Loeb, L. (1908b). *Proc. Soc. Exp. Biol. Med.* **5**, 102.

Long, J. A., and Evans, H. M. (1922). *Mem. Univ. Calif.* **6**, 1.

McCann, S. M. (1970). *In* "Hypophysiotropic Hormones of the Hypothalamus" (J. Meites, ed.), p. 90. Williams & Wilkins, Baltimore, Maryland.

McCann, S. M., and Friedman, H. M. (1960). *Endocrinology* **67**, 597.

McDonald, G. J., Armstrong, D. T., and Greep, R. O. (1967). *Endocrinology* **80**, 172.

McGuire, J. L., and DeDella, C. (1971). *Endocrinology* **88**, 1099.

McLaren, A. (1968). *J. Endocrinol.* **42**, 453.

McLaren, A. (1970a). *J. Embryol. Exp. Morphol.* **20**, 1.

McLaren, A. (1970b). In "Ovoimplantation, Human Gonadotropins and Prolactin" (P. O. Hubinont, F. Leroy, C. Robyn, and P. Leleux, eds.), p. 18. Karger, Basel.

Madhwa Rau, H. G., Sairam, M. R., and Moudgal, N. R. (1968). *J. Reprod. Fert.* **17**, 335.

Marcus, G. J. (1970). *Annu. Meet. Soc. Study Reprod., 3rd, 1970* Abstr. No. 46.

Marcus, G. J., and Shelesnyak, M. C. (1967). *Endocrinology* **80**, 1028.

Martin, L., and Finn, C. A. (1969). *J. Endocrinol.* **44**, 279.

Martin, L., and Finn, C. A. (1970). *J. Endocrinol.* **48**, 109.

Martinez-Manautou, J., Cortez, V., Giner, J., Aznar, R., Casasola, J., and Rudel, H. W. (1966). *Fert. Steril.* **17**, 49.

Mayer, G. (1959). *Mem. Soc. Endocrinol.* **6**, 76.

Mayer, G., Nilsson, O., and Reinus, S. (1967). *J. Anat.* **126**, 43.

Meites, J., Nicoll, C. S., and Talwalker, P. K. (1963). *Advan. Neuroendocrinol., Proc. Symp., Miami, Fla., 1961* p. 238.

Mešter, J., Robertson, D. M., Feherty, P., and Kellie, A. E. (1970). *Biochem. J.* **120**, 831.

Mešter, J., Martel, D., and Psychoyos, A. (1973). Unpublished data.

Meyer, R. K., Prasad, M. R. N., and Cochrane, R. L. (1958). *Anat. Rec.* **130**, 339.

Meyers, K. (1970). *J. Endocrinol.* **46**, 341.

Milgrom, E., and Baulieu, E. E. (1970). *Endocrinology* **87**, 276.

Milgrom, E., Atger, M., and Baulieu, E. E. (1971). *Advan. Biosci.* **7**, 235.

Milgrom, E., Atger, M., Perrot, M., and Baulieu, E. E. (1972). *Endocrinology* **90**, 1071.

Mintz, B. (1965). *Preimplantation Stages Pregnancy, Ciba Found. Symp.* p. 145.

Mohla, S., Prasad, M. R. N., and Dass, C. M. S. (1970). *Endocrinology* **87**, 383.

Monesi, V., and Salfi, V. (1967). *Exp. Cell Res.* **46**, 632.

Nicoll, C. S., Fiorindo, R. P., McKennee, C. T., and Parsons, J. A. (1970). In "Hypophysiotropic Hormones of the Hypothalamus" (J. Meites, ed.), p. 115. Williams & Wilkins, Baltimore, Maryland.

Nilsson, O. (1970). In "Ovoimplantation, Human Gonadotropins and Prolactin" (P. O. Hubinont, F. Leroy, C. Robyn, and P. Leleux, eds.) p. 52. Karger, Basel.

Nilsson, O. (1972). *J. Ultrastruct. Res.* **40**, 572.

Nimrod-Zmigrod, A., Ladany, S., and Lindner, H. R. (1972). *J. Endocrinol.* **53**, 249.

Noyes, R. W., Hertig, A. T., and Rock, J. (1950). *Fert. Steril.* **1**, 3.

Noyes, R. W., Dickman, Z., Doyle, L., and Gates, A. H. (1963). In "Delayed Implantation" (A. C. Enders, ed.), p. 197. Univ. of Chicago Press, Chicago, Illinois.

Nutting, E. F., and Meyer, R. K. (1963). In "Delayed Implantation" (A. C. Enders, ed.), p. 233. Univ. of Chicago Press, Chicago, Illinois.

O'Malley, B. W., McGuire, W. L., Kohler, P. O., and Korenman, S. G. (1969). *Recent Progr. Horm. Res.* **25**, 105.

Orsini, M. W., and Meyer, R. K. (1959). *Anat. Rec.* **134**, 619.

Orsini, M. W., and Psychoyos, A. (1965). *J. Reprod. Fert.* **10**, 300.

Peckmam, B. M., and Greene, R. R. (1947). *Endocrinology* **41**, 273.

Peckham, B. M., and Greene, R. R. (1950). *Endocrinology* **46**, 489.

Potts, M. (1967). *J. Anat.* **101**, 622.

Potts, M. (1969). *Advan. Reprod. Physiol.* **4**, 241.

Potts, M., and Psychoyos, A. (1967a). *C. R. Acad. Sci., Ser.* D **264**, 370.

Potts, M., and Psychoyos, A. (1967b). *C. R. Acad. Sci., Ser.* D **264**, 956.

Prasad, M. R. N., Dass, C. M. S., and Mohla, S. (1968). *J. Reprod. Fert.* **16**, 97.

Psychoyos, A. (1960). *C. R. Soc. Biol.* **154**, 1384.

Psychoyos, A. (1961). *C. R. Acad. Sci.* **253**, 1616.

Psychoyos, A. (1963a). *C. R. Acad. Sci.* **257**, 1153.

Psychoyos, A. (1963b). *C. R. Acad. Sci.* **257**, 1367.

Psychoyos, A. (1963c). *J. Endocrinol.* **27**, 337.

Psychoyos, A. (1964). *Proc. 2nd Intern. Congr. Endocrinol. London, 1964. Excerpta Med. Found. Int. Congr. Ser.* **83**, 508.

Psychoyos, A. (1966a). *Ciba Found. Study Group* [Pap.] **23**, 4.

Psychoyos, A. (1966b). *Nature (London)* **211**, 864.

Psychoyos, A. (1966c). *C. R. Acad. Sci., Ser.* D **263**, 1755.

Psychoyos, A. (1966d). *C. R. Acad. Sci., Ser.* D **263**, 986.

Psychoyos, A. (1967a). *Advan. Reprod. Physiol.* **2**, 257.

Psychoyos, A. (1967b). *Arch. Anat. Microsc. Morphol. Exp.* **56**, Suppl. 304, 616.

Psychoyos, A. (1968). *J. Reprod. Fert., Suppl.* **4**, 47.

Psychoyos, A. (1969a). *Proc. 3rd Intern. Congr. Endocrinol., Mexico 1968. Excerpta Med. Found. Int. Congr. Ser.* **184**, 935.

Psychoyos, A. (1969b). *Advan. Biosci.* **4**, 275.

Psychoyos, A. (1970). *In* "Ovoimplantation, Human Gonadotropins and Prolactin" (P. O. Hubinont, F. Leroy, C. Robyn, and P. Leleux, eds.), p. 101. Karger, Basel.

Psychoyos, A. (1973). *In* "Handbook of Physiology" (E. B. Astwood and R. Greep, eds.), Sect. 7: Endocrinology, Vol. II, p. x. Amer. Physiol. Society, Washington, D. C.

Psychoyos, A., and Alloiteau, J. J. (1962). *C. R. Soc. Biol.* **254**, 46.

Psychoyos, A., and Bitton-Casimiri, V. (1969). *C. R. Acad. Sci., Ser.* D **268**, 188.

Psychoyos, A., and Mandon, P. (1971a). *J. Reprod. Fert.* **26**, 137.

Psychoyos, A., and Mandon, P. (1971b). *C. R. Acad. Sci., Ser.* D **272**, 2723.

Psychoyos, A., Alloiteau, J. J., and Acker, G. (1966). *J. Reprod. Fert.* **12**, 419.

Psychoyos, A., Alberga, A., and Baulieu, E. E. (1968). *C. R. Acad. Sci., Ser.* D **266**, 1407.

Psychoyos, A., Casimiri, V., Fridlanski, E., and Brun, J. L. (1973). Unpublished data.

Roser, S., and Bloch, R. B. (1969). *C. R. Acad. Sci., Ser.* D **268**, 1318.

Rossi-Cartoni, C., and Bignami, G. (1969). *Ann. Ist. Super. Sanita* **5**, 107.

Rothchild, I. (1960). *Endocrinology* **67**, 9.

Rothchild, I., and Meyer, R. K. (1942). *Physiol. Zool.* **15**, 216.

Runner, M. N. (1947). *Anat. Rec.* **98**, 1.

Sananès, N., and Psychoyos, A. (1970). *C. R. Acad. Sci., Ser.* D **271**, 430.

Sananès, N., Roche, D., and Psychoyos, A. (1973). Unpublished data.

Sanyal, M. K., and Meyer, R. K. (1970). *Endocrinology* **86**, 976.

Saxen, L., and Saksela, E. (1971). *Exp. Cell Res.* **66**, 369.

Schally, A. V. (1970). *Res. Reprod.* **2**, 2.

Schayer, R. W. (1963). *Ann. N. Y. Acad. Sci.* **103**, 264.

Schlough, J. S. (1969). *Biol. Reprod.* **1**, 315.

Schwartz, N. B., and Talley, W. L. (1968). *J. Reprod. Fert.* **15**, 39.

Scommegna, A., Pandya, N., Lee, C. M., Christ, M., and Cohen, M. R. (1970). *Fert. Steril.* **21**, 2.

Segal, S. J., and Nelson, W. O. (1958). *Proc. Soc. Exp. Biol. Med.* **98**, 431.

Segal, S. J., and Scher, W. (1967). *In* "Cellular Biology of the Uterus" (R. M. Wynn, ed.), p. 114. Appleton, New York.

Shaikh, A. A. (1971). *Biol. Reprod.* **5**, 297.

Shaikh, A. A., and Abraham, G. E. (1969). *Biol. Reprod.* **1**, 378.

Shelesnyak, M. C. (1957). *Recent Progr. Horm. Res.* **13**, 269.

Shelesnyak, M. C. (1960). *Endeavour* **19**, 81.

Shelesnyak, M. C. (1962). *Perspect. Biol. Med.* **5**, 503.

Shelesnyak, M. C., and Kraicer, P. F. (1960). *Proc. Int. Congr. Endocrinol., 1st, Copenhagen* p. 547.

Shelesnyak, M. C., and Kraicer, P. F. (1963). *In* "Delayed Implantation" (A. C. Enders, ed.), p. 265. Univ. of Chicago Press, Chicago, Illinois.

Shelesnyak, M. C., and Tic, L. (1963a). *Acta Endocrinol. (Copenhagen)* **42**, 465.

Shelesnyak, M. C., and Tic, L. (1963b). *Acta Endocrinol. (Copenhagen)* **43**, 462.

Shelesnyak, M. C., Kraicer, P. F., and Zeilmaker, G. H. (1963). *Acta Endocrinol.* **42**, 225.

Short, R. V., and Hay, M. T. (1965). *J. Reprod. Fert.* **9**, 372.

Smith, J. A., Martin, L., King, R. J. B., and Vertes, M. (1970). *Biochem. J.* **119**, 773.

Tachi, S., Tachi, C., and Lidner, H. R. (1970). *J. Reprod. Fert.* **21**, 37.

Tachi, S., Tachi, C., and Lidner, H. R. (1972). *J. Reprod. Fert.* **31**, 59.

Taleisnik, S., and Orias, R. (1966). *Endocrinology* **78**, 522.

Talwar, G. P., Segal, S. J., Evans, A., and Davidson, O. (1964). *Proc. Nat. Acad. Sci. U. S.* **52**, 1059.

Toft, D., and Gorski, J. (1966). *Proc. Nat. Acad. Sci. U. S.* **55**, 1574.

Uchida, K., Kakowaki, M., and Miyake, T. (1969). *Endocrinol. Jap.* **16**, 227.

Vickery, G. H., Erickson, G. I., Bennet, J. P., Mueller, N. S., and Haleblian, J. K. (1970). *Biol. Reprod.* **3**, 154.

Vittorelli, M. L., Harrison, R. A. P., and Lutwak-Mann, C. (1967). *Nature (London)* **214**, 980.

Waynforth, H., Pope, B., and Hosking, Z. D. (1972). *J. Reprod. Fert.* **28**, 191.

Weichert, C. K. (1928). *Proc. Soc. Exp. Biol. Med.* **25**, 490.

Weichert, C. K. (1940). *Anat. Rec.* **77**, 31.

Weichert, C. K. (1941). *Anat. Rec.* **81**, 106.

Weichert, C. K. (1942). *Anat. Rec.* **83**, 1.

Weitlauf, H. M. (1969). *J. Exp. Zool.* **171**, 481.

Weitlauf, H. M., and Greenwald, G. S. (1965). *J. Reprod. Fert.* **10**, 203.

Weitlauf, H. M., and Greenwald, G. S. (1967). *Anat. Rec.* **159**, 249.

Weitlauf, H. M., and Greenwald, G. S. (1968). *J. Exp. Zool.* **169**, 463.

Whitten, W. K. (1956). *Nature (London)* **176**, 96.

Whitten, W. K. (1958). *J. Endocrinol.* **16**, 435.

Wiest, W. G. (1970). *Endocrinology* **87**, 43.

Yochim, J. M., and De Feo, V. J. (1963). *Endocrinology* **72**, 317.

Yoshinaga, K. (1961). *J. Reprod. Fert.* **2**, 35.

Yoshinaga, K. (1972). *Biol. Reprod.* **6**, 51.

Yoshinaga, K., and Greep, R. O. (1970). *Proc. Soc. Exp. Biol. Med.* **134**, 725.

Yoshinaga, K., and Greep, R. O. (1971). *Endocrinology* **88**, 627.

Yoshinaga, K., Hawkins, R. A., and Stocker, J. F. (1969). *Endocrinology* **85**, 103.

Zeilmaker, G. H. (1963). *Acta Endocrinol. (Copenhagen)* **44**, 355.

Zeilmaker, G. H. (1964). *Acta Endocrinol. (Copenhagen)* **46**, 483.

Hormonal Effects on Human Myometrial Activity

LARS PHILIP BENGTSSON

Department of Obstetrics and Gynecology, University Hospital, Lund, Sweden

I. Introduction

The myometrium differs from all skeletal muscles and most smooth muscles by the fact that its activity is controlled in a very complicated way, in which hormones play a most prominent role. Furthermore, the myometrium is engaged in the perpetuation of life in a specific way by being of decisive importance through the whole reproductive cycle, from menstruation throughout pregnancy and to well after delivery.

Consequently the hormonal control of the myometrium has attracted lively interest for many decades. Research work in this field has been complicated by the fact that hormonal effects on myometrial activity obviously differs from one species to another. This difference is clearly indicated, for example, by the various roles of female sex hormones (Bedford *et al.*, 1972) and of fetal corticosteroids (see below) in the maintenance and termination of pregnancy.

Therefore, it was decided to restrict the presentation to the human being; animal studies will be quoted only exceptionally. In order to keep this chapter within reasonable dimensions, further limitations were needed:

Muscular activity can be studied from different angles, e.g., anatomical, chemical, histochemical, histological, physiological, electrophysiological, and pharmacological. I have concentrated on *physiological and pharmacological effects of hormones, effects that can be studied either by recording myometrial activity or by analyzing the consequences of myometrial activity in pregnancy, i.e., abortion and labor.*

Furthermore, I have confined this chapter mainly to *in vivo* studies. There is no doubt that *in vitro* studies of the hormonal control of myometrial activity in animals have given important information. However, *in vitro* studies on the human myometrium have yielded confusing results that have contributed but little to our understanding of myometrial control throughout the reproductive cycle.

Stress will be laid on hormones to which the control of myometrial activity has traditionally been attributed, i.e., female sex hormones and posterior pituitary hormones. Corticosteroids, biogenic amines, and prostaglandins will be discussed, but less comprehensively than those above mentioned.

Prostaglandins are at present subjected to almost monthly reviews and are also dealt with in special journals: *Prostaglandins* and *Research in Prostaglandins.* Therefore, by following the rapid evolution in this field through these journals, the interested reader can easily complement the brief review given in this chapter.

II. Estrogen and Gestagen

A. Principal Effects of Estrogen and Gestagen

Estrogen produces a series of changes in the myometrium. In this context the following effects should be mentioned: (1) hypertrophy and hyperplasia of the myometrial cells (Brody and Wiqvist, 1961; Laguens and Lagrutta, 1964; Silva, 1967); (2) increase in contractile proteins (Csapo, 1950); (3) increase in the supply of biologically useful energy (Eggleton and Eggleton, 1929–1930; Walaas and Walaas, 1950a,b; Borell, 1951a,b; Menckes and Csapo, 1952; Cretius, 1957a,b; Villee et al., 1960; Jung, 1965); (4) increase in membrane potential (Marshall, 1959, 1962; Goto and Csapo, 1959; Kuriyama, 1961; Jung, 1965); (5) increase in spontaneous activity (see below); (6) increase in sensitivity (see below).

It is considerably more difficult to define the specific effects of progesterone than those of estrogen.

The name progesterone indicates that this hormone is supposed to protect and maintain pregnancy. This is true for some animals, e.g., the rabbit (Corner and Allen, 1929; Csapo, 1956; Fuchs and Fuchs, 1958). The effect is dependent upon two different capacities of the hormone: (1) to prepare the endometrium for implantation and subsequently maintain the decidua (Fraenkel and Cohn, 1902; Allen and Corner, 1930); (2) to depress myometrial activity and sensitivity (Knaus, 1926, 1930; Csapo and Corner, 1952; Schofield, 1954, 1955).

The history of progesterone as an inhibitor of myometrial activity and sensitivity to posterior pituitary hormones dates back to Knaus (1926, 1929) and Allen and Reynolds (1935). This effect, demonstrated in rabbits, was further analyzed, among others, by Csapo (1955, 1956, 1961a, 1971), Csapo and Corner (1952), and Schofield (1955).

The conclusion of the exhaustive work done by Csapo and his group, mainly on rabbits, was that progesterone exerts a "block" on the myometrium, decreasing the conduction of impulses and the coordination of contractions as well as the sensitivity to oxytocin. This theory strongly stimulated research on the hormonal control of pregnancy and parturition. However, the theory has also been increasingly criticized: Some of the essential facts on which the theory is based have not been fully confirmed: e.g., (1) that progesterone increases the membrane potential (Jung, 1956; Kao and Nishiyama, 1964) and decreases the conduction (Henriksen and Wagner, 1969); (2) that progesterone blocks myometrial activity in the human (see below). Thus, enthusiasm for the progesterone block theory has cooled off.

In the absence of estrogen, progesterone and other gestagens have very little effect on the female genital target organs. Thus, it is not possible to study the effects of endogenous or exogenous gestagen in the absence of endogenous or exogenous estrogen. Therefore, in the following the two hormones will be dealt with mostly under the same headings.

B. EFFECTS OF ESTROGEN AND GESTAGEN IN NONPREGNANT WOMEN

1. Spontaneously Occurring Conditions

a. The Normal Menstrual Cycle. Since the pioneer recording of Knaus (1929), a series of research workers have studied uterine activity in normal menstrual cycles with different techniques and with varying results. The reason why I here describe definite activity patterns is not only that we have found them in our studies (Bengtsson and Theobald, 1966; Moawad and Bengtsson, 1967), but also that most modern authors have found the same patterns (Henry *et al.*, 1950; Karlson, 1954; Garret, 1956; Hoff and Bayer, 1956; Posse, 1958; Hendricks, 1965, 1966; Cibils, 1967; Baumgarten, 1970; Eskes *et al.*, 1970; Roth-Brandel *et al.*, 1970; Braaksma, 1970). It should also be stressed that the same patterns

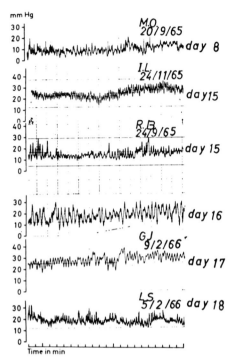

FIG. 1. Intrauterine recordings from day 8 to day 18 of normal menstrual cycles. From Moawad and Bengtsson (1967), by permission of *Amer. J. Obstet. Gynecol.*

were obtained by a technique using no intrauterine devices (Joelsson and Odeblad, 1972). Contradictory results have been obtained by Csapo and Pinto-Dantas (1966), Behrman and Burchfield (1968), and to some extent also by Gibor *et al.* (1971).

Figures 1–3 illustrate the patterns of myometrial activity in normal menstrual cycles: from day 6 to day 18 (of 28-day cycles) the contractions, recorded as pressure changes, are frequent (2–4 per minute), have low amplitude (3–10 mm Hg) and short duration. Around the middle of the secretory phase a new type of contraction appears, showing lower frequency (every 2–3 minutes), higher amplitude (about 25 mm Hg), a duration of 1–2 minutes and a rather slow rise and fall. As the next menstruation is approached, the stronger, infrequent contractions become more pronounced, the amplitude increases, the onset is sharper, relaxation between the contractions becomes more complete and the resting pressure decreases. Hendricks (1965, 1966) has called this type of activity "pre-laborlike." Around the onset of menstruation, the small, frequent contractions have disappeared, the stronger contractions appear

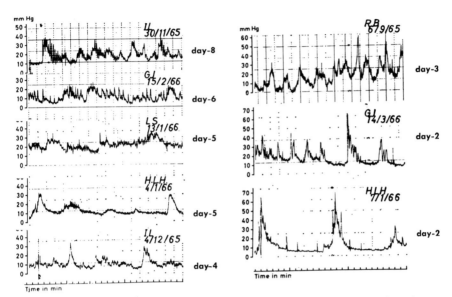

Fig. 2. Intrauterine recordings from mid- and late secretory phase of ovulatory cycles. Left: from day 8 to day 4 before menstruation. Right: from day 3 to day 2 before menstruation. From Moawad and Bengtsson (1967), by permission of *Amer. J. Obstet. Gynecol.*

at intervals of about 2–3 minutes, reaching a pressure of 100–200 mm Hg, and showing a sharp rise and fall. A record from the onset of menstruation cannot be distinguished from a record obtained during active labor, when propagating waves are sweeping over the uterus. This type of activity, therefore, has been called "laborlike" (Hendricks, 1965, 1966) or "propagating" (Csapo and Pinto-Dantas, 1966).

There is a well known time sequence in the production of estrogen and progesterone during the menstrual cycle: in the proliferative phase mainly estrogen is produced, in the secretory phase estrogen and increasing amounts of progesterone are produced until, some few days before the next menstruation, the production of both hormones decreases. The above-mentioned time sequence of the activity patterns during the cycle indicates that estrogen alone induces small and frequent contractions, the combination of estrogen and progesterone induces "prelaborlike" activity and the withdrawal of the two hormones induces "laborlike" activity. As will be shown below, these effects of female sex hormones on myometrial activity have been verified in several different ways.

According to Csapo (see p. 259), progesterone depresses the *prop-*

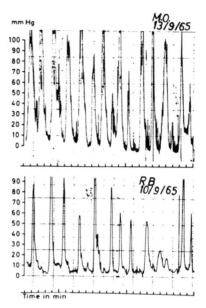

Fig. 3. Intrauterine recordings from the first menstrual day. From Moawad and Bengtsson (1967), by permission of *Amer. J. Obstet. Gynecol.*

agation and coordination of myometrial contractions. If so, there would be propagated and coordinated contractions in the proliferative phase and only local, noncoordinated and nonpropagating contractions in the secretory phase. As this is an important problem, we have subjected it to a study by our team (Martinez-Gaudio *et al.*, 1973). We found that in the proliferative phase there are only local, independent, and nonpropagating contractions. From the midsecretory phase to the onset of menstrual bleeding, a gradual change is observed from local contractions toward the propagated ones, typical of those at the onset of menstruation. During menstrual bleeding propagation is improved, and contraction waves can be observed, sometimes going upward, sometimes downward, and sometimes starting in the middle of the uterus, propagating in both directions. Really synchronous contractions were but rarely observed. This is illustrated in Figs. 4 and 5. These findings *do not* suggest that propagation and coordination of uterine contractions in the nonpregnant woman are depressed by progesterone.

The fact that in all these experiments—except the rare occasions of synchrony—different pressures were recorded at different levels of the uterine cavity clearly demonstrates that the "cavity" is only a potential cavity—in fact a mere slit.

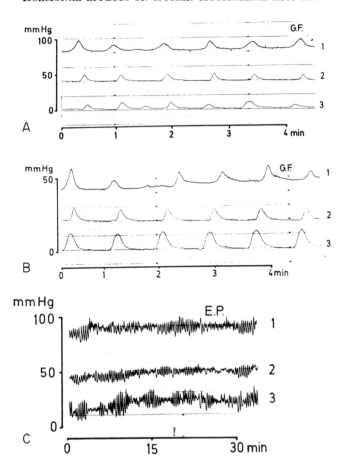

FIG. 4. Intrauterine recordings from (1) upper, (2) middle, and (3) lower portion of the uterus on day 12 of the menstrual cycle. Record B (day 12) was obtained some minutes after A. The lack of relation between the activities at the three different levels indicates purely local contractions. (C) Records with lower paper speed, from another subject on day 14, show periodical and independent changes in amplitudes at the different levels. From Martinez-Gaudio *et al.* (1973), by permission of *Amer. J. Obstet. Gynecol.*

b. Anovulatory Cycles and Stein-Leventhal's Syndrome. In anovulatory cycles, where a lack of ovulation generally excludes ovarian progesterone production, the myometrium consistently shows the proliferative phase type of activity, i.e., small, frequent contractions (Wilson and Kurzrok, 1938, 1940; Bickers, 1941; Henry and Browne, 1943; Henry *et al.*, 1950; Garret, 1956; Cibils, 1967; Moawad and Bengtsson, 1967). This is il-

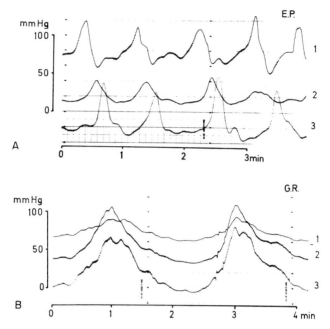

FIG. 5. Intrauterine recordings from (1) upper, (2) middle, and (3) lower portion of the uterus. (A) From menstrual day 3, indicating downward propagation. (B) From day 3 in another subject, indicating synchronous contractions. From Martinez-Gaudio *et al.* (1972), by permission of *Amer. J. Obstet. Gynecol.*

lustrated in Fig. 6. Also in cases of Stein-Leventhal syndrome, estrogen alone is continuously produced; consequently only proliferative phase activity is found (Fig. 7).

c. Postmenopause. A lack of ovarian hormones in postmenopausal and castrated women reduces the uterine activity but does not abolish it (Figs. 8 and 15a).

2. Estrogen Administration and Withdrawal

Estrogen administration to postmenopausal and castrated women rapidly restores myometrial activity to the proliferative phase type (Bickers, 1941; Henry *et al.*, 1950; Bengtsson and Theobald, 1966; Moawad and Bengtsson, 1967, 1968; Coutinho, 1968b). This is illustrated in Fig. 9, a recording from a woman 6 years after castration and after an estrogen treatment copying the estrogen influence in a normal menstrual cycle. *Withdrawal* of estrogen treatment is followed by withdrawal bleeding, but no laborlike activity is observed (Fig. 10).

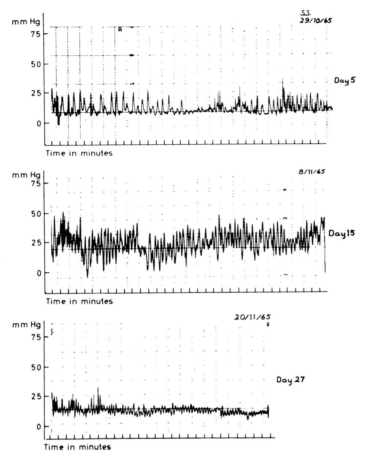

Fig. 6. Intrauterine recordings on days 6, 15, and 27 in an anovulatory cycle. Note the lack of "pre-laborlike" activity on day 27, which was the day before the onset of bleeding. From Moawad and Bengtsson (1968), by permission of *Acta Obstet. Gynecol. Scand.*

3. *Gestagen Administration (without Estrogen)*

As mentioned above, estrogen priming is a prerequisite for a gestagen effect on the endometrium. This seems to be valid also for the myometrium, because gestagen given alone to postmenopausal women has only a small effect on myometrial activity as is demonstrated in Fig. 11. The effect of gestagen withdrawal in this condition has not been studied.

The above-mentioned studies have indicated that estrogen alone produces the proliferative phase type of activity, i.e., small, frequent

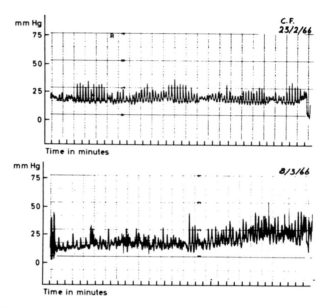

FIG. 7. Intrauterine recordings 2 weeks apart in a case of Stein-Leventhal syndrome. From Moawad and Bengtsson (1968), by permission of *Acta Obstet. Gynecol. Scand.*

contractions, but that the addition of progesterone from the corpus luteum changes the activity pattern into pre-laborlike activity and the withdrawal of estrogen and progesterone induces the observed laborlike pattern. We have carefully studied whether the activity changes, presumably due to a gestagen effect, can be mimicked by induced progesterone production and by exogenous gestagen administration.

4. *Endogenous Progesterone*

In amenorrheic women we induced ovulation by clomiphene. The increase in pregnanediol excretion after the treatment is illustrated in Fig. 12. The changes in myometrial activity are shown in Fig. 13, where panel A demonstrates the activity before treatment; panel B, the pre-laborlike activity of the day of maximal pregnanediol excretion; and panel

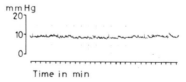

FIG. 8. Intrauterine record from a woman 6 years after castration. From Moawad and Bengtsson (1968), by permission of *Acta Obstet. Gynecol. Scand.*

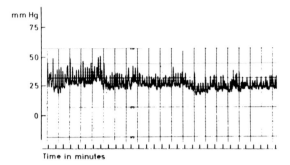

FIG. 9. Intrauterine recording from a castrated woman (the same as in Fig. 8) after 26 days of estrogen treatment (10–100 μg of ethynylestradiol per day in a schedule copying estrogen influence in the menstrual cycle). From Moawad and Bengtsson (1968), by permission of *Acta Obstet. Gynecol. Scand.*

C, the laborlike activity when pregnanediol values had approached pre-treatment values and the bleeding started. Thus, this artificially produced secretory phase was accompanied by changes in myometrial activity similar to those in spontaneously occurring cycles.

5. Addition of Exogenous Gestagen to Endogenous Estrogen

It has been stated above that endogenous progesterone changes the myometrial activity pattern from the weak, frequent contractions of the

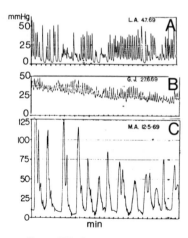

FIG. 10. Intrauterine recordings (A) from a woman 4 hours after the onset of estrogen withdrawal bleeding, (B) from a woman 10 hours after the onset of such bleeding. (C) A record for comparison, obtained a few hours after the onset of menstruation in a normal ovulatory cycle. From Moawad and Bengtsson (1970), by permission of *Acta Obstet. Gynecol. Scand.*

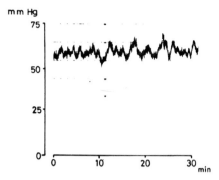

FIG. 11. Intrauterine recording after 4 mg of norethisterone daily for 10 days to a woman 6 years after menopause. From Bengtsson (1968a) by permission of *Rev. Fr. Gynecol. Obstet.*

proliferative phase to the stronger and less frequent contractions of the secretory phase. The same change in activity is produced by exogenous progesterone in anovulatory but estrogen-producing women (Wilson and Kurzrok, 1938, 1940; Bickers, 1941; Henry *et al.*, 1950; Coutinho, 1967). If progesterone is given in the proliferative phase of normally menstruating women, a rapid evolution of pre-laborlike activity is obtained; cessation of the treatment is followed by laborlike activity and bleeding (Bengtsson, 1970a). This is illustrated in Fig. 14.

    a. Combined Estrogen and Gestagen Administration. In castrated

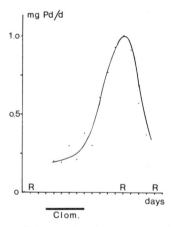

FIG. 12. Urinary pregnanediol excretion in an amenorrheic woman treated with clomiphene (—). At R the recordings in Fig. 13 were obtained. From Bengtsson (1970a), by permission of *Acta Obstet. Gynecol. Scand.*

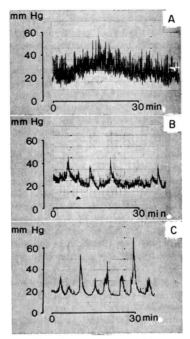

Fig. 13. Intrauterine recordings in an amenorrheic woman. (A) Two days before clomiphene treatment. (B) At the peak of pregnanediol excretion. (C) At the onset of bleeding. Compare with Fig. 12. From Bengtsson (1970a), by permission of *Acta Obstet. Gynecol. Scand.*

women sequential administration of estrogen and progesterone mimics in detail the sequence of activity patterns found in ovulatory cycles (Wilson and Kurzrok, 1940; Henry and Browne, 1943; Henry *et al.*, 1950; T. Eskes *et al.*, 1969).

The same is mainly true also for synthetic, orally active steroids. The larger the doses, the more rapidly the activity changes are produced. If

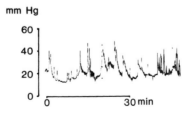

Fig. 14. Intrauterine recording after 100 mg of progesterone given intramuscularly for 2 days. From Bengtsson (1970a), by permission of *Acta Obstet. Gynecol. Scand.*

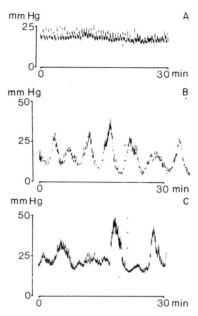

FIG. 15. Intrauterine recordings in a castrated woman. (A) Before treatment, (B) After 2 days. (C) After 5 days of treatment with 8 mg of norethisterone and 0.1 mg of ethynylestradiol. From Bengtsson (1970a), by permission of *Acta Obstet. Gynecol. Scand.*

big doses of both estrogen and gestagen are given, drastic activity changes are observed after only a few days (Fig. 15). It is suggested by the presented records that, after combined estrogen + gestagen administration, details of the recorded activity do not quite correspond to those from normal ovulatory cycles. This was observed also by Hendricks (1965, 1966).

However, after *prolonged* combined estrogen plus gestagen treatment there seems to be a reduction of uterine activity toward small, infrequent contractions (Cibils, 1967).

In preliminary experiments on the *effect of gestagen on the coordination of myometrial contractions* in nonpregnant women (Bengtsson and Martinez-Gaudio, unpublished), we found that conventional contraceptive pills (estrogen plus gestagen) do not increase coordination, but produce a rather bizzarre pattern of incoordination, illustrated in Fig. 16.

The increase in *myometrial compliance* observed in the secretory phase can be copied by gestagen administration (Sharp and Wood, 1966). A further increase takes place during pregnancy, and may be due to increasing production of estrogen and progesterone (Wood, 1964).

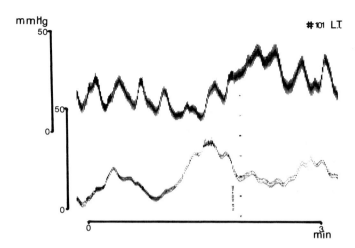

FIG. 16. Intrauterine recordings at two different levels of the uterus after 5 days daily administration of 2 mg of norethisterone and 0.1 mg of mestranol. Upper tracing: fundal position, lower tracing: mid-uterus position of the catheter. (The small, very frequent amplitudes indicate the pulse.) The tracings indicate completely independent contractions. From L. P. Bengtsson and M. Martinez-Gaudio (unpublished).

b. The Effect of Estrogen and Gestagen on Myometrial Sensitivity

i. Sensitivity to posterior pituitary hormones. See Section V.

ii. Sensitivity to mechanical stimuli. Any foreign body in the uterine cavity, e.g., an intrauterine device, may mechanically stimulate the myometrium. We have studied the effect of Lippes' loop on myometrial activity, and found that the pre-laborlike activity of the secretory phase develops precociously in the presence of the loop (Bengtsson and Moawad, 1967; Moawad and Bengtsson, 1970). This may suggest that the sensitivity to mechanical stimulation increases in the secretory phase. Similar results have been obtained by Maia and Coutinho (1970) dissimilar by Johnson *et al.* (1966) and Behrman and Burchfield (1968).

C. EFFECTS OF ESTROGEN AND GESTAGEN IN PREGNANCY AND LABOR

1. Estrogen

a. Estrogen for Induction of Myometrial Activity

i. At term. From the fact that—even in the human—estrogen is needed for the growth and strength of the myometrium, it has been extrapolated that estrogen also stimulates myometrial activity and sensitivity. It is demonstrated above that this is not true for the nonpregnant human uterus.

As far as the estrogen and the activity of the pregnant uterus are concerned, several authors have through many decades reported the successful use of estrogen for the induction of labor (Robinson *et al.*, 1935; Jeffcoate, 1950; Kalkschmied, 1958, 1960; Tappfer, 1959; Vara *et al.*, 1961; Järvinen and Luukkainen, 1962; Järvinen and Huhmar, 1963; Pinto *et al.*, 1966; Pinto, 1967; Järvinen *et al.*, 1965).

The theory concerning the stimulatory effect of estrogen on the pregnant uterus may be supported by the fact that estriol excretion increases during pregnancy, most pronouncedly toward its end (Klopper *et al.*, 1961). The same increase has been demonstrated also in plasma estriol concentration (Masson and Klopper, 1972).

However, intravenous administration of large doses of estrogen does not stimulate the uterus at term (Kelly, 1961). Furthermore, carefully performed double blind tests have not proved any *consistent* effect of estrogen administration in starting or shortening labor. Thus, Klopper and Dennis (1962) studied the effect on induction-delivery time and on length of labor of oral administration of estriol and stilbestrol to pregnant women who were to be subjected to induction of labor by means of artificial rupture of the membranes. They found no effect of the estrogens given. Intra-amniotic injections of estriol sulfate have a certain but not very convincing effect on myometrial activity at term (Klopper *et al.*, 1969, 1973). The authors' conclusion from these studies is very cautious: "This study, however, does not show that changes in the oestriol concentration at the myometrial level play a dominant, or indeed any, part in the onset of labour."

The inability of estrogen to induce effective myometrial activity in human pregnancy is also suggested by the fact that administration of estrogen, once a rather popular therapeutic procedure, has nowadays been almost totally abandoned.

ii. In "missed abortion." As mentioned above, there is no proof that estrogen plays an important role in the onset of human labor. However, in order to start myometrial activity in missed abortion, estrogen therapy has long been used and is still advocated. Two facts must be borne in mind: (1) that the hormonal conditions in missed abortion differ considerably from those in normal pregnancy, and (2) that in missed abortion estrogen is used not as an oxytocic drug, but in order to rebuild myometrial strength. It has been assumed that missed abortion occurs only when the fetus dies before the placenta (Rongy and Arluck, 1921). If this situation is produced by rupturing the membranes and ligation of the

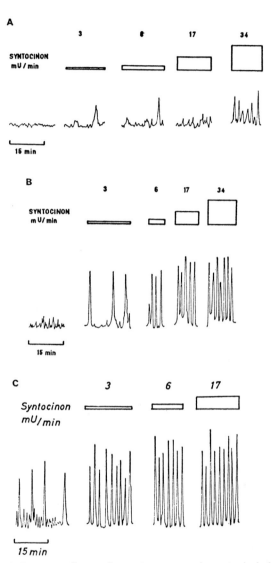

Fig. 17. Intrauterine recordings of spontaneous and oxytocin-induced uterine activity in a case of missed abortion, 8 weeks after fetal death. (A) Before treatment. (B) After 2 days and (C) after 4 days of treatment with 0.5 mg ethynylestradiol daily. From Bengtsson (1962), by permission of *Lancet*.

umbilical cord in order to induce therapeutic abortion (Cassmer, 1959), the estrogen production ceases rapidly, while progesterone production is maintained. We have shown that in cases of spontaneous intrauterine fetal death which turn into missed abortion, the sequence of hormonal changes are closely similar: a rapid drop in the urinary excretion of estrogen, while pregnanediol excretion drops very slowly and may be normal for up to 4 weeks (Bengtsson and Forsgren, 1966). This specific sequence of hormonal changes may be an important factor in the etiology of missed abortion (Bengtsson, 1962). Some months after fetal death the production of estrogen and progesterone is extremely low, and the myometrium, being devoid of the normal hormonal influence, is incapable of effective contraction and insensitive to stimulation. In these cases, i.e., months after fetal death, estrogen administration builds up the myometrium again and restores its strength and sensitivity. This is illustrated in Fig. 17, which demonstrates a case of fetal death during week 25. The recording started 2 months after fetal death. Before treatment, the spontaneous activity as well as the oxytocin sensitivity was low. After 4 days of treatment with ethinylestradiol in an oral dose of 0.5 mg daily, both myometrial activity and oxytocin sensitivity increased and continuation of the oxytocin drip induced abortion.

We also observed (1) that the urinary excretion of estriol and pregnanediol indicates how long the fetus has been dead (Bengtsson and Forsgren, 1966), and (2) that in a group of 27 women with fetal death about 4 weeks earlier, 20 aborted after estrogen treatment, in some cases completed with intravenous oxytocin infusion (Bengtsson and Falk, 1964).

2. *Progesterone*

Studies on the effects of progesterone on myometrial activity in pregnancy have been performed along two different lines, one concerning endogenous progesterone, i.e., the amount of progesterone which, during stages of myometrial quiescence and activity, respectively, is produced, circulates in the blood and is present in the myometrium, and one concerning the effect of exogenous gestagen on myometrial activity. These two lines will be discussed separately.

a. Normal Pregnancy and Labor. During pregnancy the *daily production of progesterone* increases from 30 mg (Corner, 1937; Dominguez et al., 1965) to 75 mg in midpregnancy (Ejarque and Bengtsson, 1962) and further to 250 mg close to term (Zander and von Münstermann, 1956; Pearlman, 1957; Solomon et al., 1962; Bengtsson and Ejarque, 1964; Dominguez et al., 1965). There is an indication that the production of progesterone is influenced by the number of fetuses, as this production was found to be no less than over 500 mg per 24 hours in a twin pregnancy at term (Bengtsson and Ejarque, 1964).

For practical reasons, progesterone production before and after the onset of myometrial activity can be judged only from progesterone concentrations in blood (see below).

Progesterone concentration in maternal peripheral blood increases during pregnancy (Fig. 18), and there is generally no fall before labor starts (Aitken *et al.*, 1958; Short and Eton, 1959; Simmer and Simmer, 1959; Deshpande *et al.*, 1960; Zander, 1961; van der Molen, 1963; Kumar *et al.*, 1964; Sommerville *et al.*, 1963; Woolever and Goldfien, 1965). Contrary to all these reports, Csapo *et al.* (1971) found a drop in blood progesterone levels shortly before labor. However, it is interesting to observe that there is a drop in blood progesterone concentration between week 8 and week 10 of pregnancy (Fig. 18), i.e., at a stage when many spontaneous abortions occur. This might be one of the few facts that indicate that progesterone influences myometrial activity in human pregnancy. Another positive observation was made by Johansson (1968): higher myometrial sensitivity to oxytocin close to term was demonstrated in combination with lower blood progesterone levels. However, Fylling (1971) found no relation between urinary pregnanediol excretion and the effect of oxytocin injections.

Studies of *progesterone concentrations in umbilical vein blood* (Aitken

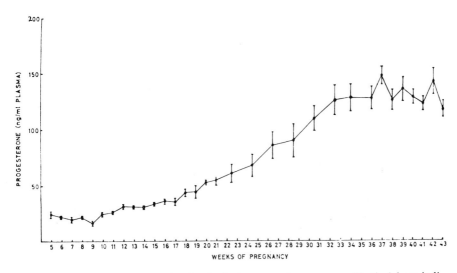

FIG. 18. Plasma progesterone levels during normal pregnancy. Vertical bars indicate the standard error of the mean. From Johansson (1969), by permission of *Acta Endocrinol. (Copenhagen)*.

et al., 1958) do not indicate any difference between cases with myometrial activity (spontaneous labor) and cases without such activity (elective cesarean sections).

Also *urinary pregnanediol excretion* increases during pregnancy. Most modern authors agree that there is no fall prior to labor, among others, Klopper *et al.* (1961) and Furuhjelm (1962).

The most important parameter, as far as progesterone and myometrial activity are concerned, is *progesterone concentration in the myometrium*. A careful study of this problem was performed by Runnebaum and Zander (1971). They found (1) that the myometrial progesterone concentration did not follow the blood progesterone concentration and (2) that a difference in progesterone concentration between the placental and the antiplacental sites was demonstrable in early pregnancy but not at term (Figs. 19 and 20). These findings are not in accordance with the theory of Csapo (1959, 1961a,b) concerning a local effect of the placenta and a progesterone block as important factors in the maintenance and termination of human pregnancy.

It is a common clinical experience that rupture of the fetal membranes stimulates uterine activity close to term. The mechanism behind this effect is unknown. Pulkkinen and Enkola (1972) found that the *progesterone concentration in the fetal membranes* did not change after the membranes were ruptured. Thus, the effect is not mediated by progesterone.

Exogenous gestagen. Several trials have been made to stop early stages

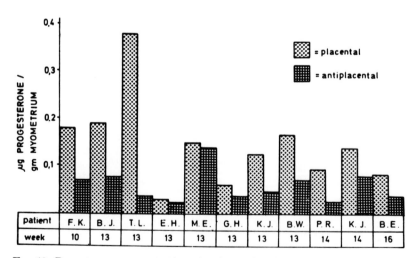

Fig. 19. Progesterone concentrations in placental and antiplacental myometrium in early pregnancy. From Runnebaum and Zander (1971), by permission of *Acta Endocrinol.*

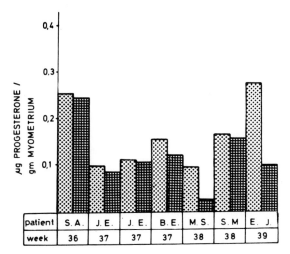

Fig. 20. Progesterone concentrations in placental (stripped bars) and antiplacental (crosshatched bars) myometrium in week 36 to week 39 of gestation. From Runnebaum and Zander (1971), by permission of *Acta Endocrinol. (Copenhagen)*.

of term labor or to prolong pregnancy by gestagen administration, but without success (Page and Woods, 1943; Kaiser and Will, 1953; Pose and Fielitz, 1961; Brenner and Hendricks, 1962). Even very large doses of synthetic gestagen have very limited effect: Csapo *et al.* (1966) gave 4 gm of 6α-methyl-17α-acetoxyprogesterone intramuscularly and observed only a slight and transient depressive effect on myometrial activity. Kumar *et al.* (1963) gave an intravenous infusion of 6–7 mg of progesterone per minute to ten women and found a moderate effect in four, minimal effect in one, and no effect in five cases (total dose up to 1 gm).

b. Abnormal Pregnancy and Labor

i. Threatened abortion and threatened premature labor. Some decades ago it was assumed that spontaneous labor should be preceded by a drop in pregnanediol excretion (see above). Consequently, many authors have expected a fall in pregnanediol excretion also in other stages of pregnancy before uterine activity starts. The studies on this problem are too well known and too many to be quoted here. Suffice it to say that most attempts to prove such a fall have failed (e.g., Borth and de Watteville, 1952; Zander, 1967). On the other hand, a severely damaged conceptus may produce a decreased amount of progesterone. Thus, combined with other tests, pregnanediol determination may be used for evaluation of the prognosis of threatened abortion (Borglin and Willert, 1957).

ii. Exogenous gestagen. Some pharmaceutical firms still advertise that gestagen protects pregnancy. This may be true in some respects, but not as far as myometrial activity after the first trimester is concerned. Before the placenta has taken over most of the progesterone production, the corpus luteum seems to be indispensable for the maintenance of pregnancy, as recently demonstrated by Csapo et al. (1972a) in an experimental study. Removal of the corpus luteum around week 7 resulted in a decreased blood progesterone concentration, an increase in spontaneous and oxytocin induced activity, and abortion. Removal of the corpus luteum after week 7 was not followed by any changes in blood progesterone concentration, in myometrial activity, or in sensitivity to oxytocin, and the pregnancy was maintained.

Thus, gestagen administration may be indicated in those cases of *early* pregnancy in which corpus luteum insufficiency is probable or proved. (This may be the only indication for gestagen therapy in pregnancy.)

In the second and third trimesters there is no proof that gestagen administration depresses myometrial activity or sensitivity. In threatened abortion and threatened premature labor, double-blind tests with gestagen and placebo administration have shown no difference in effect (Fuchs and Stakemann, 1958; Brenner and Hendricks, 1962; Shearman and Garret, 1963; Øvlisen and Iversen, 1963; Nilsson, 1964; Alling-Møller and Fuchs, 1965; Govaerts-Videtzky et al., 1965). Nor could Zander (1967), a distinguished author in the progesterone field, prove any effect of gestagen treatment in threatened abortion.

Based upon the idea that what matters in the effect of gestagen on myometrial activity is the myometrial concentration of the hormone, *intramyometrial administration of gestagen* has been tried in order to depress myometrial activity in the second and third trimester (Coutinho et al., 1960; Theobald and Lundborg, 1962; Bengtsson and Siener, 1964). These studies have all shown a certain, but far from 100%, success. There seems to be a general opinion that the effect of the treatment decreases by increasing cervical dilatation. The number of women studied is small in all these experiments, because the treatment is painful and poorly accepted by the women.

There are no indications that *prolonged pregnancy* is combined with increased progesterone production, judged from the urinary excretion of pregnanediol (Kaiser and Will, 1953; Borth and Stamm, 1958).

c. Therapeutic Abortion. Therapeutic abortion performed by means of intrauterine injection of solutions, mostly hypertonic sodium chloride, seemingly offers an excellent opportunity to study the mechanisms behind the onset of myometrial activity after injection. However, the factors involved in the effect of hypertonic saline may be as many as those engaged in the onset of normal labor. We know that the sodium chloride injected into the pregnant uterus produces fetal death, enters into the placenta and the decidua (Gustavii, 1971), damages the placenta, fetal membranes (Bengtsson and Stormby, 1962), and decidua (Gustavii and Brunk, 1972), and changes the osmolarity of the blood with consequent effects upon oxytocin and vasopressin release (Hendricks et al., 1959).

As the placenta is damaged, it has been suspected that the progesterone production decreases. According to the "progesterone block" theory (Csapo, 1961a,b), this would induce myometrial activity and be respon-sible for the abortion (Bengtsson and Csapo, 1962). Consequently, several authors have studied blood progesterone concentrations before and after intrauterine injection of 20% saline, but various results have been reported. There are no consistent progesterone concentration changes in the uterine vein blood after intra-amniotic saline (Fuchs et al., 1965). In the peripheral blood, Csapo et al. (1969) found a significant drop of progesterone concentration before the clinical onset of abortion. In a larger study of similar cases, Holmdahl et al. (1971) confirmed that after saline injection there is a decrease in blood progesterone but—what is important—they found no relation whatsoever between blood progesterone concentration and the onset or outcome of abortion. In our team we have studied blood progesterone concentrations in 20 cases of saline-induced

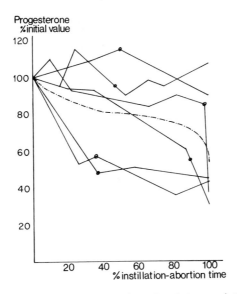

Fig. 21. Plasma progesterone concentration after intra-amniotic injection of 20% sodium chloride in six representative cases (out of 20). Solid lines: individual cases, dashed lines: mean values. Circles: onset of clinical signs of abortion. From L. P. Bengtsson, B. Gustavii, and J. Nilsson (unpublished).

abortions (Bengtsson, Gustavii, and Nilsson, unpublished) and have got exactly the same results as Holmdahl et al. (1971), as illustrated in Fig. 21.

A decrease in progesterone production induced by saline injection should be compensated by gestagen administration, which should postpone abortion. In a small series (6 cases) Bengtsson and Csapo (1962) produced a certain delay by giving 6α-methyl-17α-acetoxyprogesterone. However, in a larger series (15 cases) Møller et al. (1964) could not confirm these results. Intra-aortic infusion of the same substance (0.72–5.40 mg per minute) depressed myometrial activity in one out of three cases (Wiqvist, 1963). Thus, at present it is not proved that the myometrial activity after hypertonic saline injection is triggered by decreased progesterone production.

On the other hand, according to earlier theories, administration of estrogen should improve myometrial activity after saline injection and should, therefore, shorten the injection-abortion period. However, intra-amniotic administration of estriol sulfate before hypertonic saline injection has no such effects (Dennis et al., 1973).

III. CORTICOSTEROIDS

In the woman there are but few observations indicating that corticosteroids influence myometrial activity (see below). However, in some animals the influence of maternal and fetal corticosteroids has been clearly demonstrated. This effect is so interesting, and will certainly stimulate human research in the hormonal control of myometrial activity to such an extent, that a short presentation of important observations in animals is included in this chapter.

A. MATERNAL CORTICOSTEROIDS

In the late-pregnant cow, two intramuscular injections with 3–6 days interval of 10–12 mg dexamethasone induce labor (Edqvist et al., 1971). During this treatment, blood estrogen increases and blood progesterone decreases. In the late-pregnant ewe, bigger doses of corticosteroids are needed to induce parturition but are supposed to act via the fetus (Liggins, 1969). In the pregnant rhesus monkey dexamethasone administration increases progesterone and decreases estrogen in the blood and does not induce labor (Bosu et al., 1972).

In the human, the production of corticosteroids increases during labor, obviously as an effect of the stress situation (Gemzell, 1953). However, there are no indications that these changes influence myometrial activity or that corticosteroid administration is capable of inducing labor in the human.

B. Fetal Corticosteroids

In cattle (Kennedy *et al.*, 1957) and sheep (Binns *et al.*, 1964) congenital absence of the fetal hypophysis with concomitant atrophy of the fetal adrenal cortex causes prolongation of gestation. It has also been demonstrated in sheep that removal of the fetal adrenal or the fetal hypophysis (which causes atrophy of the adrenal cortex) prolongs pregnancy, while infusion of ACTH or corticosteroids into the fetal abdomen interrupts gestation. The effect of corticosteroid on the myometrium seems to be mediated via the placenta: The administered corticosteroid depresses placental progesterone production and increases the production of estrogen and $PGF_{2\alpha}$ (Liggins *et al.*, 1967; Liggins and Kennedy, 1968).

In women it had already been observed by Malpas (1933) that pregnancy is considerably prolonged when the fetus is anencephalic with the hypophysis lacking and the adrenal cortex atrophic. As the adrenal cortex produces the estriol precursor, estriol excretion in these cases is very low, as demonstrated by Frandsen and Stakemann (1961, 1964).

Unlike the ewe, the woman does not go into labor after corticosteroid infusion into the fetus (Liggins, 1969). However, a relation between the fetal adrenal cortex and the onset of labor is indicated not only by the anencephalic fetuses mentioned above, but also by the fact that the size of the adrenal glands is related to the length of gestation (Turnbull and Anderson, 1969).

IV. Biogenic Amines

A. Epinephrine

There is general agreement that epinephrine depresses myometrial activity, in the nonpregnant as well as in the pregnant woman (Reynolds *et al.*, 1954; Garret, 1954; Pose *et al.*, 1962; Zuspan *et al.*, 1962).

In pregnant women at term, intravenous infusion of 5–70 μg of epinephrine induces within some few minutes a drop in frequency and amplitude of the contractions. After about 20 minutes of infusion a recovery starts, which later becomes sometimes total, sometimes partial. After discontinuation of the infusion, a "rebound" effect is observed, with increased uterine activity and pronouncedly elevated tonus. For these reasons epinephrine is not suitable for clinical depression of uterine activity in pregnancy.

The depression of uterine activity by epinephrine may have clinical significance as women in prolonged labor have higher blood levels of epinephrine than those in normal labor (Hochuli et al., 1956).

B. NOREPINEPHRINE

This circulating hormone stimulates myometrial activity, also in the pregnant woman (Kaiser, 1950; Garret, 1954; Cibils et al., 1962; Zuspan et al., 1962). Intravenous infusion of 2–10 μg per minute almost immediately increases the tonus, amplitude, and frequency of myometrial contractions. A maximum is reached after about 6 minutes; thereafter a slow decrease in the effect is observed, but not to preinfusion values. The contractions elicited by the injection are incoordinated. The rapid subsidence of the effect and the incoordinated character of the contractions make norepinephrine less suitable for induction and stimulation of labor than oxytocin.

C. NEURONAL CATECHOLAMINES

The distribution and identity of neuronal catecholamines in the human uterus have been elucidated by combined fluorescence histochemistry and fluorometric quantitations. Dopamine and epinephrine do not occur in the tissue in measurable amounts; norepinephrine is exclusively present in sympathetic nerves, which are unique in that they arise close to the effector organ from peripheral ganglia ("short adrenergic neurons"), which can be directly visualized histochemically (Owman et al., 1967). The myometrial nerve terminals run close to the smooth muscle cells. The density of innervation is comparatively low in the fundus region (corresponding to a mean norepinephrine concentration of 0.12 μg/gm), higher in the corpus (0.16 μg/gm) and maximal in the cervix (0.45 μg/gm).

Animal experiments have revealed that the uterine short adrenergic neurons are also functionally unique. Their norepinephrine transmitter is almost abolished through a combination of humoral and mechanical factors at the end of pregnancy (Rosengren and Sjöberg, 1968; Sjöberg, 1968a). The norepinephrine content is doubled under the influence of estrogen (Sjöberg, 1968b; Falck et al., 1969a) and is reduced with the addition of progesterone (Falck et al., 1969b).

D. SEROTONIN

This tissue hormone stimulates myometrial activity in all animals studied, but the effect varies from species to species (Gaddum and Hameed, 1954; Robson et al., 1954; Fuchs, 1971).

In the human the effect is most pronounced in early pregnancy and decreases toward term (*in vitro* experiments, Fuchs, 1971). *In vivo* experiments have shown that intravenous infusion of 10–40 μg per minute increases uterine activity at term (Urban, 1965); such doses are supposed to be above physiological levels. Some findings have been presented in order to demonstrate that serotonin plays a role in the control of myometrial activity in pregnancy and labor. The serotonin content of the placenta increases during pregnancy (Koren *et al.*, 1965). Intra-amniotic injection of pargyline hydrochloride, which blocks serotonin breakdown, starts myometrial activity, and can be used for therapeutic abortion (Koren *et al.*, 1966). However, Fuchs (1971) concluded that there is no experimental support for the idea that serotonin plays a significant role in myometrial control during pregnancy and labor.

V. Posterior Pituitary Hormones

A. Oxytocin

The myometrium-stimulating action of posterior pituitary extracts was discovered by Dale (1906). Since then we have learned much about oxytocin; and since the introduction of the intravenous oxytocin drip by Theobald (Theobald *et al.*, 1948), we know how to use it safely in inducing and stimulating labor.

The effect of oxytocin on the myometrial cell. In animals oxytocin increases myometrial activity and sensitivity by lowering the membrane potential of the myometrial cell (Jung, 1957). This effect may be brought about by an increase of the number of sodium gates in the cell membrane (Kleinhaus and Kao, 1969). However, it has been suggested that oxytocin may also act directly inside the myometrial cell by activating the contractile elements (Evans *et al.*, 1958).

1. Myometrial Sensitivity to Oxytocin in Nonpregnant Women

During the ovulatory menstrual cycle, the actions of estrogen and progesterone on the myometrium change in a typical way. Since these hormones are supposed to change myometrial activity as well as sensitivity, one would expect oxytocin to elicit different response at different stages in the cycle. However, there is a remarkable disagreement about myometrial sensitivity to oxytocin during the menstrual cycle. Almost all kinds of sensitivity changes have been reported: (a) increased sensitivity in the proliferative phase (Knaus, 1929, 1930; Adair and Haugen, 1939; Csapo and Pinto-Dantas, 1966; Joelsson *et al.*, 1966; Kerenyi *et al.*, 1969); (b) increased sensitivity in the secretory phase (Moir, 1944; Henry *et al.*, 1950; Garret, 1954; Embrey and Moir, 1967; Coutinho and Lopes, 1968); (c) very low and unchanged oxytocin sensitivity through-

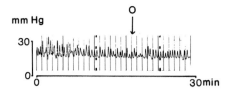

FIG. 22. Intrauterine recording on day 9 of the cycle, showing the lack of effect of 0.1 IU of oxytocin. From Bengtsson (1970c), by permission of *Acta Obstet. Gynecol. Scand.*

out the cycle (Torpin and Woodburry, 1947; Dahle, 1950; Caldeyro-Barcia and Sereno, 1961; Hendricks, 1965).

Some of these differences may be due to variations in technique and in doses of oxytocin. When high oxytocin doses are used, e.g., 0.5–2.0 IU, which are giant doses compared with what is highly effective at term, a certain but weak response is obtained in the proliferative, but not in the secretory, phase (Kerenyi *et al.*, 1969; Baumgarten, 1970).

If somewhat smaller doses, 0.1–0.2 IU of oxytocin are used (which still can be regarded rather as pharmacological than as physiological doses), there is no effect in any period of the cycle. This is illustrated by Figs. 22 and 23. In these experiments the myometrial activity was recorded by an intrauterine small rubber balloon catheter or a sponge-tipped catheter (Bengtsson, 1968b). These techniques give closely similar results (Braaksma, 1970).

Thus, in the doses used, 0.1–0.2 IU of Syntocinon, oxytocin did not elicit any response in the myometrium of nonpregnant women irrespective of changes in ovarian hormones.

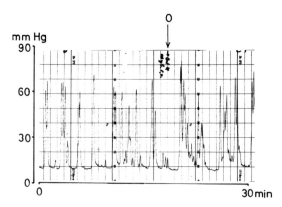

FIG. 23. Intrauterine recording on menstrual day 2. At 0 (arrow), intravenous injection of 0.1 IU of oxytocin, followed by insignificant change in myometrial activity. From Bengtsson (1970c), by permission of *Acta Obstet. Gynecol. Scand.*

2. Myometrial Sensitivity to Oxytocin in Pregnant Women

Nobody doubts that exogenous oxytocin stimulates the myometrium in the pregnant woman. However, there are still some doubts, namely, concerning (a) the physiological role of oxytocin in the initiation and successful outcome of labor, (b) the increase in oxytocin sensitivity during pregnancy, (c) the role of fetal oxytocin production.

The view that oxytocin plays a *physiological* role in labor is supported by the close similarity between normal, spontaneous myometrial contractions during labor and contractions induced at term by intravenous administration of oxytocin in suitable doses (Caldeyro-Barcia et al., 1957; Poseiro and Noriega-Guerra, 1961).

Theoretically, oxytocin could play a physiological role in the onset of labor in two ways: either by an increase in oxytocin release or by a rapid increase in myometrial sensitivity to oxytocin. Both ways would trigger the onset of labor contractions. Concerning increase in oxytocin release, most authors have found that if there is an increased blood oxytocin concentration, it does not occur until the *second* stage of labor (Coch et al., 1965; Fitzpatrick and Walmsley, 1965; Coutinho, 1964). Even more confusing are the studies of Chard et al. (1970, 1971), who found (a) that the oxytocin blood levels are very low throughout labor, (b) that the level changes during delivery but has no relation to the myometrial contractions, and (c) that there is no increase at the end of labor.

The idea that the evolution of myometrial activity in labor takes place without any increase in oxytocin release was earlier suggested by Cobo (1968), who recorded intrauterine and intraductal mammary gland pressures during spontaneous labor and found increasing uterine activity, unchanged oxytocin sensitivity but no significant milk-ejecting activity.

Concerning the *increase in myometrial response* to oxytocin during pregnancy there is a general agreement that there *is* an increase. But there the agreement stops. As to the time relation of the increase, there are controversial views. Caldeyro-Barcia and Poseiro (1959) have found a steady increase in oxytocin sensitivity up to, but not after, week 36. In contrast to that, Theobald et al. (1969) and to some extent Smyth (1958) and Csapo and Sauvage (1968) found no or very little increase in oxytocin sensitivity until close to the onset of labor, when the increase was drastic.

The first view implies that labor may start owing to an increase in oxytocin production, the latter that it may start without such an increase, but because of an increase in myometrial sensitivity to oxytocin.

Caldeyro-Barcia and Theobald (1968) finally agreed upon the following conclusion: the difference between the two views of the increase in oxytocin sensitivity during pregnancy is due to different test doses: On big doses the myometrium responds according to the Caldeyro-Barcia curve, on small doses, according to that of Theobald. This explanation satisfies a clinician, because the *clinical* experience has always been that there is a drastic increase in oxytocin sensitivity close to term.

3. *Fetal Oxytocin Production*

The possibility that the human fetus contributes to the oxytocin production was mentioned already by Bell and Robson (1937) and later by Theobald (1968). It has recently been reported that the fetus produces considerable amounts of oxytocin and vasopressin (Chard *et al.,* 1971; Chard, 1972). The concentration of oxytocin in the umbilical artery is considerable and higher than in the umbilical veins (Fig. 24). Furthermore, the concentration in the umbilical artery is higher when the myometrium has been working than when the fetus has been delivered by elective cesarean section (Fig. 24). This shows a relation between fetal oxytocin production and myometrial activity, but does not clearly indicate what comes first.

Chard himself hesitates to draw conclusions from these results (Chard, 1972). He points out that oxytocin passes the placenta (Noddle, 1964) and could thus reach the myometrium from the fetus. On the other

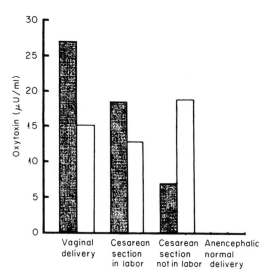

Fɪɢ. 24. Oxytocin level in umbilical cord blood obtained at different kinds of delivery. Stippled areas: umbilical arterial blood. Clear areas: umbilical venous blood. From Chard *et al.* (1971), by permission of *Nature (London).*

hand, he stresses that, in cases with an anencephalic fetus, there is no fetal oxytocin but a delayed but otherwise normal labor.

B. VASOPRESSIN

1. *Myometrial Sensitivity to Vasopressin in Nonpregnant Women*

Contrary to the oxytocin sensitivity (see above) the vasopressin sensitivity changes in a typical way during the menstrual cycle. Coutinho and Lopes (1968) found that the myometrial response to vasopressin changes "from positive (early proliferative) to absent (midproliferative) to negative (late proliferative), and during the secretory phase the response reverts to positive."

We have confirmed these results, except for the late proliferative phase, which we have not specifically studied. On day 9 (of a 28-day cycle), intravenous injection of 0.2 IU of vasopressin induced a limited increase in the tonus (Fig. 25). The same transient response was observed after 0.1 IU of vasopressin intravenously on day 10 of a 32–36-day-cycle. On day 20, the same dose of vasopressin gave a significantly stronger response. The strongest, remarkably long-lasting response was observed on the first menstrual day (Fig. 26). Thus, the addition of endogenous progesterone increases the myometrial response to vasopressin, which is further increased at the onset of menstrual bleeding, when the production of both ovarian sex hormones has decreased.

Also *exogenous* progesterone drastically increases the myometrial sensitivity to vasopressin. This is illustrated in Fig. 27.

2. *Myometrial Sensitivity to Vasopressin in Pregnancy*

The names "vasopressin" and "antidiuretic hormone" indicate two effects of this hormone, which have been carefully studied. (It should be noted that the effect on blood pressure in the *human* is very weak, except

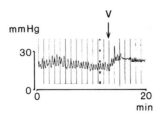

FIG. 25. Intrauterine recording showing the effect of intravenous injection of 0.2 IU of vasopressin: only increase in tonus. From Bengtsson (1970c), by permission of *Acta Obstet. Gynecol. Scand.* The effect of larger doses of vasopressin is demonstrated in Fig. 29.

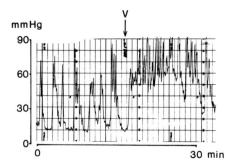

FIG. 26. Intrauterine recording on menstrual day 2. At V (arrow) injection of 0.1 IU of vasopressin, followed by strong and long-lasting increase in activity. From Bengtsson (1970c), by permission of *Acta Obstet. Gynecol. Scand.*

in huge doses .) The effect of vasopressin on the activity of the pregnant uterus has been rather neglected. Oxytocin, being a most potent and therapeutically important drug at the end of pregnancy, has dominated the field almost completely, and there are only a few reports of the effect of vasopressin on the myometrium of the pregnant woman (Moir, 1944; Dahle, 1950; Schild *et al.*, 1951; Cibils *et al.*, 1962; Embrey and Moir, 1967): In the beginning of pregnancy, oxytocin and vasopressin elicit about the same myometrial response. Toward term the sensitivity to oxytocin widely surpasses that to vasopressin. However, it has been clearly demonstrated that, in the nonpregnant woman, vasopressin is a much more potent oxytocic agent than oxytocin itself (Dahle, 1950; Bygdeman and Eliasson, 1964; Joelsson *et al.*, 1966; Coutinho and Lopes, 1968; Bengtsson, 1970c).

It is also possible that there are other relations between vasopressin

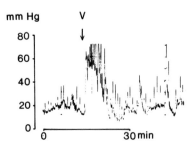

FIG. 27. Intrauterine recording showing the effect of 0.1 IU of vasopressin after progesterone treatment: 100 mg of progesterone intramuscularly for 2 days. Note the strong and long-lasting effect. From Bengtsson (1970c), by permission of *Acta Obstet. Gynecol. Scand.*

and myometrial activity. In rabbits even small amounts of vasopressin given intravenously severely depress uteroplacental blood flow (Carter *et al.*, 1968). An acute reduction of uterine blood flow influences myometrial activity, at least in primates (Whiteside *et al.*, 1967). Also a prolonged action of vasopressin could have similar effects by reducing placental blood flow, thereby interfering with placental hormone production. It is an interesting observation that the uterine circulation in pregnant women (judged from cervical circulation) is reduced not only during myometrial contractions, but also immediately before them (Brotánek *et al.*, 1969a,b).

3. Fetal Vasopressin Production

The high levels of oxytocin in umbilical cord vessels during parturition have been mentioned above. It is interesting to observe that Chard *et al.* (1971) have found considerably higher concentrations of vasopressin, which is illustrated in Fig. 28. This figure also shows that the highest levels are found when the myometrium has been working.

These findings indicate that also the fetal production of vasopressin

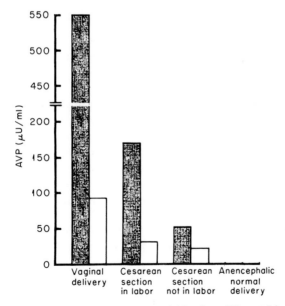

FIG. 28. Vasopressin levels in umbilical cord blood at different kinds of delivery. Stippled areas: umbilical arterial blood. Clear areas: umbilical venous blood. From Chard *et al.* (1971), by permission of *Nature (London)*.

may be relevant in the control of myometrial function in pregnancy and labor.

The possibility of vasopressin as a factor in the control of labor may be supported by the finding that reduction of uterine blood flow appears to stimulate myometrial activity (Brotánek et al., 1969a,b).

VI. Prostaglandins

For many years the research work on prostaglandins was confined to Sweden: The discovery of prostaglandins (von Euler, 1934), the effect of intravaginal injection of seminal fluid or extracts of it on myometrial activity (Karlson, 1959; Eliasson and Posse, 1960), the clarification of the chemical structure (Bergström et al., 1963) and analysis of the effects in pregnant and nonpregnant women (Bygdeman, 1964; Bygdeman et al., 1968; Wiqvist et al., 1968). The interest in prostaglandins then spread over the world, and the clinical use of prostaglandins in inducing therapeutic abortion and labor has been widely studied, especially $PGF_{2\alpha}$ and PGE_2, which have the most selective action on the myometrium of the pregnant human uterus.

A. Effects of Prostaglandins in Nonpregnant Women

Intravaginal application of semen (Karlson, 1959) and of seminal fluid extracts containing prostaglandins (Eliasson and Posse, 1960) has a varying but mainly stimulatory effect on the nonpregnant uterus in vivo.

Irrespective of the route of administration, pure prostaglandins always stimulate myometrial activity in the nonpregnant woman (Roth-Brandel et al., 1970; Karim et al., 1971). An increase in tonus is constantly found; at higher doses, also an increase in amplitude and frequency. This is illustrated in Figs. 29 and 30. The stimulatory effect of prostaglandins may vary in the different phases of the menstrual cycle, but definitely not as drastically as does the effect of vasopressin (Roth-Brandel et al., 1970).

Given intravenously in single doses, PGE_1 is at least two times more effective than $PGF_{2\alpha}$ (Roth-Brandel et al., 1970; Karim et al., 1971). Given by other routes (intramuscular, intravaginal, oral), ten to hundred times higher doses are needed but are often accompanied by gastrointestinal side effects (Karim, 1971a,b; Karim et al., 1971).

It is interesting to observe that also small amounts of prostaglandins administered into the uterine cavity of the nonpregnant woman increase myometrical activity (Embrey, 1970). Based on this fact, Pickles et al. (1966) suggested that the increase in myometrial activity around the

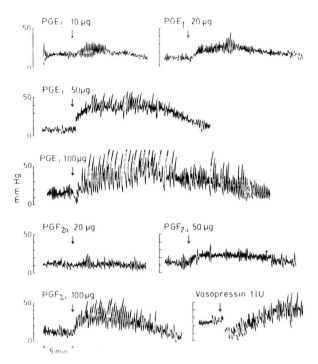

FIG. 29. Intrauterine recordings showing the effects of intravenous injections of PGE₁, PGF₂ₐ (and vasopressin) in the proliferative phase (day 13 of the cycle). From Roth-Brandel *et al.* (1970), by permission of *Acta Obstet. Gynecol. Scand.*

onset of menstruation may be due to absorption of prostaglandins from the endometrium.

B. Effects of Prostaglandins in Pregnancy

1. *Therapeutic Abortion*

Three years ago two groups reported independently that intravenous administration of PGF₂ₐ could be used for induction of abortion (Karim and Filshie, 1970; Wiqvist and Bygdeman, 1970). However, the results varied. The period of treatment approached 24 hours, and the side effects on the intestine were considerable.

Owing to these disadvantages, other routes of administration are now being tested. Intravaginal injections of PGF₂ₐ have a debatable effect and a high incidence of side effects (Karim and Sharma, 1971; Brenner *et al.*, 1972; Béguin *et al.*, 1972).

Single intra-amniotic injections of PGF₂ₐ are effective only when high

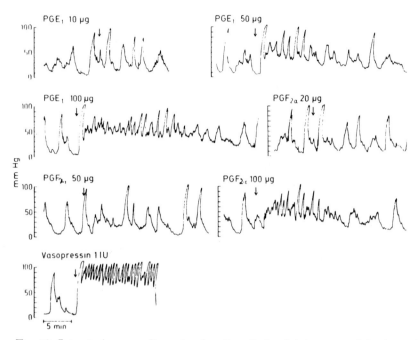

Fɪɢ. 30. Intrauterine recordings showing the effects of intravenous injections of PGE₁, PGF₂α (and vasopressin) on day 28 of the cycle. From Roth-Brandel *et al.* (1970), by permission of *Acta Obstet. Gynecol. Scand.*

doses (40 mg) are used (Bygdeman *et al.*, 1972; Anderson *et al.*, 1972). (One wonders what would happen if such doses were accidentally injected into the blood stream.)

At present the most promising route of administration is the *extra-amniotic* (Wiqvist and Bygdeman, 1970; Wiqvist *et al.*, 1972a). Such injections of $PGF_{2\alpha}$ or PGE_2 repeated at 2-hour intervals are effective within 24 hours, and the incidence of side effects is rather low (Embrey *et al.*, 1972; Bygdeman *et al.*, 1972). Single extra-amniotic injections of $PGF_{2\alpha}$ require large doses of the drug and therefore might be dangerous (Csapo *et al.*, 1972b).

As prostaglandins are capable of inducing strong uterine contractions, they have been tentatively used as postimplantation and defertility agents. Karim (1971c) reported success in some small groups of women, while Wiqvist (1963) had less successful results. Some derivatives of $PGF_{2\alpha}$ and PGE_2, e.g., 15-me-$PGF_{2\alpha}$ and 15-me-PGE_2, have been reported to have a stronger and more long-lasting effect than the original compounds (Toppozada *et al.*, 1972; Wiqvist *et al.*, 1972).

The use of prostaglandins in therapeutic abortion is of great theoretical and practical interest. However, the present techniques should be improved before clinicians can replace conventional abortion methods by prostaglandin treatment.

An interesting theory has recently been presented (Gustavii and Brunk, 1971; Gustavii and Gréen, 1972) that prostaglandins are engaged in the mechanism of effect of therapeutic abortion, induced by intra-uterine injection of hypertonic sodium chloride. The theory is based upon the following observations: (a) high concentration of prostaglandin $F_{2\alpha}$ ($PGF_{2\alpha}$) in decidua during labor; (b) advanced regressive changes in the decidual cells following both intra-amniotic and extra-amniotic injection of hypertonic saline (Gustavii and Brunk, 1972); (c) release of $PGF_{2\alpha}$ into amniotic fluid following extra-amniotic injection of hypertonic saline (Gustavii and Gréen, 1972). The $PGF_{2\alpha}$ concentration rose before clinically effective uterine contractions appeared. This hypothesis may be supported by the successful use of intra-amniotic and extra-amniotic injection of $PGF_{2\alpha}$ for the induction of abortion and by the fact that inhibition of prostaglandin synthesis postpones saline-induced abortions (Waltman et al., 1973).

2. Induction of Labor

Induction of labor at term by means of prostaglandin administration has been studied by several authors (Bygdeman et al., 1968; Karim et al., 1969; Embrey, 1970; Beazley et al., 1970). Also at term PGE_2 has proved to be more effective than $PGF_{2\alpha}$.

It has not yet been proved that prostaglandins are more effective or safer than intravenous oxytocin drip in induction of labor at term (Beazley and Gillespie, 1971).

3. Comments on Endocrine Factors in Labor

The literature reviewed above reveals two theories as to the onset of human labor: (a) that labor starts because some protective factor is withdrawn (e.g., the "progesterone block"), (b) that labor starts because some factor increases in importance or a new factor is added (e.g., increase in oxytocin release, increase in fetal corticosteroid production, prostaglandin release).

The second theory has gained support from experiments on sheep showing the effect of fetal corticosteroids on placental hormone production and prostaglandin release. There are also other theories concerning the addition of new factors, triggering myometrial activity at term. Recently Gustavii (1972) proposed that the lysosomes in decidual cells might act as a trigger for parturition. The lytic enzymes in these organelles are capable of breaking down all cellular constituents and thus also the cellular membrane system, which is built up partially from the prostaglandin precursor arachidonic acid. Since steroid sex hormones labilize lysosomal membranes (Szego et al., 1971), Gustavii suggested that after a certain steroid concentration was reached at the end of pregnancy, leakage of enzymes from lysosomes into the cytoplasm might occur, resulting in prostaglandin synthesis and finally uterine contraction.

VII. Summary

There was a time, not long ago, when the problem of the endocrine control of myometrial activity in the woman was assumed to be solved. The balance between estrogen, stimulating the activity of the myometrium and increasing its sensitivity, on the one hand, and progesterone, depressing activity and sensitivity, on the other, was thought to direct myometrial activity during the menstrual cycle as well as the maintenance and termination of pregnancy. In this endocrine interplay, oxytocin had some diffuse kind of triggering effect in the onset and successful outcome of labor.

However, recent research has obscured this picture. It is true that *estrogen and progesterone* influence the myometrial activity and sensitivity in the nonpregnant woman, but not in the way earlier assumed. Endogenous and exogenous estrogen produce small, frequent, local and nonpropagated contractions. Endogenous and exogenous gestagen produce contractions with higher amplitude, longer duration and lower frequency, and improve propagation. They also increase myometrial sensitivity (e.g., to vasopressin and mechanical stimuli). These effects of estrogen and gestagen have been much discussed, but skepticism is rapidly abating.

It is also true that estrogen and progesterone are prerequisites for the beginning, the maintenance and termination of pregnancy—but not necessarily through their effects on the myometrium. Thus, there are but few facts indicating that estrogen and progesterone influence myometrial activity and sensitivity in pregnancy, thereby being of importance for the termination of pregnancy—at term or prematurely.

Maternal and fetal *corticosteroids* are of importance for myometrial activity in some pregnant animals. Their role in human pregnancy is obscure.

As for *biogenic amines,* epinephrine depresses and norepinephrine stimulates myometrial activity in the woman. However, they seem to be of doubtful physiologic and therapeutic importance. Neuronal norepinephrine may play a role in myometrial control in all mammals. So far, it has been studied almost exclusively in animals. Serotonin stimulates myometrial activity also in the woman. Its physiological role in human pregnancy and labor has been discussed but remains unproved.

In large doses, *oxytocin* has a certain stimulatory effect in the proliferative phase; in smaller doses it is ineffective throughout the menstrual cycle. In pregnancy it is increasingly effective in stimulating myometrial activity, with a drastic increase close to term. Its therapeutic value in starting and stimulating labor is unquestioned. Its physiological role in the onset and continuation of labor is still debated.

Vasopressin stimulates myometrial activity in the secretory phase and even more around the onset of menstruation. In pregnancy, its effect is lower than that of oxytocin and does not show the same increase toward term. Its role in labor is unknown.

Recent studies have indicated that in connection with labor the fetus produces considerable amounts of oxytocin and vasopressin. The significance of the fetal contribution of posterior pituitary hormones is still unknown.

Prostaglandins, especially $PGF_{2\alpha}$, PGE_1 and PGE_2 are potent stimulators of myometrial activity in both pregnant and nonpregnant women. They have been utilized for induction of therapeutic abortion and labor. There is some indication that prostaglandins have a physiological role in the onset of myometrial activity, but final proof is still lacking.

REFERENCES

Adair, F. L., and Haugen, J. A. (1939). *Amer. J. Obstet. Gynecol.* **37**, 753.

Aitken, E. H., Preedy, J. R. K., Eton, B., and Short, R. V. (1958). *Lancet* **ii**, 1096.

Allen, W. M., and Corner, G. W. (1930). *Proc. Soc. Exp. Biol. Med.* **27**, 403.

Allen, W. M., and Reynolds, S. R. M. (1935). *Amer. J. Obstet. Gynecol.* **30**, 309.

Alling-Møller, K. J., and Fuchs, F. (1965). *J. Obstet. Gynaecol. Brit. Commonw.* **72**, 1042.

Anderson, A. B. M., Pierrepoint, C. G., Griffiths, K., and Turnbull, A. C. (1972). *J. Reprod. Fert., Suppl.* **16**, 25.

Baumgarten, K. (1970). *Geburtsh. Frauenheilk.* **30**, 921.

Beazley, J. M., and Gillespie, A. (1971). *Lancet* **i**, 152.

Beazley, J. M., Dewhurst, C. J., and Gillespie, A. (1970). *J. Obstet. Gynaecol. Brit. Commonw.* **77**, 193.

Bedford, C. A., Challis, J. R. G., Harrison, F. A., and Heap, R. B. (1972). *J. Reprod. Fert., Suppl.* **16**, 1.

Béguin, F., Bygdeman, M., Toppozada, M., and Wiqvist, N. (1972). *Prostaglandins* **1**, 397.

Behrman, S. J., and Burchfield, W. (1968). *Amer. J. Obstet. Gynecol.* **100**, 194.

Bell, G. H., and Robson, J. M. (1937). *Quart. J. Exp. Physiol. Cog. Med. Sci.* **27**, 205.

Bengtsson, L. P. (1962). *Lancet* **i**, 339.

Bengtsson, L. P. (1968a). *Rev. Fr. Gynecol. Obstet.* **63**, 73.

Bengtsson, L. P. (1968b). *J. Reprod. Fert.* **16**, 115.

Bengtsson, L. P. (1970a). *Acta Obstet. Gynecol. Scand. Suppl.* **49**(6), I.

Bengtsson, L. P. (1970b). *Acta Obstet. Gynecol. Scand. Suppl.* **49**(6), II.

Bengtsson, L. P. (1970c). *Acta Obstet. Gynecol. Scand. Suppl.* **49**(6), III.

Bengtsson, L. P., and Csapo, A. (1962). *Amer. J. Obstet. Gynecol.* **83**, 1083.
Bengtsson, L. P., and Ejarque, P. (1964). *Acta Obstet. Gynecol. Scand.* **43**, 49.
Bengtsson, L. P., and Falk, V. (1964). *In* "Obstetrik and Gynekologi 2" (A. Sjövall and S. Kullander, eds.), pp. 77–83. Lund, Sweden.
Bengtsson, L. P., and Forsgren, B. (1966). *Acta Obstet. Gynecol. Scand.* **45**, 155.
Bengtsson, L. P., and Moawad, A. H. (1967). *Amer. J. Obstet. Gynecol.* **98**, 957.
Bengtsson, L. P., and Siener, H. (1964). *Bibl. Gynaecol.* **42**, 79.
Bengtsson, L. P., and Stormby, N. (1962). *Acta Obstet. Gynecol. Scand.* **41**, 115.
Bengtsson, L. P., and Theobald, G. W. (1966). *J. Obstet. Gynaecol. Brit. Commonw.* **73**, 273.
Bergström, S., Ryhage, R., Samuelsson, B., and Sjövall, J. (1963). *J. Biol. Chem.* **238**, 3555.
Bickers, W. (1941). *Amer. J. Obstet. Gynecol.* **42**, 1023.
Binns, W., James, J. F., and Shupe, J. L. (1964). *Ann. N. Y. Acad. Sci.* **111**, 571.
Borell, U. (1951a). *Acta Endocrinol. (Copenhagen)* **7**, 17.
Borell, U. (1951b). *Acta Endocrinol. (Copenhagen)* **8**, 131.
Borglin, N. E., and Willert, B. (1957). *Acta Obstet. Gynecol. Scand.* **36**, 382.
Borth, R., and de Watteville, H. (1952). *Vita. Horm. (New York)* **10**, 141.
Borth, R., and Stamm, O. (1958). *Geburtsh. Frauenheilk.* **18**, 600.
Bosu, W. T. K., Edqvist, L.-E., and Johansson, E. D. B. (1972). *Acta Pharmacol. Toxicol. Suppl.* **1**, 31, 76.
Braaksma, J. T. (1970). "Pressure Recording in the Non Pregnant Uterus *In Vivo*." G. van Soest N.V., Amsterdam.
Brenner, W. E., and Hendricks, C. H. (1962). *Amer. J. Obstet. Gynecol.* **83**, 1094.
Brenner, W. E., Hendricks, C. H., Braaksma, J. T., Fishburne, J. I., Jr., and Staurovsky, L. G. (1972). *Prostaglandins* **1**, 455.
Brody, S., and Wiqvist, N. (1961). *Endocrinology* **68**, 971.
Brotánek, V., Hendricks, C. H., and Yoshida, T. (1969a). *Amer. J. Obstet. Gynecol.* **103**, 1108.
Brotánek, V., Hendricks, C. H., and Yoshida, T. (1969b). *Amer. J. Obstet. Gynecol.* **105**, 535.
Bygdeman, M. (1964). *Acta Physiol. Scand., Suppl.* **242**, 1.
Bygdeman, M., and Eliasson, R. (1964). *J. Reprod. Fert.* **7**, 47.
Bygdeman, M., Kwon, S. U., Mukherjee, T., and Wiqvist, N. (1968). *Amer. J. Obstet. Gynecol.* **102**, 317.
Bygdeman, M., Beguin, F., Toppozada, M., and Wiqvist, N. (1972). *Advan. Biosci.* **9**, 86.
Caldeyro-Barcia, R., and Poseiro, J. J. (1959). *Ann. N. Y. Acad. Sci.* **78**, 813.
Caldeyro-Barcia, R., and Sereno, J. A. (1961). *In* "Oxytocin" (R. Caldeyro-Barcia and H. Heller, eds.), p. 177. Pergamon, Oxford.
Caldeyro-Barcia, R., and Theobald, G. W. (1968). *Amer. J. Obstet. Gynecol.* **102**, 1181.
Caldeyro-Barcia, R., Sica-Blanco, Y., Poseiro, J. J., González-Panizza, V., Méndez-Bauer, C., Fielitz, C., Alvarez, H., Pose, S. V., and Hendricks, C. H. (1957). *J. Pharmacol. Exp. Ther.* **121**, 18.
Carter, A. M., Göthlin, J., and Bengtsson, L. P. (1968). *J. Reprod. Fert.* **17**, 419.
Cassmer, O. (1959). *Acta Endocrinol. (Copenhagen), Suppl.* **45**.
Chard, T. (1972). *J. Reprod. Fertil.* **16**, Suppl., 121.
Chard, T., Boyd, N. R. H., Forsling, M. L., McNeilly, A. S., and Landon, J. (1970). *J. Endocrinol.* **48**, 223.

Chard, T., Boyd, N. R. H., Edwards, C. R. W., and Hudson, C. N. (1971). *Nature (London)* **234,** 352.

Cibils, L. A. (1967). *Obstet. Gynecol.* **30,** 441.

Cibils, L. A., Pose, S. V., and Zuspan, F. P. (1962). *Amer. J. Obstet. Gynecol.* **84,** 307.

Cobo, E. (1968). *J. Appl. Physiol.* **24,** 317.

Coch, J. A., Brovetto, J., Cabot, H. M., Fielitz, C. A., and Caldeyro-Barcia, R. (1965). *Amer. J. Obstet. Gynecol.* **91,** 10.

Corner, G. W. (1937). *Cold Spring Harbor Symp. Quant. Biol.* **5,** 62.

Corner, G. W., and Allen, W. M. H. (1929). *Amer. J. Physiol.* **88,** 326.

Coutinho, E. M. (1964). *Proc. Int. Congr. Endocrinol., 2nd, Excerpta Med. Found. Int. Congr. Ser.* **64,** 742.

Coutinho, E. M. (1967). *Proc. Int. Conf. IPPF (Int. Planned Parenthood Fed.), 8th, Santiago* p. 432.

Coutinho, E. M. (1968a). *Proc. World Congr. Fert. Steril., 6th, Tel Aviv.*

Coutinho, E. M. (1968b). *Proc. Int. Planned Parenthood Fed., World Conf., 8th, Santiago, Chile, 1967.*

Coutinho, E. M. (1968c). *Progr. Endocrinol., Proc. Int. Congr. Endocrinol., 3rd, Mexico, D.F., Excerpta Med. Found. Congr. Ser.* **184,** p. 945.

Coutinho, E. M., and Lopes, A. C. V. (1968). *Amer. J. Obstet. Gynecol.* **102,** 479.

Coutinho, E. M., Fisher, G., and Mascarenhas, G. B. (1960). *Brazil. Congr. Obste. Gynecol.*

Cretius, K. (1957a). *Z. Geburtsh. Gynaekol.* **149,** 114.

Cretius, K. (1957b). *Z. Geburtsh. Gynaekol.* **149,** 131.

Csapo, A. (1950). *Amer. J. Physiol.* **162,** 406.

Csapo, A. (1955). *In* "Modern Trends in Obstetrics and Gynecology" (K. Bowes, ed.), pp. 20–49. Butterworth, London.

Csapo, A. (1956). *Amer. J. Anat.* **98,** 273.

Csapo, A. (1959). *Ann. N. Y. Acad. Sci.* **75,** 790.

Csapo, A. (1961a). *In* "Progesterone" (A.-C. Barnes, ed.), pp. 7–23. Brook Lodge Press, Augusta, Michigan.

Csapo, A. (1961b). *Ciba Found. Study Group [Pap.]* **9,** 3–31.

Csapo, A. (1971). *In* "International Encyclopedia of Pharmacology and Therapeutics" (M. Tausk, ed.), Vol. 1, pp. 123–203. Pergamon, Oxford.

Csapo, A., and Corner, G. W. (1952). *Endocrinology* **51,** 378.

Csapo, A., and Pinto-Dantas, C. R. (1966). *Fert. Steril.* **17,** 34.

Csapo, A., and Sauvage, J. (1968). *Acta Obstet. Gynecol. Scand.* **47,** 181.

Csapo, A., de Sousa-Filho, M. B., de Souza, J. C., and de Souza, O. (1966). *Fert. Steril.* **17,** 621.

Csapo, A., Knobil, R., Pulkkinen, M., van der Molen, H. J., Sommerville, I. F., and Wiest, W. G. (1969). *Amer. J. Obstet. Gynecol.* **105,** 1132.

Csapo, A., Knobil, E., van der Molen, H. J., and Wiest, W. G. (1971). *Amer. J. Obstet. Gynecol.* **110,** 630.

Csapo, A., Pulkkinen, M. O., Ruttner, B., Sauvage, J. P., and Wiest, W. G. (1972a). *Amer. J. Obstet. Gynecol.* **112,** 1061.

Csapo, A., Ruttner, B., and Wiest, W. G. (1972b). *Prostaglandins* **1,** 365.

Dahle, T. (1950). *Acta Obstet. Gynecol. Scand., Suppl.* **30**(4).

Dale, H. H. (1906). *J. Physiol. (London)* **34,** 163.

Dennis, K. J., Farr, V., and Klopper, A. (1973). *J. Obstet. Gynaecol. Brit. Commonw.* **80,** 41.

298   LARS PHILIP BENGTSSON

Deshpande, G. N., Turner, A. K., and Sommerville, I. F. (1960). *J. Obstet. Gynaecol. Brit. Commonw.* **67,** 954.
Dominguez, O. V., François, G. D., Watanabe, M., and Solomon, S. (1965). *In* "Metabolism of Steroid Hormones" (R. I. Dorfman and F. Ungar, eds.), pp. 611–612. Academic Press, New York.
Edqvist, L.-E., Ekman, L., Gustafsson, B., Jacobson, S. O., Johansson, E. D. B., and Lindell, J.-O. (1971). *Sv. Vet. Tidskr.* **21,** 1.
Eggleton, G. P., and Eggleton, P. (1929–1930). *J. Physiol. (London)* **68,** 193.
Ejarque, P., and Bengtsson, L. P. (1962). *Acta Endocrinol. (Copenhagen)* **69,** 521.
Eliasson, R., and Posse, N. (1960). *Acta Obstet. Gynecol. Scand.* **39,** 112.
Embrey, M. P. (1970). *Brit. Med. J.* **ii,** 256.
Embrey, M. P., and Moir, J. O. (1967). *J. Obstet. Gynaecol. Brit. Commonw.* **74,** 648.
Embrey, M. P., Hillier, K., and Mahendran, P. (1972). *Brit. Med. J.* **iii,** 146.
Eskes, T. K. A. B., Hein, P. R., Kars-Villanueva, E. B., Braaksma, J. T., Janssens, J., and Kollerie, A. (1969). *Arch. Int. Pharmacodyn. Ther.* **182,** 409.
Eskes, T. K. A. B., Hein, P. R., Stolte, L. A. M., Kars-Villanueva, E. B., Crone, A., Braaksma, J. T., and Janssens, J. (1970). *Amer. J. Obstet. Gynecol.* **106,** 1235.
Evans, D. H. L., Schild, H. O., and Thesleff, S. (1958). *J. Physiol. (London)* **143,** 474.
Falck, B., Owman, C., Rosengren, E., and Sjöberg, N.-O. (1969a). *Acta Endocrinol. (Copenhagen)* **62,** 77.
Falck, B., Owman, C., Rosengren, E., and Sjöberg, N.-O. (1969b). *Endocrinology* **84,** 958.
Fitzpatrick, R. J., and Walmsley, C. F. (1965). *In* "Advances in Oxytocin Research" (J. H. M. Pinkerton, ed.), pp. 51–73. Pergamon, Oxford.
Fraenkel, L., and Cohn, F. (1902). *Anat. Anz.* **20,** 294.
Frandsen, V. A., and Stakemann, G. (1961). *Acta Endocrinol. (Copenhagen)* **38,** 383.
Frandsen, V. A., and Stakemann, G. (1964). *Acta Endocrinol. (Copenhagen)* **47,** 265.
Fuchs, A.-R. (1971). *In* "Endocrinology of Pregnancy" (F. Fuchs and A. Klopper, eds.), pp. 286–305. Harper, New York.
Fuchs, F., and Fuchs, A.-R. (1958). *Acta Endocrinol. (Copenhagen)* **29,** 615.
Fuchs, F., and Stakemann, G. (1958). *Congr. Int. Gynecol. Obstet. 2nd, Montreal* **2,** 533. (Abstr.)
Fuchs, F., Fuchs, A.-R., Short, R. V., and Wagner, G. (1965). *Acta Obstet. Gynecol. Scand.* **44,** 63.
Furuhjelm, M. (1962). *Acta Obstet. Gynecol. Scand.* **41,** 370.
Fylling, P. (1971). "Studies in Plasma Progesterone in Women and Sheep During Pregnancy." Universitetsforlaget, Oslo.
Gaddum, J. H., and Hameed, K. A. (1954). *Brit. J. Pharmacol. Chemother.* **9,** 240.
Garret, W. J. (1954). *J. Obstet. Gynaecol. Brit. Emp.* **61,** 586.
Garret, W. J. (1956). *J. Physiol. (London)* **132,** 553.
Gemzell, C. A. (1953). *J. Clin. Endocrinol. Metab.* **13,** 898.
Gibor, Y., Pandya, G. N., Bieniarz, J., and Scommengna, A. (1971). *Amer. J. Obstet. Gynecol.* **109,** 542.

Goto, M., and Csapo, A. I. (1959). *J. Gen. Physiol.* **43**, 455.

Govaerts-Videtzky, M., Martin, L., and Hubinont, P. O. (1965). *J. Obstet. Gynaecol. Brit. Commonw.* **72**, 1034.

Gustavii, B. (1971). *Acta Obstet. Gynecol. Scand.* **50**, 43.

Gustavii, B. (1972). *Lancet* **ii**, 1149.

Gustavii, B., and Brunk, U. (1971). *Lancet* **ii**, 826.

Gustavii, B., and Brunk, U. (1972). *Acta Obstet. Gynecol. Scand.* **51**, 121.

Gustavii, B., and Gréen, K. (1972). *Amer. J. Obstet. Gynecol.* **114**, 1099.

Hendricks, C. H. (1965). *In* "Muscle" (W. M. Paul, E. E. Daniel, and C. M. Kay, eds.), pp. 349–362. Pergamon, Oxford.

Hendricks, C. H. (1966). *Amer. J. Obstet. Gynecol.* **96**, 824.

Hendricks, C. H., Helfand, T., and Caldeyro-Barcia, R. (1959). *Amer. J. Obstet. Gynecol.* **77**, 387.

Henriksen, J., and Wagner, G. (1969). *10th Meeting, Nord. Fertil. Club, Copenhagen.*

Henry, J. S., and Browne, J. S. L. (1943). *Amer. J. Obstet. Gynecol.* **45**, 927.

Henry, J. S., Browne, J. S. L., and Venning, E. H. (1950). *Amer. J. Obstet. Gynecol.* **60**, 471.

Hochuli, E., Kaiser, O., and Burger, M. (1956). *Experientia* **12**, 356.

Hoff, F., and Bayer, R. (1956). "Ovarialhormone und Uterusmotilität." Enke, Stuttgart.

Holmdahl, H. T., Johansson, E. D. B., and Nilsson, B. A. (1971). *Acta Endocrinol. (Copenhagen)* **66**, 82.

Järvinen, P. A., and Huhmar, E. (1963). *Ann. Chir. Gynaecol. Fenn.* **52**, 361.

Järvinen, P. A., and Luukkainen, T. (1962). *Ann. Chir. Gynaecol. Fenn.* **51**, 438.

Järvinen, P. A., Luukkainen, T., and Väistö, L. (1965). *Acta Obstet. Gynecol. Scand.* **44**, 258.

Jeffcoate, T. N. A. (1950). *Proc. Roy. Soc. Med.* **43**, 734.

Joelsson, J., and Odeblad, E. (1972). *Acta Obstet. Gynecol. Scand.* **71**, 297.

Joelsson, J., Ingelman-Sundberg, A., and Sandberg, F. (1966). *J. Obstet. Gynaecol. Brit. Commonw.* **73**, 832.

Johansson, E. D. B. (1968). *Lancet* **1**, 570.

Johansson, E. D. B. (1969). *Acta Endocrinol. (Copenhagen)* **61**, 607.

Johnson, W. L., Ek, T. W., and Brenner, L. L. (1966). *Obstet. Gynecol.* **28**, 526.

Jung, H. (1956). *Pfluegers Arch. Gesamte Physiol. Menschen Tiere* **263**, 427.

Jung, H. (1957). *Arch. Gynaekol.* **190**, 194.

Jung, H. (1965). *Bibl. Gynaecol.* **33** .

Kaiser, I. H. (1950). *Surg., Gynecol. Obstet.* **90**, 649.

Kaiser, R., and Will, I. (1953). *Arch. Gynaekol.* **184**, 159.

Kalkschmied, W. (1958). *Geburtsh. Frauenheilk.* **18**, 380.

Kalkschmied, W. (1960). *Wien. Med. Wochenschr.* **110**, 546.

Kao, C. Y., and Nishiyama, A. (1964). *Amer. J. Physiol.* **207**, 793.

Karim, S. M. M. (1971a). *J. Obstet. Gynaecol. Brit. Commonw.* **78**, 289.

Karim, S. M. M. (1971b). *In* "Prostaglandins, Progress in Research I" (S. M. M. Karim, ed.), pp. 71–164. Med. Tech. Publ., Aylesbury, England.

Karim, S. M. M. (1971c). *Contraception* **3**, 173.

Karim, S. M. M. (1972). *J. Reprod. Fert., Suppl.* **16**, 105.

Karim, S. M. M., and Devlin, J. (1967). *J. Obstet. Gynecol. Brit. Commonw.* **74**, 230.

Karim, S. M. M., and Filshie, G. M. (1970). *Lancet* **i,** 157.

Karim, S. M. M., and Sharma, S. D. (1971). *J. Obstet. Gynaecol. Brit. Commonw.* **78,** 294.

Karim, S. M. M., Trussell, R. R., Hillier, K., and Patel, R. C. (1969). *J. Obstet. Gynaecol. Brit. Commonw.* **76,** 769.

Karim, S. M. M., Hillier, K., Somers, K., and Trussel, R. R. (1971). *J. Obstet. Gynaecol. Brit. Commonw.* **78,** 172.

Karlson, S. (1954). *Acta Obstet. Gynecol. Scand.* **33,** 253.

Karlson, S. (1959). *Acta Obstet. Gynecol. Scand.* **38,** 503.

Kelly, J. V. (1961). *Amer. J. Obstet. Gynecol.* **82,** 1207.

Kennedy, P. C., Kendrick, J. W., and Stormont, C. (1957). *Cornell Vet.* **47,** 160.

Kerenyi, T. D., Pinto-Dantas, C. A., de Sousa, O., and Darze, E. (1969). *Ciba Found. Study Group [Pap.]* **34,** 120–132.

Kleinhaus, A. L., and Kao, C. Y. (1969). *J. Gen. Physiol.* **53,** 758.

Klopper, A., and Dennis, K. J. (1962). *Brit. Med. J.* **ii,** 1157.

Klopper, A., MacNaughton, M. C., and Michie, E. A. (1961). *J. Endocrinol.* **22,** XIV.

Klopper, A., Dennis, K. J., and Farr, V. (1969). *Brit. Med. J.* **ii,** 786.

Klopper, A., Farr, V., and Dennis, K. J. (1973). *J. Obstet. Gynaecol. Brit. Commonw.* **80,** 34.

Knaus, H. (1926). *J. Physiol. (London)* **61,** 383.

Knaus, H. (1929). *Zentralbl. Gynaekol.* **53,** 2193.

Knaus, H. (1930). *Arch. Gynaekol.* **140,** 181.

Koren, Z., Pfeifer, Y., and Sulman, F. G. (1965). *Amer. J. Obstet. Gynecol.* **93,** 411.

Koren, Z., Pfeifer, Y., and Sulman, F. G. (1966). *J. Reprod. Fert.* **12,** 75.

Kumar, D., Goodno, J. A., and Barnes, A. C. (1963). *Bull. Johns Hopkins Hosp.* **113,** 53.

Kumar, D., Ward, E. F., and Barnes, A. C. (1964). *Amer. J. Obstet. Gynecol.* **90,** 1360.

Kuriyama, H. (1961). *Ciba Found. Study Group [Pap.]* **9,** 51.

Laguens, R., and Lagrutta, J. (1964). *Amer. J. Obstet. Gynecol.* **89,** 1040.

Liggins, G. C. (1969). *In* "Foetal Autonomy" (G. E .W. Wolstenholme and M. O'Connor, eds.), pp. 218–231. Churchill, London.

Liggins, G. C., and Kennedy, P. C. (1968). *J. Endocrinol.* **40,** 333.

Liggins, G. C., Kennedy, P. C., and Holm, L. W. (1967). *Amer. J. Obstet. Gynecol.* **98,** 1080.

Maia, H. S., and Coutinho, E. M. (1970). Personal communication.

Malpas, P. (1933). *J. Obstet. Gynaecol. Brit. Emp.* **40,** 1046.

Marshall, J. M. (1959). *Amer. J. Physiol.* **194,** 935.

Marshall, J. M. (1962). *Physiol. Rev.* **42,** Suppl. 5, 213.

Martinez-Gaudio, M., Yoshida, T., and Bengtsson, L. P. (1973). *Amer. J. Obstet. Gynecol.* **115,** 107.

Masson, G. M., and Klopper, A. (1972). *J. Obstet. Gynaecol. Brit. Commonw.* **79,** 970.

Menkes, J. A., and Csapo, A. (1952). *Endocrinology* **50,** 37.

Moawad, A. H., and Bengtsson, L. P. (1967). *Amer. J. Obstet. Gynecol.* **98,** 1057.

Moawad, A. H., and Bengtsson, L. P. (1968). *Acta Obstet. Gynecol. Scand.* **47,** 225.

Moawad, A. H., and Bengtsson, L. P. (1970). *Acta Obstet. Gynecol. Scand., Suppl.* **49**(6), V.

Møller, K. J. A., Wagner, G., and Fuchs, F. (1964). *Amer. J. Obstet. Gynecol.* **90**, 694.

Moir, C. (1944). *J. Obstet. Gynaecol. Brit. Emp.* **51**, 181.

Nilsson, L. (1964). *Acta Obstet. Gynecol. Scand., Suppl.* **42**(6), 128.

Noddle, B. A. (1964). *Nature (London)* **203**, 414.

Øvlisen, B., and Iversen, J. (1963). *Amer. J. Obstet. Gynecol.* **86**, 291.

Owman, C., Rosengren, E., and Sjöberg, N.-O. (1967). *J. Obstet. Gynecol.* **30**, 763.

Page, E. W., and Woods, L. (1943). *West. J. Surg., Obstet. Gynecol.* **51**, 225.

Pearlman, W. H. (1957). *Biochem. J.* **67**, 1.

Pickles, V. R., Hall, W. J., Clegg, P. C., and Sullivan, T. J. (1966). *Mem. Soc. Endocrinol.* **14**, 89.

Pinto, R. M. (1967). *J. Int. Fed. Gynaecol. Obstet.* **3**, 171.

Pinto, R. M., Lerner, U., Mazzocco, N., and Glauberman, M. (1966). *Amer. J. Obstet. Gynecol.* **94**, 876.

Pose, S. V., and Fielitz, C. (1961). *In* "Oxytocin" (R. Caldeyro-Barcia and H. Heller, eds.), pp. 229–239. Pergamon, Oxford.

Pose, S. V., Cibils, L. A., and Zuspan, F. P. (1962). *Amer. J. Obstet. Gynecol.* **84**, 297.

Poseiro, J. J., and Noriega-Guerra, L. (1961). *In* "Oxytocin" (R. Caldeyro-Barcia and H. Heller, eds.), pp. 158–174. Pergamon, Oxford.

Posse, N. (1958). *Acta Obstet. Gynecol. Scand. Suppl.* **37**(2).

Pulkkinen, M. O., and Enkola, K. (1972). *Int. J. Gynecol. Obstet.* **10**, 93.

Reynolds, S. R. M., Harris, J. S., and Kaiser, I. H. (1954). "Clinical Measurements of the Uterine Forces in Pregnancy and Labor," 1st Ed. Thomas, Springfield, Illinois.

Robinson, A. L., Datnow, M. M., and Jeffcoate, T. N. A. (1935). *Brit. Med. J.* i, 749.

Robson, J. M., Trounce, J. R., and Didcock, K. A. H. (1954). *J. Endocrinol.* **10**, 129.

Rongy, A. J., and Arluck, S. S. (1921). *Surg., Gynecol. Obstet.* **32**, 171.

Rosengren, E., and Sjöberg, N.-O. (1968). *Acta Physiol. Scand.* **72**, 412.

Roth-Brandel, U., Bygdeman, M., and Wiqvist, N. (1970). *Acta Obstet. Gynecol. Scandinav., Suppl.* **49**(5), 19.

Runnebaum, B., and Zander, J. (1971). *Acta Endocrinol. (Copenhagen), Suppl.* **150.**

Schild, H. O., Fitzpatrick, R. J., and Nixon, W. C. W. (1951). *Lancet* i, 250.

Schofield, B. M. (1954). *Endocrinology* **55**, 142.

Schofield, B. M. (1955). *J. Physiol. (London)* **129**, 289.

Sharp, A. H., and Wood, C. (1966). *Aust. N. Z. J. Obstet. Gynaecol.* **6**, 321.

Shearman, R. P., and Garret, W. J. (1963). *Brit. Med. J.* i, 292.

Short, R. V., and Eton, B. (1959). *J. Endocrinol.* **18**, 418.

Silva, D. (1967). *In* "Modern Trends in Obstetrics" (R. J. Kellou, ed.), Vol. 4, p. 58. Butterworth, London.

Simmer, H., and Simmer, I. (1959). *Klin. Wochenschr.* **37**, 971.

Sjöberg, N.-O. (1968a). *Acta Physiol. Scand.* **72**, 510.

Sjöberg, N.-O. (1968b). *Acta Endocrinol. (Copenhagen)* **57**, 405.

Smyth, C. N. (1958). *Lancet* i, 237.

Solomon, S., Watanbe, M., Dominguez, D. V., Gray, M. J., Meeker, C. I., and Sims, E. A. H. (1962). *Excerpta Med. Found. Int. Congr. Ser.* **51**, 267.

Sommerville, I. F., Pickett, M. T., Collins, W. P., and Denyer, D. C. (1963). *Acta Endocrinol. (Copenhagen)* **43**, 101.

Szego, C. M., Seeler, B. J., Steadman, R. A., Hill, D. F., Kimura, A. K., and Roberts, J. A. (1971). *Biochem. J.* **123**, 523.

Tappfer, S. (1959). *Geburtsh. Frauenheilk.* **19**, 170.

Theobald, G. W. (1968). *Amer. J. Obstet. Gynecol.* **102**, 1181.

Theobald, G. W., and Lundborg, R. A. (1962). *J. Obstet. Gynaecol. Brit. Commonw.* **69**, 417.

Theobald, G. W., Graham, A., Campbell, J., Gange, P. D., and Driscoll, W. J. (1948). *Brit. Med. J.* **ii**, 123.

Theobald, G. W., Robards, M. F., and Suter, P. E. N. (1969). *J. Obstet. Gynaecol. Brit. Commonw.* **76**, 385.

Toppozada, M., Beguin, F., Bygdeman, M., and Wiqvist, N. (1972). *Prostaglandins* **2**, 239.

Torpin, R., and Woodburry, R. A. (1947). *Amer. J. Obstet. Gynecol.* **54**, 766.

Turnbull, A. C., and Anderson, A. B. M. (1969). *Ciba Found. Study Group* [*Pap.*] **34**, 106.

Urban, J. (1965). *Ginekol. Pol.* **36**, 1219.

van der Molen, H. J. (1963). *Clin. Chim. Acta* **8**, 943.

Vara, P., Timonen, S., and Järvinen, P. A. (1961). *Int. Fed. Gynaekol. Obstet., World Congr., 3rd, Vienna* **2**, 433.

Villee, C. A., Hagerman, D. D., and Joel, P. B. (1960). *Recent Progr. Horm. Res.* **16**, 49.

von Euler, U. S. (1934). *Naunyn-Schmiedebergs Arch. Exp. Pathol. Pharmakol.* **175**, 78.

Walaas, O., and Walaas, E. (1950a). *Acta Physiol. Scand.* **21**, 1.

Walaas, O., and Waalas, E. (1950b). *Acta Physiol. Scand.* **21**, 18.

Waltman, R., Tricomi, V., and Palav, A. (1973). *Prostaglandins* **3**, 47.

Whiteside, J. H., Brame, R. G., and McGaugher, H. S., Jr. (1967). *Surg. Forum* **18**, 422.

Wilson, L., and Kurzrok, R. (1938). *Endocrinology* **23**, 79.

Wilson, L., and Kurzrok, R. (1940). *Endocrinology* **26**, 587.

Wiqvist, N. (1963). "Proceedings of the Interdisciplinary Conference on the Initiation of Labor" (J. M. Marshall, ed.), pp. 115–157. U. S. Dep. Health, Educ. Welfare, Princeton, New Jersey.

Wiqvist, N., and Bygdeman, M. (1970). *Lancet* **i**, 889.

Wiqvist, N., Kwon, S. U., Mukherjee, T., and Roth-Brandel, U. (1968). *Amer. J. Obstet. Gynecol.* **102**, 327.

Wiqvist, N., Béguin, F., Bygdeman, M., and Toppozada, M. (1972a). *In* "Prostaglandins in Fertility Control" (S. Bergström, K. Gréen, and B. Samuelsson, eds.), Vol. 2, pp. 118–128. WHO Res. Training Cent. Hum. Reprod., Karolinska Inst., Stockholm.

Wiqvist, N., Béguin, F., Bygdeman, M., and Toppozada, M. (1972b). *Advan. Biosci.* **9**, 831.

Wood, C. (1964). *J. Obstet. Gynecol. Brit. Commonw.* **71**, 615.

Woolever, C. A., and Goldfien, A. (1965). *In* "Hormonal Steroids" (L. Martini and A. Pecile, eds.), Vol. 2, pp. 253–262. Academic Press, New York.

Zander, J. (1961). *In* "Progesterone" (A. C. Barnes, ed.), pp. 77–89. Brook Lodge Press, Augusta, Michigan.

Zander, J. (1967). *Arch. Gynaekol.* **204,** 92.

Zander, J., and von Münstermann, A. M. (1956). *Klin. Wochenschr.* **34,** 944.

Zuspan, F. P., Cibils, L. A., and Pose, S. V. (1962). *Amer. J. Obstet. Gynecol.* **84,** 841.

Author Index

Numbers in italics refer to the pages on which the complete references are listed.

Subject Index